The Science of Catering

J Audrey Stretch
BSc MI Biol

H A Southgate
MHCIMA FCFA Cert Ed

Edward Arnold

A division of Hodder & Stoughton

LONDON   BALTIMORE   MELBOURNE   AUCKLAND

The publishers would like to thank the following for permission to include copyright photographs: Food Research Institute: pp. 58 left and right, 188 left and right; M.A.F.F., Slough Laboratory, Crown Copyright: p. 67 top right and left, bottom right and left; The Health Education Council: p. 68; Flour, Milling and Baking Research Association: pp. 83, 85, 109 left, centre, and right; Wellcome Biotechnology Ltd: p. 84; Olis, O.L. Smith and Co Ltd: p. 98 top and centre right; Moorwood Vulcan Limited: pp. 98 centre left, 99 top right and centre left; Zanussi, C.L.V. Systems Ltd: pp. 98 bottom, 99 top left; Merrychef: p. 99 centre right; M. Gilbert (Greenford) Ltd: p. 99 bottom; Catering Times and British Airways: p. 204; Burridge Savill: p. 227.

The publishers would like to thank the following for permission to include copyright material: Bell & Hyman Limited for *The Complete Vegetarian Recipe Book* (p. 182); the British Gas Corporation (p. 105); Butterworth Scientific Ltd for A E Bender: *Dictionary of Nutrition and Food Technology 5th edn* (p. 250); Craigmillar (a division of Van den Berghs & Jurgens Ltd) (p. 122); Her Majesty's Stationery Office for data from the *Composition of Foods* and the *Manual of Nutrition* which is used by permission of the Controller (pp. 153, 168, 169, 182); D G Mackean for 2 figures from *Introduction to Biology*, John Murray 1973 (p. 146); Macmillan, London and Basingstoke for O Kilgour: *Mastering Biology* (p. 79); John Murray (Publishers) Ltd for H C Q Rowett: *Basic Anatomy and Physiology* (p. 141); International Thomson Publishing Ltd for B J Ford: *Microbiology and Food* (p. 81); T J Parry & R K Pawsey for their *Principles of Microbiology* (p. 81); Unilever Ltd for *Plant Protein Foods* and Weight Watchers (U.K.) Ltd for *Weight Watchers – a Way of Life* (pp. 174-5).

First published in Great Britain 1986
Second impression 1988

British Library Cataloguing in Publication Data

Stretch, J.A.
· The science of catering.
1. Food service management.
I. Title   II. Southgate, H.A.
647'.95'068   TX911.3.M27

ISBN 0-7131-7431-5

Typeset in 10/11 pt English Times Compugraphic by Colset Singapore
Printed and bound in Great Britain for Edward Arnold, the educational, academic and medical publishing division of Hodder and Stoughton Limited, 41 Bedford Square, London WC1B 3DQ by Richard Clay Ltd.

Contents

Introduction

This book is intended for students taking City & Guilds catering courses, HCIMA Parts A and B and BTEC courses in Hotel Catering and Institutional Management Operations. We hope chefs and managers in the industry will also find it useful.

The book is based on the practical work of the industry — buying, storing, cooking and serving food. The scientific content is linked to these functions, so that students are encouraged to acquire the knowledge which must accompany skill and artistic flair in the catering industry today. Science has been interpreted in the broadest sense to cover any aspect which can be classified, observed or calculated with a degree of accuracy.

Most chapters are divided into two parts; Part A is introductory or deals with practical work in the storeroom, larder, kitchen or restaurant; Part B deals with the explanatory scientific facts.

The book has been arranged so that it can be dipped into to extract information on particular areas of catering. For this reason, there is a certain amount of duplication which would not be necessary in a conventional textbook. Self assessment of multiple-choice questions have been provided at the end of each section to enable students to test their understanding of each topic.

Acknowledgements

I wish to thank all my colleagues in the Hotel Operations and Cuisine departments at Thanet Technical College, and in the Science & Food Technology and Food & Fashion departments of Grimsby College of Technology who knowingly or unknowingly contributed ideas to this book.

In particular, I would like to thank Dr Robert Knight for his advice on a numerical approach to nutrition and for his permission to include his Food Tables and summary in this book. I also wish to thank Mrs M. McGeown, Miss J. Duncan, Miss S. Loseby, Mrs J. Monaghan and Miss D. Stretch for their assistance in preparing the typescript.

J. Audrey Stretch

1
What is food? — Plant foods

Part A

Plant food commodities. Definitions, quality, uses, storage of cereals, vegetables, fruits and nuts, flavourings, beverages, sugar, fats and oils. Questions.

The word 'food' covers a wide variety of commodities from Witchety grubs to pâté de foie gras. Anything which can be safely digested and assimilated by the human body can be food for somebody. Foods can be divided into four main categories:

Natural fresh foods   plant and animal foods used in their native state.

Preserved foods   foods treated in various ways to increase their shelf life.

Processed foods   foods refined or modified to improve their quality or to provide variety in the diet.

Additives   materials added to flavour, preserve or modify foods in some way.

A detailed knowledge of the different types and varieties of food is essential to caterers. It enables them to select the quality of ingredients which are needed to maintain a high standard of cuisine. Knowing the purchasing points for each commodity helps catering students to learn to identify the quality of foods using their senses of sight, smell, touch and taste.

Foods, once purchased, must be stored in such a way that they keep their quality until required. Knowing the best storage conditions for different types of food prevents waste and loss of profit. Understanding the rates at which foods deteriorate during storage assists in estimating how much of each commodity to purchase.

In the kitchen, a knowledge of the origin and composition of foods and their behaviour during cooking will help the chef to obtain the best results.

Cereals

Cereals are cultivated grasses which are used for food, and include wheat, maize, oats, barley, rice and rye. These are the main cereals used in the Western World. Also included in the term 'cereals' are arrowroot, tapioca and sago, although these are not true cereals but farinaceous products. These three 'cereals' are obtained from forms of vegetation other than grasses, but are used in a similar manner in cookery. Diagrams of these cereals are given in Fig. 1.1.

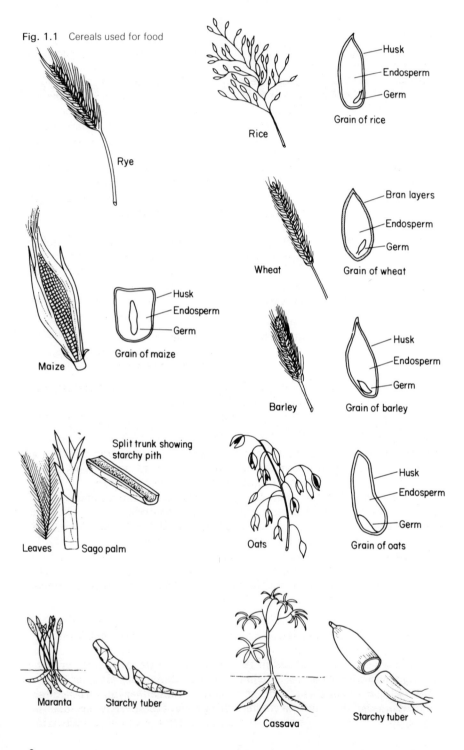

Fig. 1.1 Cereals used for food

Rye

Rice

Grain of rice
- Husk
- Endosperm
- Germ

Maize

Grain of maize
- Husk
- Endosperm
- Germ

Wheat

Grain of wheat
- Bran layers
- Endosperm
- Germ

Barley

Grain of barley
- Husk
- Endosperm
- Germ

Leaves Sago palm

Split trunk showing starchy pith

Oats

Grain of oats
- Husk
- Endosperm
- Germ

Maranta Starchy tuber

Cassava

Starchy tuber

2

Wheat

There are three main types of wheat used in cookery: bread wheats, macaroni wheats and English wheats.

Bread wheat has a high gluten content of 11–15%, which makes it suitable for bread, yeast doughs and puff pastry. Bread wheat is grown in Canada, North America and the U.S.S.R. Because of its high gluten content it is known as strong flour, once it has been milled. The gluten gives elasticity to the dough, which, when combined with yeast, gives the required crumb and texture we associate with yeast products.

Macaroni wheats (or durum wheats) have a gluten content of 11–13%, which makes them suitable for the manufacture of varieties of pasta and macaroni. The gluten content is required to give the pasta its characteristic shape without collapsing during and after shaping. Durum wheat is also grown in Canada and North America.

English wheat has a low gluten content of 8–10%, which makes it suitable for cakes, pastries and biscuits. English wheat is grown throughout Europe, South America and Australia, and when milled it produces a soft flour which, when baked, produces goods which are short and light in texture.

Wheat is generally a good source of nutrition because on average it contains:

70% carbohydrate (endosperm)	2% fat (germ)
12% protein (gluten)	2% minerals and vitamins
12% water	2% crude fibre bran

Whole wheat grains are processed into a variety of breakfast cereals; for example, Weetabix, Puffed Wheat and Wheat Flakes.

The main use for wheat is the production of flour, and the different types are blended to produce flour for specific purposes.

Wholemeal flour	contains the germ, bran and the endosperm, and has a extraction rate of 100%. It is the most nutritious flour, but may be indigestible because of the bran.
Wheatmeal flour	contains the germ, inner bran layers and the endosperm, and has an extraction rate of 85–95%.
Hovis flour	contains the germ, endosperm and additional germ. The extraction rate is 85%.
White flour	contains the endosperm only, and has an extraction rate of 72–75%.
High ratio or Patent flour	is a very fine flour containing the endosperm only. It has an extraction rate of 40%.

The extraction rate of flour is the proportion of wheat entering the mill which is recovered as flour. The higher the extraction rate, the more nutritious the flour.

Good quality white flour can be recognised by the fineness of the grains, the very white colour and the freedom from infestation (see Chapter 3).

It is more difficult to determine the quality of wheatmeal and wholemeal flours because of their natural colour, which varies according to the amount of bran and the degree of milling. If the flour is fresh it will have a pleasant

3

aroma. Staleness can be detected by a rancid smell caused by the deterioration of the oil in the germ. Again, there should be no signs of infestation. Because wheatmeal and wholemeal flours contain oil in the germ they should be used within 12 weeks. After this time there is rapid deterioration, due to the oil going rancid.

Semolina
This is obtained from the large uncrushed particles of wheat during the milling of flour, and is used for milk puddings and pasta paste.

Semolina can be produced as white semolina or wholewheat semolina. Good quality semolina should be fairly coarse in texture and creamy-white or light brown in colour, according to variety.

Pasta
Pasta paste is made from durum wheat semolina enriched with egg yolks. Pasta contains carbohydrate and protein, but the main nutritional value is obtained from the sauces and garnishes served with it.

Good quality pasta can be recognised in the dry state by the golden-yellow colour, brittle texture, freedom from white specks, and the sheen. When it is cooked it should double its size and hold its shape, and the water should be clear.

Maize
Maize, or sweetcorn as it is more commonly known, originated in America. The nutritional value of maize is not as high as wheat. It contains:

69% carbohydrate	4% fat
12% water	2% fibre
11% protein	2% vitamins and minerals

Maize is a useful cereal because it can be used as a vegetable. The starch is extracted and dried to produce cornflour or corn starch. The germ contains a good quality cooking oil. The whole kernels can be crushed to produce corn meal. The kernels are also processed into a range of breakfast cereals.

Fresh sweetcorn, or corn-on-the-cob, should be moist and slightly milky and the kernels a bright yellow colour.

Cornflour should be very fine, pure white and odourless.

Oats
Oats are a hardy cereal that can withstand cold climates, and are grown extensively in Scotland. It is the most nutritious of all the cereals and contains:

66% carbohydrate	9% fat
11% protein	2% fibre
10% water	2% vitamins and minerals

Oats are processed into various grades of oatmeal, oatflakes and rolled oats, which are mainly used for porridge.

Processed oats keep well because the steam used during the processing kills the enzyme lipase, which prevents the fat turning rancid. These products should be clean and free from weevil.

Barley
Barley is the hardiest of all cereals, and can grow in very cold climates. It contains:

75% carbohydrate	1% fat
12% water	2% fibre
8% protein	2% vitamins and minerals

The only form of barley widely used in catering is pearl barley, which is used for garnishing soups and stews, and can also be used for making barley water. Barley is widely used for malting in beer and whisky production.

Good quality pearl barley should be light brown in colour and free from excess husk.

Rice
Rice forms the staple diet of many countries throughout Asia, where it is grown extensively. Other rice growing areas are the U.S.A., Australia and Italy. The nutritional value of rice varies according to whether it is white (or polished) rice or brown rice. Rice contains the following nutrients:

77% carbohydrate	1% fat
12% water	1% fibre
7% protein	2% vitamin and minerals

but thiamine, niacin, riboflavin, iron and calcium are only present in brown rice, which contains the inner layers of the husk. Most of the rice sold is white (or polished) rice, and this has a greatly reduced nutritional value.

The three main varieties of rice used in Western cookery are Patna (or long grain), Carolina (or short grain [round grain]) and Piedmont, which has a medium grain.

Good quality white rice should be creamy-white in colour and free from husk, should have few or no broken grains and no signs of grain weevil. Brown rice varies in its grain colour, but it is generally yellow-brown. There should be no signs of grain weevil, but there may be a little husk.

Rye
Rye is a grain which is not widely used, except for making a dark flour which is used for rye bread and biscuits. It is the only cereal which contains gluten unsuitable for making bread. Rye contains the following nutrients:

72% carbohydrate	2% fat
15% water	1% fibre
8% protein	2% vitamins and minerals

Rye flour is darker that wheat flour, and should be free from any form of grain weevil and debris.

The following products are farinaceous, because they are obtained from

5

starchy forms of vegetation and, when purified, are almost pure starch.

Arrowroot
The starch is obtained from the tubers of the maranta plant, which is grown on the island of St Vincent. The leaves of the maranta are shaped like arrows, hence the name arrowroot.

Arrowroot should be very fine, white and odourless, and is still often sold as St Vincent arrowroot.

Tapioca
Tapioca is made into pellets or flakes from the starch obtained from the long starchy tubers of the cassava, or manioc plant. Cassava is grown in Africa and Indonesia and formed into small- or medium-sized pellets.

The quality is determined by the evenness in size of the variety and the colour, which should be very white. If the colour is off-white it is a sign that the tapioca is old.

Sago
This is the purified starch obtained from the pith of the sago palm, grown in the Philippines and Malaysia. The starch or sago meal is formed into small pellets similar to tapioca.

The sago pellets are darker in colour than tapioca, which distinguishes the two.

Self assessment questions

Cereals
1 What does the term cereals refer to?
2 Why is English wheat suitable for cakes and pastries?
3 Why is it necessary to have a flour with a high gluten content for yeast work?
4 Name four varieties of wheat flour.
5 Which is the most nutritious cereal?
6 Name the sources of the following: arrowroot, sago, tapioca.

Vegetables

The plants which are generally known as vegetables from the cooking angle have a savoury taste. For a biological definition, see Part B of this chapter. Vegetables can be divided up according to the various parts of the plants which are eaten. Table 1.1 lists the main vegetables and their sub-categories.

Vegetables can be eaten raw in salads, or cooked and served as part of a meal to accompany a dish of meat, poultry, fish or game. Certain vegetables can be served as a course on their own. Vegetarians rely heavily on vegetables for their nutrients.

Table 1.1   Main vegetables

Sub-category	Varieties
Tubers	Potatoes, Jerusalem artichokes, sweet potatoes
Leaves	Brassicas — all cabbages, lettuces, sprouts, spinach
Seeds	Leguminous plants — all peas and beans
Flowers	Broccoli, calabrese, cauliflowers, globe artichokes
Stems	Asparagus, cardoons, seakale, celery
Roots	Carrots, swedes, turnips, parsnips, beetroots
Bulbs	Onions, shallots, leeks
Fungi	Mushrooms, morels, chanterelles, truffles
Fruits	Tomatoes, peppers, marrows, cucumbers, avocado pears, aubergines

Generally speaking, vegetables provide vitamins, minerals, carbohydrate, protein and roughage, but some of the vitamins can be lost through careless preparation, cooking and serving.

The seeds of leguminous plants, when dried, are known as pulses. These have a protein content of 20%, but lack vitamin C. Some pulses, such as mung beans, if allowed to sprout, will produce bean shoots or bean sprouts that contain vitamins B and C.

Tubers
Tubers should be of medium size for the variety and free from soil, with no signs of damage or decomposition. The texture should be crisp and firm, not soft or spongy.

Leaves
The brassicas should have tight heads and the leaves should be crisp and green, not limp or discoloured. Brussels sprouts should be even in size and tightly closed, with no discolouration or signs of rotting.

Spinach leaves should be crisp, with no discolouration, and should be free from excess stalk. Lettuce heads should be fairly tight, according to variety. The leaves should not be limp and there should be no sign of discolouration or rotting.

Seeds
When peas and broad beans are purchased in the pod they should be green and crisp. The peas and beans should be moist and a good size and colour. Peas are best picked when they are small, because they will then be sweet and tender, while large peas become dry and hard.

Flowers
The heads of cauliflowers should be white, tightly closed and firm to the touch. Broccoli and calebrese should have flowers which are closed and should have no excess stalk. Globe artichokes must be harvested before the flower opens, the outer leaves must be succulent. To ensure that artichokes are tender, they must be young flowers.

Stems

Asparagus stems should be moist with a fresh appearance, not too long for the type, or too thick and woody. The points should be well-formed and undamaged.

Celery should be white or green, according to the method of production. The stems should be crisp, with no signs of decomposition. Seakale should be white and crisp, with a fresh appearance.

Roots

Roots should not be too small or too large for the variety. Small roots may lack flavour, and are wasteful through peeling. Large roots may be woody or coarse. There should be no signs of decomposition. The texture should be firm and crisp, and the roots free from soil.

Bulbs

Onions and shallots should be dry and firm, with no signs of rotting — which is indicated by the bulbs feeling soft when pressed lightly.

Leeks should be crisp and fresh. The stems should have no discolouration and should be free from excess soil. If too large, they will be coarse and strong.

Fungi

Mushrooms are purchased as buttons when the caps are tightly closed and small, cups when the caps are slightly opened, and open when the caps are fully opened and the gills exposed. Mushrooms should be crisp, clean and firm, with no signs of moisture or decomposition.

Morels, chanterelles and truffles are usually purchased in jars, canned or dried.

Fruits

Cucumbers and marrows should not be too large, and should be firm to the touch, with no signs of bruising. Tomatoes should be firm and of good even shape and size, with no signs of decomposition.

Aubergines should have a glossy skin and should give slightly when lightly pressed. If hard when pressed, they need to be left to ripen. There should be no signs of decomposition.

Self assessment questions

Vegetables
1 Name the nine categories into which vegetables can be divided.
2 Name two vegetables for each category.
3 What general points would you look for to determine the quality of the types of vegetables named?
4 What is the name given to the dried seeds of leguminous plants, and what important part do they play in cookery?
5 List the various ways in which vegetables may be used in the kitchen.

Fruits

Fresh fruits, as used in catering, may be described as plant foods with a sweet or sweet/sharp taste. For the biological classification, see Part B of this chapter.

Fruits can be sub-categorised according to the composition of the types of fruit as given in Table 1.2.

Table 1.2   Fruit categories

Sub-category	Varieties
Citrus fruits	Lemons, limes, grapefruits, ugli fruits, oranges, mandarins
Stone fruits	Greengages, plums, damsons, apricots, peaches, nectarines, cherries
Soft or berry fruits	Blackberries, redcurrants, blackcurrants, grapes, raspberries, strawberries, loganberries, cranberries
Fleshy fruits	Apples, pears, pineapples, bananas, melons, mangoes

Fresh fruits play an important part in our daily diet, providing vitamins, fibre, carbohydrate and minerals. Fruits have many uses in cookery because they are so versatile, and may be used for garnishing meat and fish dishes: for example, poached Sole Veronique — white grapes; braised duck — oranges; braised ham — peaches or pineapple.

The soft fruits may be used for flavouring ice creams, sorbets and bavarois, and other sweet dishes. Citrus fruits are used for marmalades, and lemons are served with fish dishes to add flavour and aid digestion of deep-fried fish.

Apples are made into a sauce to be served with rich fatty meats (for example, roast pork, roast duck and roast goose) to aid the digestion.

Most fruits are suitable to serve as dessert fruits at the end of a meal.

Citrus fruits
These should be of good size for the variety, and be firm to the touch, not soft or spongy. The skin should not be too thick or dry, and should have a bright colour. Tangerines and similar fruits have a looser skin, which may give a spongy texture.

Stone fruits
These should be no signs of bruising or mould, and the fruit should be free from stalk and leaves. The fruit should be firm, but not hard, and when ripe the general appearance should be good and bright.

Soft fruits
These should be firm with no signs of bruising or mould.

Fleshy fruits
The skins should be free from blemishes and insect marks, and the flesh should be firm. Pineapples should be of medium size with a fresh

appearance. The ripeness can be judged by the size of the holes (or eyes) of the skin — when these holes are fully open, the fruit is ready for eating.

Bananas should be firm, have yellow skins tinged with green, with no signs of decomposition.

Melons can be tested for ripeness by lightly pressing the opposite end to the stalk with the thumbs. If soft, it is ready for eating.

Nuts

Nuts may be defined as any seeds with hard shells and edible kernels, which are the nuts. There are many varieties of nuts which may be used as a source of food to provide protein, fat, carbohydrate, traces of minerals and vitamins of the B group.

The nuts in general use are brazils, hazelnuts, almonds, walnuts, chestnuts, pistachios and cashews. Peanuts (or groundnuts) are not true nuts, as they are grown in a casing below the ground, but they are used as nuts.

Vegetarians use nuts in cookery to provide protein and other nutrients. Most people regard nuts as a food to be nibbled at with drinks, instead of as a source of food. The varieties of nuts are put to many uses in the catering industry. Table 1.3 gives the uses of the various nuts and the forms in which they are available.

Quality
The quality of nuts in the shell is very difficult to assess, as no visual indication is available. The shelled nuts should be whole, if purchased as such. They should not be shrivelled or too dry, and should not have a rancid taste.

Self assessment questions

Fruits
1 List the various categories of fruits.
2 List as many different uses for them as you can.
3 What points would you look for to recognise good quality in the different kinds of fruit?

Nuts
1 Write down a suitable definition for nuts.
2 What is the nutritional value of the various types of nuts?
3 Suggest ways in which nuts may be used.

Flavourings

Nearly all of the foods used for flavourings are from various forms of plant. The exception is salt, which is a mineral. Flavourings may be classified as herbs, spices or aromatic seeds.

Table 1.3 Nuts and their uses

Variety	Form	Uses
Almonds	Whole	Fruit bowl
	Shelled	Pastry work
	Blanched	Cakes
	Nibbed	Gateaux, petits fours
	Flaked	Gateaux
	Split	Cakes
	Ground	Almond paste, gateaux, pastries, petits fours
Brazils	Whole	Fruit bowl
	Shelled	Petits fours, vegetarian cookery
Walnuts	Whole	Fruit bowl
	Shelled	Cakes, gateaux, salad oil
Hazelnuts	Whole	Fruit bowl
	Shelled	Pastry work, petits fours, vegetarian cookery
Pistachio	Salted	Cocktail snacks
	Shelled	Pork pies, boars heads, galantines, terrines
Cashew	Salted	Cocktail snacks, drinks
	Shelled	Vegetarian cookery
Chestnuts	Whole (shelled)	Turkey stuffing, Brussels sprouts
	Glacé	Pastry work, sweets
	Purée	Pastry work, game dishes
Peanuts	Salted	Cocktail snacks and drinks
	Roasted	Cocktail snacks and drinks
	Fresh	Not generally used

Herbs

Generally speaking, herbs are the leaves of plants which have no woody stems, and may be used fresh or dried for flavouring a variety of dishes. The characteristic flavour of herbs is obtained from an aromatic volatile oil contained in the leaves. This oil aids the digestion, as well as adding to the flavour of the dish. With the exception of parsley, herbs have no food value.

To retain the flavour of herbs they must be kept in sealed airtight containers. When purchased, dried herbs should have a natural characteristic aroma, and not smell of damp vegetation or dried grass.

Fresh herbs have crisp green leaves with a fresh, delicate aroma — this may not be noticeable until the leaves are lightly pressed with the finger and thumb to release the smell. The leaves should not be discoloured or limp, and should have no signs of decomposition.

A list of the herbs extensively used in cooking is given in Table 1.4.

Spices

Spices are obtained from the roots, flowers, fruits and bark of plants and shrubs. These natural products are sun-dried, and may be left whole or ground.

Table 1.4 Herbs commonly used in cooking

Variety	Uses
Bay leaves	Soups, sauces, stews, marinades
Basil	Tomato dishes, rice and pasta dishes
Borage	Salads, fruit cups, flowers for fruit drinks
Chervil	Meat and poultry dishes, cold decorative work, sauces
Chives	Salads, potatoes, hors d'oeuvre
Garlic	Meat, poultry and vegetable dishes
Marjoram	Salads, soups, stews and stuffings
Parsley	Meat, poultry, fish dishes and sauces
Rosemary	Lamb dishes, marinades
Sage	Stuffing — pork, duck, goose
Tarragon	Meat, poultry, cold decorative work, sauces
Thyme	Stuffing–lamb, veal, poultry, soups, sauces, stews, marinades

Most spices originated in the Molluca Islands, but are now grown in many other countries — India, Africa, the West Indies and the Far East. Spices also contain oils which aid the digestion by stimulating the gastric juices. As well as aiding digestion, spices are a source of natural colourings which enhance the appearance of food as well as adding a variety of flavours. Common uses of spices are shown in Table 1.5. Because spices are dried products, they have a concentrated flavour and must be used sparingly, otherwise instead of improving the foods they will make them unpalatable.

Table 1.5 Spices and their uses

Type	Variety	Uses
Roots	Ginger	Cakes, biscuits, melon, curry powder
	Turmeric	Chutneys, piccalilli, curry powder
Flowers	Cloves	Stocks, sauces, apple dishes
	Saffron	Rice dishes, fish stews
Fruits	Mace	Meat dishes, fish dishes, fish sauces
	Nutmeg	Potato dishes, spinach dishes, milk puddings
	Chillies	Pickles, chutneys, curry powder
	Allspice	Sausages, sauces, fruit cakes
	Paprika	Meat and poultry dishes, egg dishes
	Pepper (cayenne)	Shellfish dishes, cheese dishes
Barks	Cinnamon	Apple dishes, cakes, mulled wine
	Cassia	Mixed spice, apple dishes

It is very difficult to determine the quality of spices, generally because of the variation in colour, country of origin, variation in size, whether whole or ground, and the method of storage by the spice merchant. Some general points for guidance for whole spices are the following:

Cinnamon	even thinness and colour, freedom from signs of insects.
Nutmegs	size variable, freedom from insect marks.
Cloves	dark brown to black, strong aroma.
Turmeric	yellow-coloured roots free from insect marks.

Chillies	colour varies from red to yellow-brown, even and whole fruits.
Saffron	fine strands, orange in colour.
Ginger	various sizes, unbleached roots are fawn in colour. Bleached roots are white, with no signs of insect marks.

Guidelines for ground spices are the following:

Cinnamon	fine with pleasant aroma, and cinnamon brown in colour.
Nutmeg	light to dark brown in colour with a definite aroma.
Turmeric	fine bright yellow powder with a bitter taste.
Chillies	variable in colour. Hot taste.
Saffron	fine orange-coloured powder.
Ginger	fawn-coloured fine powder with a rich, clean tang.

Aromatic seeds

Aromatic seeds may be classified as spices, but as they are all seeds it is more convenient to classify them separately. As the name implies, they are seeds which have aroma and flavour, which add to the flavour of a variety of foods and dishes. Seeds contain fat, protein, carbohydrate and traces of vitamins but they are not generally consumed in sufficient quantities to be of any nutritional value. Many of these seeds are obtained from herbs, flowers, shrubs and evergreen trees. Common uses are shown in Table 1.6.

Table 1.6   Aromatic seeds and their uses

Seed	Uses
Cardamom	Danish pastries, sausages, curry powder, coffee
Caraway	Cheeses, seed cakes, curry powder, kummel
Coriander	Soups, pickles, meat dishes
Dill	Pickled cucumbers, gherkins, chutneys, fish
Fennel	Various breads, cheeses, fish
Juniper berries	Sauerkraut, marinades, stews, gin, pork
Poppy	Various breads and pastries
Sesame	Buns, hors d'oeuvre, salads, breads
Vanilla pods	Custards, ice cream, bavarois
Cumin	Curry powders

Self assessment questions

Herbs
1 What are herbs, and why are they used in cookery?
2 Name five herbs, and state how they may be used in cookery with various foods.
3 What substance is responsible for the individual flavours of herbs?
4 How would you preserve the flavour of dried herbs?

Spices
1 Define the term 'spices'.

2 List the various reasons for using spices in cookery.
3 Name five spices, and state which part of the plant they come from.

Aromatic seeds
1 List as many aromatic seeds as you can, and say how they may be used in cookery.

Vegetable fats and oils

Vegetable fats and oils are extracted from seeds and fruits of various plants and trees. Oils are fats which are liquid at room temperature. The main sources of these oils and fats are given in Table 1.7.

Table 1.7 Vegetable fats and oils

Oil source	Main countries of origin
Sunflower seeds	Europe, India, China, America
Sesame seeds	India, Sri Lanka, China, Africa
Olives	Italy, Spain, France
Groundnuts	U.S.A., Africa
Soya beans	China, America
Oil palm	West Africa, Malaysia, Indonesia
Coconuts	Indonesia, Malaysia, Philippines
Cotton seeds	India, U.S.A., Middle East, China
Maize	America, Canada
Rape seed	China, India

Oils are extracted from clean seeds by pressure and solvent extraction. The oil extracted by pressure only is known as cold pressed oil, and is the best quality. It contains vitamin E, which is a natural anti-oxidant that prevents the oil from turning rancid. Mechanical extraction is carried out by heating the seeds and crushing them by machine. The heat destroys the vitamin E, and the oils are liable to turn rancid more quickly. The crushed seeds from the mechanical extraction are treated with a solvent that dissolves the oil in the seeds. The solvent is then evaporated to leave a crude oil.

Cold pressed oil contains the minimum of impurities and is suitable for use in cooking without further refining. Examples of these oils are walnut oil and olive oil. Oils extracted by mechanical and solvent methods contain impurities and colouring matter, making them unsuitable for use in cooking. For this reason, these oils must be refined to make them suitable for cooking and eating.

The refining process removes all impurities, colour, aroma and flavour from the oils, leaving them tasteless, odourless, crystal clear and pale yellow in colour, and suitable for culinary purposes. An anti-oxidant is added to prevent them from turning rancid.

For many purposes in the food industry it is desirable to use vegetable oils which have been hardened into solid fats. Oils can be converted to solid fats by a process of hydrogenation, when the oils are treated with fragments of nickel and hydrogen gas under pressure (see Chapter 5). The nickel fragments are removed by filtration, and when cool the hydrogenated oils will set solid to become a fat. These vegetable fats have a higher melting point than animal fats, and may either be used in the solid state or be melted and used in the liquid state. Hydrogenated fats will always set solid when cold.

Hardened vegetable fats are used in the manufacture of margarine and shortenings — these are fats which shorten doughs and pastes i.e. make them light and tender. Fats split the gluten by forming a film which weakens the gluten sufficiently to make it tender, shortening the dough or paste.

Margarine
Margarine was invented in 1869 by Mèges-Mouriés as a substitute for butter. It contained beef dripping and sour milk, emulsified together. Today the product is made from blends of vegetable fats, skimmed milk or whey, lecithin, flavouring, salt, colouring and vitamins A and D, emulsified together to give a texture suitable for cooking and table use. The blends of oils used can be varied to produce margarines with different textures for specific purposes.

Cake margarine
Cake margarine is made from a blend of oils which have a low melting point, and from vegetable fats. As the name suggests, it is used for cakes because it creams easily and has good egg absorption, resulting in cakes which have bulk and lightness.

Pastry margarine
Pastry margarine is produced for making puff pastry, and it must be able to stand up to machine rolling and still produce a light puff paste. This product is a blend of oils and fats with a firm but waxy texture enabling the margarine to be folded into the dough without oozing out when rolled. The baked goods have lightness, but may be hard to the tooth because of the blend of fats used.

Table margarine
Table margarine is prepared by blending oils and fats which have low melting points. This enables them to be spread easily. Table margarines are fortified with vitamins A and D, as vegetable oils and fats do not contain these nutrients.

Quality
Oils and fats are widely used in the kitchen for a variety of recipes and uses, and the type of oil or fat is very important. Even after refining the oils retain some of their original flavour and colour, and if used for mayonnaise or salad dressings will leave an unpleasant flavour in the mouth. Generally, edible oils should be light golden in colour, with no rancid smell. Always purchase oils and fats from reputable manufacturers if quality is to be maintained.

Oil is the most popular deep-frying medium and it undergoes changes when continually used. If fats are used for deep frying, care must be taken when melting prior to use to ensure that a fierce or full heat is avoided, since this can cause the fat in contact with the elements on the bottom of the fryer to scorch, giving an undesirable flavour and reducing the life of the fat. Vegetable fats and oils have different temperatures at which they are suitable for deep frying. They should not be allowed to reach smoke point, as this also causes deterioration. A fat or oil is ready for deep frying when a haze is seen on the surface and the surface of the fat or oil is perfectly still.

Self assessment questions

Vegetable fats and oils
1 Name four sources of vegetable oils.
2 Briefly describe how vegetable oils are refined.
3 Suggest ways of using vegetable oils in the kitchen.
4 How are oils converted to solid fats?
5 What is the purpose of converting oils to solid fats?
6 How are the different textures in margarine obtained?
7 What are shortenings, and why are they used in cookery?

Tea

The tea with which we are familiar is obtained by processing the leaves of *Camellia sinensis*, which is commonly known as the tea plant. The plants are pruned to form bushes 1–1.4 m high to facilitate the plucking of the leaves for tea production. These bushes are cultivated on plantations in East Africa, Sri Lanka (Ceylon), India, China, Japan and Pakistan. The plantations range from sea level to 1800 m, and during the growing season the leaves are plucked every 7–10 days. The growing season varies from country to country. Only the first two leaves and the bud are plucked for tea production. It takes approximately 4.5 kg of freshly plucked leaves to produce 1 kg of black tea.

To produce black tea the leaves undergo various treatments and processes which change them from crisp green to pieces of dried black leaves which

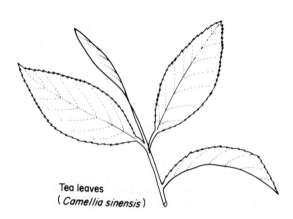

Tea leaves
(*Camellia sinensis*)

have their own characteristic shape, flavour and aroma. The main stages of manufacture are briefly described below.

The leaves are withered in currents of warm air to reduce them to a soft limp condition. The withered leaves are rolled to break the leaf cells and release the juices. During the rolling process the leaves are formed into balls, and these are separated by roll-breaking. The separated leaves are left to oxidise or ferment in a cool humid room. It is at this stage that the leaves develop their characteristic shape and the flavour. If the leaves are allowed to over-ferment they will become sour and will be useless. During this stage the leaves change colour to a bright copper, and chemical changes occur. The leaves are then dried or fired in currents of hot air to remove all the moisture, and the colour changes to dark brown or black. At this stage the tea is of all different shapes and sizes, and must be graded before being sold.

Tea is graded according to size, and not quality, into three grades, each grade having many varieties. Leaf teas generally give more flavour and

Leaf teas	Broken teas	Fannings
Darjeeling	Broken Pekoe	Pekoe fannings
Orange Pekoe	Broken Orange Pekoe	Dust

fragrance, while broken teas and fannings give teas with a darker liquor and a stronger flavour.

Once graded, the teas are placed into plywood tea chests lined with tinfoil to keep the tea dry during transit. On arrival in this country the teas are kept in bonded warehouses where they are weighed and marked. The tea is then sold to the tea merchants by auction at Sir John Lyon House, London. Most of the teas sold in this country are blended, and contain many varieties of tea from different countries.

Tea contains a small amount of caffeine, which is released slowly, acting as a stimulant.

Cocoa

The cocoa pod is the fruit of the *Theobroma cacao*, which is now grown in Ghana, Nigeria and the Cameroons. The pods contain cocoa beans, which are prepared and manufactured into cocoa powder and chocolate products. To produce cocoa the beans are allowed to ferment in the pulp in which they are embedded. This kills the germ and prevents germination: at the same time the beans absorb liquid from the pulp and swell. The beans are generally sun-dried before being packed for export.

The beans are carefully roasted to develop the flavour and aroma, and the skins are removed. The beans are crushed into pieces known as cocoa nib, which are then ground between rollers to form a semi-liquid mass. At this stage the cocoa mass contains approximately 55% fat, the cocoa butter. This must be removed to produce cocoa powder. The cocoa butter is removed by

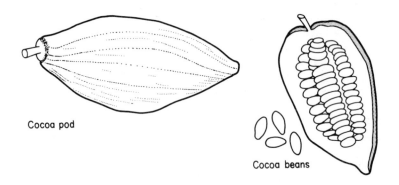

Cocoa pod

Cocoa beans

pressure, and when set is solid and white in colour. The defatted cocoa mass is allowed to set as cocoa cake, and is later ground and sifted to produce cocoa powder.

Chocolate

In the manufacture of chocolate extra cocoa butter is added to improve the texture, and milk powder and powdered sugar are added to improve the eating quality and flavour. In the manufacture of baker's chocolate a percentage of softer vegetable fat is added instead of cocoa butter to reduce the brittleness. This allows the chocolate to be cut without snapping.

Chocolate couverture is another type of chocolate which is used to cover confectionary. It must be smooth and glossy so it is melted to a temperature of 40–45°C and then cooled to below 28°C.

Cocoa powder should be very fine, and of a good colour and flavour. It may cake under pressure, but when touched should form a powder. Chocolate should be very smooth, have good flavour and colour according to whether it is plain, milk or baker's chocolate. Good quality chocolate is expensive, and price is an indication of quality.

Coffee

The two types of coffee grown commercially are the Arabica and the Canephora (which is known as robusta) coffee. Arabica coffee beans are large and oval in shape, while robusta beans are small and round.

Coffee trees are cultivated to form bushes which bear clusters of fruits, called coffee cherries. Each cherry contains two coffee beans, each with a rounded side and a flat side. Each bean is covered with a thin parchment skin, and the beans are surrounded by a pulp and the outer skin. The beans are removed from the outer skin and left to ferment before being washed and dried. At this stage the raw beans have no typical coffee flavour. They are graded according to size, variety and whether the beans are whole or broken.

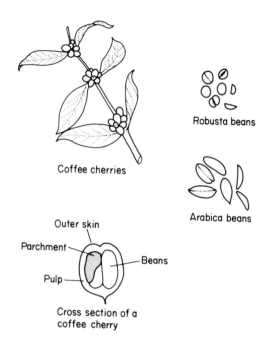

Coffee cherries

Robusta beans

Arabica beans

Outer skin

Parchment

Beans

Pulp

Cross section of a
coffee cherry

The flavour of coffee is developed by roasting the beans, which caramelises some of the sugar and makes them brittle and easily ground. The degree of roasting varies from a light to a dark roast, the darker the roast the more bitter the flavour. After roasting, the beans must be cooled and kept in airtight containers to preserve the flavour.

Coffee is ground to ensure the maximum extraction of flavour and aroma from the beans. Once ground, coffee should be percolated as soon as possible, since the essential oils are volatile and the flavour will be lost. Ground coffee must be kept in airtight containers.

The coffee beans contain caffeine, which is a stimulant, but there are brands of decaffeinated coffee available which have the caffeine removed by a special process.

Instant coffee is prepared from percolated coffee which has been dried by the spray method to form a fine soluble powder, or freeze-dried to form soluble granules. Coffee essence is prepared from percolated coffee which has the water content reduced to leave a coffee with a syrupy consistency.

The quality of coffee varies greatly, but generally speaking the Arabica varieties are the best. However, most of the coffee drunk is blended by the coffee merchants, and there are blends available to suit all tastes.

Coffee beans are named after the area or country of origin, and some of the better-known ones are Santos, Blue Mountain, Mysore, Mocha and Costa Rica.

The main coffee-producing countries of the world are the countries of South America, Jamaica, Africa and India.

Self assessment questions

Tea
1 What is the name of the tea plant, and in which countries is it grown?
2 Briefly describe the process of the manufacture of black tea.
3 How is tea graded, and what are the three grades?

Cocoa
1 Where is most of the world's cocoa grown?
2 How is cocoa powder produced from the beans?
3 How do baker's chocolate and chocolate couverture differ?

Coffee
1 What are the names of the two main types of coffee?
2 How would you recognise these two types of beans?
3 At what stage of coffee production is the flavour developed?

Sugar

The sugar generally used as a sweetening agent is obtained from sugar cane and sugar beet, and is known as sucrose. For most uses in cookery the sugar is refined to remove impurities and make it suitable for cooking and acceptable in appearance.

Sugar cane is a giant grass that resembles bamboo in appearance and is grown in the West Indies, Australia, Mauritius and South America. The sugar content, which is approximately 16%, is contained in the form of a juice in the soft fibre of the cane. This juice extracted by crushing and squeezing the cane. The juice is treated with lime and heated to neutralise the organic acids and remove impurities. It is then concentrated to form sugar crystals, which are then separated from the black molasses. The brown sugar crystals are known as Demerara sugar.

Sugar beet resembles a large parsnip in appearance. It contains approximately 18% sugar, and is grown throughout Europe, Canada and in East Anglia in Britain. The sugar is extracted by crushing the washed roots in warm water to dissolve the sugar. The resulting juice is treated as for cane sugar to form sugar crystals, also known as Demerara.

There is no difference in the chemistry of the sugar obtained from these two sources.

To remove the impurities from the brown raw sugar crystals, they are melted to form a liquid which is filtered, treated with lime and carbon dioxide, then passed through a bed of bone charcoal which removes the colour. After refining, the liquid is 99% pure sugar, and this is crystallised into many different varieties for use in the catering industry (see Table 1.8).

The fine dark brown sugars are known by various names — Muscavado, Barbados, Molasses or foot sugar. These varieties are obtained from the vats where the molasses is stored, hence the moist texture and dark colour. The fine particles of sugar settle on the bottom of the storage vats.

Table 1.8   Varieties of sugar and their uses

Variety	Colour	Size/description	Uses
Demerara	Light to dark gold	Coarse grains	Coffee, meat dishes
Barbados	Dark brown	Fine grains, moist	Cakes
Granulated	White	Medium grains, dry	General sweetening
Caster	White	Fine grains, dry	Sponges, cakes, biscuits
Icing	White	Fine powder, dry	Water icing, royal icing, dusting, pastillage
Coffee	White, brown, multi-coloured	Various, irregular sizes	Coffee
Pearls–nib	White/opaque	Irregular pieces	Buns
Cube	White	Cubes of fine or coarse grain	Sugar boiling, beverages

Sugar is also used as a medium of food preservation — see Chapter 6.

When sugar is heated to various temperatures noticeable changes occur, and this enables the confectioner or pastry chef to produce many varieties of sweet dishes, cake decorations and display pieces, as well as fondant icing (see Table 1.9 and Chapter 4). The temperature of cooking sugar is measured by a sugar thermometer (see Fig. 1.2).

Table 1.9   Stages of cooking sugar and its uses

Temperature (°C)	Stage	Uses
116	Soft ball	Marzipan
118	Ball	Fondant
121	Hard ball	Nougat
129	Light crack	
133	Crack	Dipping fruits and marzipans
143	Hard crack	Modelling, spun sugar
180	Caramel	Caramel sauce

The degree of density of a sugar solution is measured by a saccharometer. This is required for water ices, sorbets, a poaching syrup for fruits, a syrup for soaking savarins, babas and certain ice cream mixtures (see Table 1.10). The saccharometer (see Fig. 1.3) is placed in the sugar solution and rises, floats or sinks according to the density. The reading is taken at the mark level

Table 1.10   Degree of density of syrups and their uses

Degree of density (°Baumé)	Uses for the syrup
17	Water ices, sorbets
20	Poaching fruits
22	Syrup for savarins and babas
28	Bombe mixture (ice cream)
33	Candy
34	Liqueurs
42	Confectioners' glucose

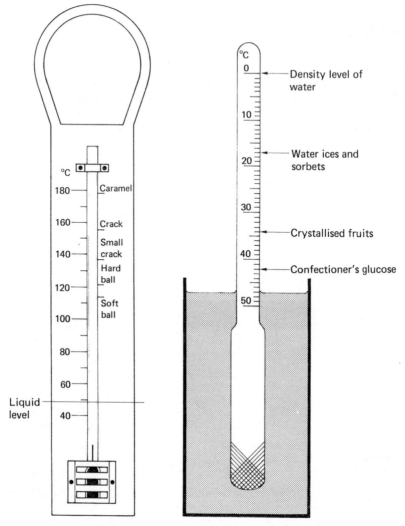

Fig. 1.2 A sugar thermometer   Fig. 1.3 A saccharometer

with the surface of the solution. The higher the reading, the denser or sweeter the syrup. The reading of the scale on a saccharometer is in degree Baumé. To test the solution for the correct density it must be at a temperature of 15°C.

Self assessment questions

Sugar
1 What are the two sources of sugar (sucrose)?
2 Briefly describe how sugar is refined.
3 Name three varieties of raw or unrefined sugar.
4 Name six varieties of white sugar.
5 What is the difference between a sugar thermometer and a saccharometer?

Part B

The origin of plant foods, photosynthesis, growth cycles, storage organs. Staple foods of the world. Plant cells and tissues. Alternative forms of food — cook–chill and cook–freeze, processed foods, new foods. Interpreting labels, additives, their uses and legislation covering their use. Questions.

Where does food come from?

Plants are the primary food producers. The green pigment, chlorophyll, in their leaves captures the radiant energy of the sun, converting it into chemical

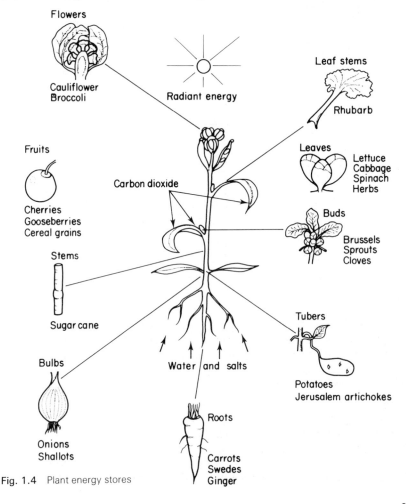

Fig. 1.4   Plant energy stores

energy to be locked safely into stores of sugars, starches or oils. These riches are intended to fuel the growth of the plant and are stored in various parts of the plant in different species (see Fig. 1.4). We, as typical animals, must rob these stores as we have no means of securing the sun's energy directly for ourselves.

On land, it is the large green plants — trees, shrubs and herbs — which are the ultimate energy producers. In the waters of the world, the food production chain begins with the smaller, simpler plants — the algae.

Food is needed for two main purposes: to provide energy and to build, and repair, our bodies.

Photosynthesis

Energy-giving foods are compounds of carbon, hydrogen and oxygen. The carbon comes from the carbon dioxide of the air. This gas enters into the spongy tissues of green leaves through small pores on their surfaces. The hydrogen comes from the water absorbed through the plant roots. The energy of sunlight splits the water molecules apart, releasing hydrogen to convert the carbon dioxide to simple sugars. At the same time, oxygen is passed into the atmosphere, allowing animals to live and breathe.

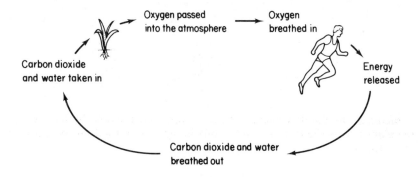

Plant food stores

The simple sugars formed by photosynthesis are bulky products. They are usually condensed to form starch, a more concentrated and less soluble material. Grains of starch can be seen in the cells of leaves which have been actively photosynthesising in sunlight. If the green chlorophyll is removed and the leaf stained with iodine, the starch grains appear as blue-black bodies. In the living plant the starch does not stay in the leaves for long. During darkness it is turned back into soluble sugar and transported to the storage organs, where it is recondensed to starch.

Some plants lay down their energy stores as oils. These reserves are mainly found in the seeds. Linseed, oil seed rape, olives and a wide variety of nuts all contain energy reserves in the form of oils.

Although plant foods are mainly thought of as energy-giving foods, they also provide us with a significant amount of the protein we require for growth and repair of tissues. Proteins, as we shall see in later chapters, differ from the energy foods in containing the element nitrogen.

Plants absorb simple nitrogen compounds from the watery solutions in the soil. The nitrogen salts are conducted from the roots to the leaves. There they combine with the products of photosynthesis to form amino acids, which are the building blocks of proteins.

Using plant energy stores

Annual plants complete their growth cycles in one season. They use most of their energy in growth, but also lay down reserves of food in their seeds for the next generation. When we grow annuals for food we use either their leaves or their seeds.

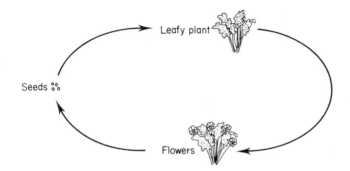

Biennials are plants which grow throughout two seasons. In the first year the plant makes the leafy growth, while in the second the flowers and seeds are formed.

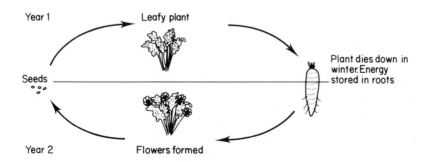

Many of our food plants are biennials. In many cases we harvest the leafy crop before the flowers are formed. We also make use of the winter stores of such plants as carrots, turnips and beets.

Perennials have a life cycle of many years. In the case of some trees it may extend to several hundred years. In these plants the energy reserves may be laid down in roots, tubers, stems and many other parts of the plant.

Plant foods originate in a variety of plant organs. Table 1.11 shows the botanical origin of a number of familiar foods. Note that some items, such as tomatoes and marrows, which are classified as fruits botanically, are termed vegetables in the kitchen because they are used for savoury dishes rather than for sweet ones.

Table 1.11 Botanical origin of familiar foods

Definition of organ	Example	
Seed Develops from the pollen and ovule — the male and female sex cells of the plant	Broad bean	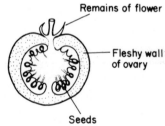 Protective seed coat Young root Young shoot Seed leaves (cotyledons) swollen with food stores
True fruit The seed box (ovary) swells when the seeds are formed. The ovary wall becomes hard (as in a nut) or fleshy (as in berries). In true fruits no other part of the plant forms part of the fruit	Tomato	Remains of flower Fleshy wall of ovary Seeds
False fruit In the false fruit, parts other than the ovary become swollen and juicy	Apple	Remains of flower Core—outer skin of the fruit Seeds Fleshy receptacle

Definition of organ	Example

Stem tuber
The tip of a stem buries itself in the ground and becomes swollen with food reserves

Jerusalem artichoke

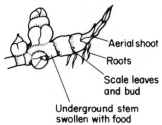

Aerial shoot
Roots
Scale leaves and bud
Underground stem swollen with food

Tap root
The main root of the plant forms the food store

Turnip

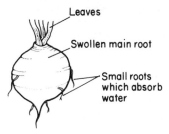

Leaves
Swollen main root
Small roots which absorb water

Flower
In a few plants the flowers are fleshy

Globe artichoke

Green bracts of flower head

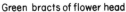

Stem
Some plants store their reserves in their main stems

Sugar cane

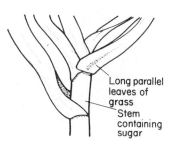

Long parallel leaves of grass
Stem containing sugar

27

Definition of organ	Example

Leaves
In most plants, the energy reserves are transferred from the leaves to other organs, but when plants are harvested while young it is often the leaves which form our food

Mint

Aromatic leaves used for flavouring

Buds
Buds are small resting shoots which grow when conditions are appropriate

Cloves

Unopened flower buds of an evergreen tree

Bulbs
In some plants, the bases of the leaves become swollen with food when the plant dies down for the winter

Onion

Protective leaf scales

Fleshy leaves

Stem

Roots

Which class do you think these plant foods belong to: potatoes, beetroot, cauliflowers, cloves, shallots, cabbages, pears, peas, plums?

Food plants

Early men were hunter-gathers who learned by trial and error which types of plants were edible. This mode of living required the expenditure of a great deal of energy just to obtain enough food to survive. A settled existence only became possible with the discovery that certain grasses — the cereals — could be grown as crops. These grasses yielded much more food for the amount of work invested in their cultivation that it was possible to obtain by gathering wild plants.

During the history of man, about 3000 species of plants have been used for food, but only about 150 species have been cultivated. Of these, around a dozen provide the staple diet of the world's population today. These are shown in Table 1.12.

Table 1.12 Staple foods of the world

	Major crops	Lesser crops
Cereals Cultivated grasses. The grains are single-seeded fruits	Wheat Rice Maize	Barley Rye Millet Oats
Starchy roots and tubers Protein content much less than that of cereals	Cassava (tapioca)	Yams Oca
Starchy fruits Protein content low	Banana	Plantain Breadfruit
Stems	Sugar cane (a cultivated grass)	Sago (from a palm)
Legumes Seeds borne in pods. Plants have nitrogen-fixing bacteria in root nodules, so are relatively independent of the need for nitrogen fertilisers	Peanut Bean Pea Lentil, etc.	
Nuts Protein content high. Energy reserves in the form of oil	Coconut	Almond Brazil Barcelona, etc.
Brassicas This genus of plants provides us with a large proportion of our vegetables	Cabbage Cauliflower Turnip Swede Radish, etc.	

Although a comparatively small number of types of plant provides the staple items of our diet, many strains and varieties have been developed within these species. Genetic manipulation and changes in crop management have produced plants which vary in their nutrient value, as well as those with increased resistance to disease and climatic damage. The different varieties lend themselves to different culinary uses as we have seen in Part A of this chapter.

Plant cells

All living organisms, apart from viruses, consist of *cells*. The taste, texture and storage characteristics of plant and animal foods depend to a large extent on the characteristics of the cells of which they are composed.

Figure 1.5 illustrates the main structures found in plant cells, as seen under the 40× lens of a microscope.

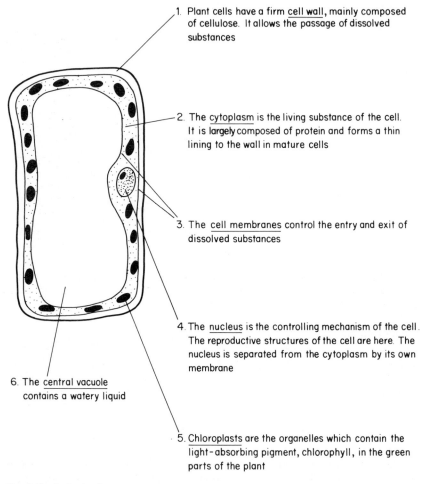

1. Plant cells have a firm cell wall, mainly composed of cellulose. It allows the passage of dissolved substances

2. The cytoplasm is the living substance of the cell. It is largely composed of protein and forms a thin lining to the wall in mature cells

3. The cell membranes control the entry and exit of dissolved substances

4. The nucleus is the controlling mechanism of the cell. The reproductive structures of the cell are here. The nucleus is separated from the cytoplasm by its own membrane

5. Chloroplasts are the organelles which contain the light-absorbing pigment, chlorophyll, in the green parts of the plant

6. The central vacuole contains a watery liquid

Fig. 1.5   A plant cell

Plant tissues

The cells which make up plants are modified to perform specialised functions. If you cut a thin slice from a potato and examine it under a microscope you will find large rounded cells packed with starch grains.

A slice down the length of a carrot will reveal in the central portion, long tubular cells with strong reinforced walls. These conduct the water from the roots to the stems and leaves.

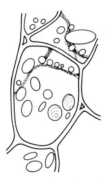

Fig. 1.6 Starch grains in potato cells

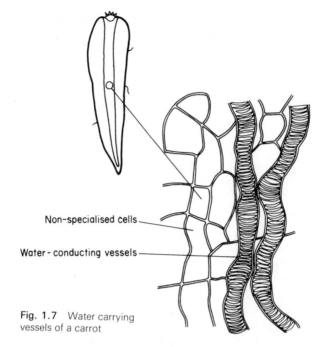

Non-specialised cells

Water-conducting vessels

Fig. 1.7 Water carrying vessels of a carrot

Groups of cells of similar shape and function are known as *tissues*. *Organs* such as stems, leaves and roots are composed of a number of different tissues each with its own function in the role of the organ as a whole.

Changes in tissues
When we are dealing with natural fresh foods, whether of plant or animal origin, we must realise that changes occur from the moment they are harvested. In later chapters we will investigate these changes as they occur during storage, cooking and preservation.

Interpreting the label

When we judge quality in fresh foods, meat, fruit and vegetables we mainly rely on our senses. Processed and convenience foods cannot be evaluated in this way. We have to depend to a large extent on information supplied by the manufacturer. In the case of prepacked goods a lot of useful information can be acquired by reading the labels critically. Manufacturers of such goods are required by The Labelling of Food Regulations 1970 (as amended) to list the ingredients in descending order by weight, and to give their name and address in case of complaint. Sometimes these lists yeild some surprising information. Water, salt or sugar may prove to be a larger proportion of many products than the buyer first supposed.

At the bottom of the list there will be some materials collectively known as 'additives'. These are substances deliberately added to foods to perform known functions. These functions include improving flavour, texture or colour, and prolonging the keeping quality. Additives may be listed by their chemical names or by 'E' numbers. The E numbers refer to the E.E.C. additive code. Each permitted additive has been given a number. Similar types are grouped together, so that a number between 100 and 199 means the substance is a colour while 200-299 covers the preservatives (Table 1.13 gives further details). While the major ingredients on labels are likely to be familiar to the purchaser, the additives are less likely to be so. Examples of the main types and their functions are given below.

Table 1.13   A guide to the E.E.C. additives code

'E' numbers	Substances
100–180	Colouring agents
200–290	Preservatives
300–321	Antioxidants
325–341(c)	pH buffering agents
400–485	Emulsifiers, stabilisers, gelling agents, humectants

Preservatives
Foods change due to microbial decay, enzymic breakdown and oxidation. Preservatives and antioxidants are added to prevent or slow down these reactions. Many substances are regarded as 'natural preservatives' because they have been used traditionally for this purpose, and often these have nutritional value in their own right. Sugar, salt, spices, alcohol, lactic acid and wood smoke come into this category. These are not regarded as chemical additives, and are not subject to food additive legislation.

Chemical preservatives fall into two main categories — organic acids and curing salts. Sulphur dioxide, benzoic, propionic and sorbic acids are the main acid materials used to preserve food (see Table 1.14). They are active at very low concentrations and are not dependent on the degree of acidity (pH) they induce in the food. Benzoic acid occurs naturally in some berries (e.g. cranberries and raspberries).

Curing salts
Sodium and potassium nitrates (and nitrites) have been used to cure meats for many centuries. The salts change the red colour of meat to pink, and inhibit the growth of bacteria. Nitrites are particularly effective in controlling the most dangerous of the food-poisoning bacteria, *Clostridium botulinum* (see Chapter 8). The maximum concentration of these salts is carefully controlled, as nitrites can react with constituents in meats to form nitrosamines which are carcinogenic.

Antioxidants
Oxidation plays an important part in a number of chemical reactions which deteriorate foods, particularly rancidity in fats and enzymic browning in fruits and vegetables. Antioxidants retard these reactions by removing the oxygen before damage can be done to the food. Vitamin E (alpha-

Table 1.14 Acid preservatives commonly used in foods

Substance	Foods permitted to contain the additive	Range permitted (ppm)	Notes
Benzoic acid (E210) and salts (E211, E212)	Soft drinks Horseradish Coffee	80–2000	Rapidly excreted from the body
Propionic acid (E280) and salts (E281–283)	Flour Bread and confectionary	1000–3000	Used to prevent 'rope' bacterial slime contamination (see Chapter 3)
Sorbic acid (E200) and salts (E201–E203)	Hard cheeses Pickles Cakes	200–1000	Particularly effective against moulds. Found naturally in some fruits
SO_2 (E220) and sulphites (E221)	Wine Fruit juices Sausages	60–2000	Destroy thiamine, so not permitted in meats or other foods which are important sources of vitamin B_1

tocopherol) is a natural antioxidant which occurs in plant oils and protects them from rancidity for a limited period. Vitamin C (ascorbic acid) also has this property, and it prevents browning in those fruits where it occurs naturally and in some manufactured products where it is added artificially.

Two synthetic substances which are related to vitamin E, B.T.H. (butylated hydroxyanisole) and B.H.T. (butylated hydroxytoluene) are the main antioxidants added to oils and fats to retard rancidity. Salts of gallic acid are also added to cooking fats and used to protect vitamin oils. Ethoxyquin is used to prevent enzymic browning in apples and pears.

Colouring agents
Many natural colours in foods are adversely affected by cooking and processing. Some manufactured foods would look very unattractive if they were not artificially coloured. However, there is a wide selection of natural products which are used to colour foods. A selection is shown in Table 1.15.

Colouring agents are controlled by The Colouring Matter in Food Regulations 1973 (as amended) and by the E.E.C. directive which approximates the laws of member states regarding colouring materials in food. This legislation:

1 Bans all added colour in:
   raw meat (not smoked),
   fresh fruit and vegetables,
   white bread and
   tea and coffee.
2 It permits only natural colours in butter and cheese.
3 It prescribes which natural and synthetic colours may be used in foods.

Table 1.15 Some natural products used to colour foods

Product	Colour	Origin
Beta-carotene	Yellow	Carrots, green vegetables, palm oil
Cochineal	Red	Extracted from the females of a Mexican insect, *Coccus cacti*
Cocoa	Brown	From the fruit of the cocoa plant, *Theobroma cacao*
Turmeric	Yellow	From the dried rhizome of a plant of the ginger family
Saffron	Yellow	Dried stigmas of *Crocus sativus*
Annatto	Yellow	From pods of a tree, *Bixa orellana*
Unrefined sugars	Brown	Sugars still retaining some molasses
Paprika	Red	From the fruits of *Capsicum annum*
Indigo	Blue	From the Indigo fern

The original synthetic dyes were developed for the textile industry. They were more intense and less likely to fade, and often cheaper than natural products, so many of them found their way into processed foods. However, over the years the safety of using some of these dyes in foods was challenged, so that only a limited number are permitted today. A selection is given below.

Substance	'E' number
Tartrazine (yellow)	102
Sunset Yellow F.C.F.	110
Green S	142
Brilliant Black BN	151
Amaranth (red)	123
Patent Blue V	131

Flavouring materials

The number of flavouring materials used in foods is much larger and less controlled than the colours. The natural flavours are due to complex mixtures of chemical substances which produce sensations of both smell and taste. In some cases, natural materials can be used in their native state to impart flavour to food, as with the herbs, spices and aromatic seeds. Other flavours can be extracted in the form of essential oils or essences. Some examples are oils of peppermint, orange, citronella, spearmint, bitter almonds and vanilla essence. The natural essences tend to be rather unstable and are often expensive, so they are supplemented with other types of substances. They may be identical with one of the constituents in a natural flavouring, if it is possible to isolate or synthesise the compound. An example of such a compound is vanillin, the main flavouring constituent of the vanilla bean.

More often, the synthetic flavouring is a chemically unrelated product which happens to produce a similar effect on the human nose and taste buds. Most of these are esters — substances produced by reactions between an alcohol and an organic acid. Some examples of these synthetic flavourings are given below.

34

Substance	Flavours
Esters	
Pentyl butanoate	Banana, peach
Ethyl ethanoate (acetate)	Apple, pear
Pentyl ethanoate (acetate)	Pear, pineapple
Aldehydes	
Benzaldehyde	Almonds
Ethyl vanillin	Vanilla

Apart from the fruity flavours, extracts and synthetic mixtures have been produced to simulate bacon, chicken, onion and smokey flavours. They are used to flavour crisps and other savoury products.

Flavour enhancers

Flavour enhancers are used to 'bring out the flavour' of foods. Beef extract, soy sauce and yeast extract are all used for this purpose. Monosodium glutamate (M.S.G.) is used to intensify the flavour of many convenience foods. The material is made by fermenting a sugary medium with a cheap source of nitrogen using a bacterium called *Micrococcus glutamicus*. The product is crystalline and smells like sauerkraut. The crystals have a sweet and salty taste, but these tastes are not passed on to the food. Their effect is to enhance the meaty or fishy flavour of the food. M.S.G. is a traditional ingredient of Chinese and Southeast Asian dishes, as well as being a common ingredient in modern processed foods. The substance can cause unpleasant symptoms such as headache, nausea and sweating if taken in excessive amounts.

Artificial sweeteners

Artificial sweeteners are used to replace sugar completely or partially in soft drinks and in many processed foods. These substances have much greater sweetening power than sugar but are non-nutritive, so they are useful in diet foods and for diabetics. The sweeteners which have been most widely used are saccharine and cyclamates.

Saccharine was discovered in 1879. It is over 500 times as sweet as sugar, but has an unpleasant bitter aftertaste. Another drawback to its use is that it decomposes on heating. Cyclamates were discovered more recently. They were found to be only 30 times as sweet as sugar, but are stable to heat and have no bitter aftertaste. A mixture of nine parts of cyclamate to one of saccharine was used extensively to sweeten soft drinks until 1970. Then research brought the safety of cyclamates into question. Rats fed large doses of the sweetener developed tumours. As a consequence cyclamates were banned, first in the U.S.A. and then in the U.K.

Many other artificial sweeteners have been discovered, but so far none have been accepted for general use. One of the most promising of these substances is aspartame, which has been approved for table use in the U.S.A.

Emulsifiers and stabilisers

Emulsifiers are substances which allow normally incompatible materials to mix together and form uniform dispersions known as emulsions (see Chapter 4, Eggs). Stabilisers are materials added to maintain emulsions. These substances are subject to The Emulsifiers and Stabilisers in Food Regulation 1980 (as amended) and a related E.E.C. directive. The legislation states that:

1 No added emulsifiers are permitted in milk, cream and flour,
2 Only specified types of emulsifiers are allowed in cheese and bread and
3 Only emulsifiers and stabilisers which are listed are permitted in other foods.

Emulsifiers are used in the preparation of solid cooking fats, salad dressings, ice cream mixes and in the preparation of bakery goods. They are essential ingredients of many convenience foods (such as instant puddings, coffee complements and soup powders) where they aid efficient dispersion of the powders on reconstitution with water.

Emulsifiers are substances with double-action molecules. One end has an affinity with the oily part of the suspension, and the other with the watery phase (see Chapter 4). A number of natural products have this ability — notably egg yolk, which is used in cakes and salad creams largely because it possesses this property.

Stabilisers change emulsions in various ways so they are less likely to break down. Many are composed of large molecules, and thicken the watery phase of the emulsion so that it does not separate from the oily part. Many natural materials have this property — starches, gums, agar, carrageen and egg albumin.

The most widely used emulsifiers are mono- and diglycerides. Normal fats are triglycerides, composed of molecules of glycerol with three fatty acids attached (see Chapter 3). In mono- and diglycerides only one or two fatty acids are attached to the glycerol. This gives emulsifying properties, since the free groups of the glycerol are water-soluble and the fatty acids are fat-soluble. When these materials are added to fats, the shortenings are known as superglycerinated or high ratio fats.

Glyceryl monostearate (G.M.S.)
This glyceride with a single fatty acid is used as a plasticiser to soften the crumb in bread-making. It is also used in the manufacture of fats where it reduces the 'spitting' during fying by preventing the dispersed water from separating from the fat.

Polyoxyethylene monostearate (P.O.E.M.S.)
This emulsifier is also used in the production of bakery goods. It differs from G.M.S. in being more water-soluble.

Sodium carboxymethyl cellulose (S.C.M.C.)
This is one of the products which can be made by chemical treatment of the cellulose from wood pulp or cotton. These materials are used to stabilise jellies and ice creams. They have no nutrient value, so are often used to provide bulk in 'slimming' foods.

Improvers and bleaches

Although wholewheat and wholemeal breads have become increasingly popular in recent years there are still a large number of people in the U.K. who prefer white bread. Consequently bread flours other than wholemeal and wheatmeal have to be chemically bleached. Bread flours also need 'ageing', as recently-milled flour makes a weak dough. Flour which has been stored for some time is 'improved', i.e. it forms a stronger dough. The effect is due to oxidation of the gluten, the protein complex which forms the structure of the bread. Flours can be improved more quickly by adding oxidising agents such as potassium bromate, chlorine dioxide or ascorbic acid.

Chlorine dioxide is very effective both in bleaching and in ageing flour, but has the disadvantage of destroying vitamin E.

Chlorine, as such, is not permitted as a bleach in bread flours, but is used in cake and biscuit flour. It softens the flour, making it more suitable for these purposes, but destroys the thiamine in the flour.

Agene (nitrogen trichloride) was once widely used as a flour improver, but is not permitted today as it was found to produce a toxic substance when it reacted with methionine, an amino acid present in flour.

Humectants

Humectants are substances which absorb and hold moisture, and so help to keep bakery products fresh and soft-textured. Examples are glucose syrup, glycerol and sorbitol.

Fortifying agents, restoration, enrichment

Vitamins, minerals and some other nutrients are added to a variety of foods for different reasons. In the case of flour and margarines the additions are legal requirements in the U.K.

Restoration of white flours

Calcium enrichment of flours began in 1942 when it was feared there might not be sufficient available calcium in the national diet. The standard wartime loaf contained more bran than the modern white loaf. Bran contains phytic acid, which is known to make calcium less soluble. Calcium enrichment was continued when the loaf became 'white' again.

At present, all flours except wholemeal and certain self-raising flours must have calcium carbonate, iron, thiamine and nicotinic acid added to bring them up to the following levels:

Calcium carbonate	235–390 mg/100 g flour
Iron	1·65 mg/100 g flour
Thiamine	0·24 mg/100 g flour
Nicotinic acid	1·60 mg/100 g flour

Margarine

The Margarine Regulations 1967 require margarines to be fortified with vitamins A and D to bring them to the same level of vitamin content as butter which has been produced in the summer.

Enrichment

Apart from the legally required additions, enrichment is practised by manufacturers of a wide range of foods. In some cases, as with breakfast cereals, it is a major selling point. Some examples are shown below.

Food	Additions
Evaporated milk	Vitamin D
Baby foods	Vitamin D
Some malted milk drinks	Vitamin D
Some breakfast cereals	Vitamins B_1, B_2, nicotinic acid, iron
Some T.V.P. products	Vitamins B_1, B_2, B_{12}, iron
Some fruit drinks	Vitamin C
Some yoghurts	Vitamins A and D
Salt	Some salt is iodised, as a precaution against goitre in areas where the water lacks this element

Alternative forms of food

The catering industry has been greatly affected by the advance of food technology over the last decade, which has led to the development of food-processing plants and large-scale kitchens which prepare, cook and preserve many classical dishes so that they only require reheating.

The two main advances which have affected the industry are cook–chill and cook–freeze. These two systems enable foods to be prepared, cooked and chilled or frozen in production kitchens, and then distributed to different outlets such as schools, canteens, hotels, restaurants and institutions. The dishes are then heated on site in microwave ovens, computerised deep friers or other rapid-heating equipment (see Chapter 4).

Other forms of processed foods are collectively known as convenience foods. These are foods which were once prepared by the consumer, but are now wholly or partly processed by the manufacturer. They are best classified by their methods of preservation (see Chapter 6). Convenience foods are valuable to caterers because they:

(a) assist in portion control,
(b) cut wastage,
(c) reduce the labour costs of preparation,
(d) are easy to store,
(e) are readily available in emergencies and
(f) are not subject to seasonal variations.

New foods

At present, global food supplies are adequate to satisfy the hunger of the world's population. These supplies are, however, very unevenly distributed, so industrial nations suffer the diseases of affluence — obesity and heart disease — while the Third World is chronically undernourished and periodically endures famine. Righting the imbalance will not be easy, as it depends on many complex geographical, climatic, political and economic factors. Greater problems, however, loom in the not too distant future as food has to be found for an ever-growing human population. New forms of food are urgently needed. The only new food developed in recent years is textured vegetable protein (T.V.P.), which is produced from defatted soya beans. The flour is spun into fine threads to represent meat fibres and then compressed and shaped into chunks or mince. Textured vegetable protein is used as a meat extender with fresh meat, and is available in various meat flavours. It absorbs the flavour and juices of any accompanying meat and has a similar flavour when cooked. It is an inexpensive form of high quality protein and unlike meat, it does not shrink so is particularly useful in pies. It has a slight beany flavour which needs disguising. Although high in protein, it lacks some of the nutrients present in meat, so requires enrichment if it is to be used to replace meat in vegetarian cookery (see Chapter 5). Although T.V.P. is mainly used in meat products at present, it can equally well be used to bulk out fish or even fruit products, as it takes up these flavours and prevents shrinkage. Other legumes are already being investigated for use as supplies of cheap protein. Lupins are being grown in the U.K. for cattle food; similar crops may prove suitable for human food.

Microorganisms grow much more rapidly than the higher plants. The novel foods of the future are likely to come from this source. We already have the technology to grow many species of microorganisms on a large scale in continuous culture. These processes have been developed in the food fermentation industries and in vaccine production. Algae, fungi and bacteria can be grown on simple media or on the wastes of existing industries — whey from cheese making and brewery or paper-making effluents.

Microbial cells produced in this way could be harvested and used to feed animals, releasing cereals and fish meal now used for this purpose for human use.

Alternatively, the proteins could be extracted and processed in a similar way to T.V.P. There will be some problems to be overcome in adapting microbial products for use as human foods. The main ones will be:

1 to modify the products so they do not produce digestive or other health problems,
2 to adapt the texture and flavour so that they are acceptable to the consumer, and
3 to produce the new foods at an economical price, since the technology is likely to remain in the industrialised West for some time, and the need likely to be in the developing countries.

Self assessment questions

Alternative forms of food
1 In what ways are convenience foods an aid to the caterer?
2 What is textured vegetable protein? What are the advantages and disadvantages of using it?

3 State two new methods of food production in the catering industry, and describe the establishments in which they may be used.
4 In a list of ingredients on food labels what do the 'E' series of numbers indicate?
5 Explain the functions of the following food additives: G.M.S., ethyl ethanoate, benzoic acid, B.H.A., sodium nitrate, chlorine dioxide, monosodium glutamate, sorbitol.
6 Which nutrients are used to fortify white flours in the U.K.?

2
What is food? — Animal foods

Part A

Animal food commodities. Definitions, quality, grading, varieties of meat, poultry, eggs, game, offal, fish, milk and cream. Questions.

Meat

The term 'meat' refers to the flesh obtained from bovines (beef-type animals) and ovines (sheep and goats).

In the catering industry the flesh obtained from these animals is classed as butcher's meat, to distinguish it from poultry and game. The flesh of meat changes its name depending on the age of the animal.

Veal is the flesh obtained from young bovines (from birth to 6 months) of either sex. Beef is the flesh obtained from heifers, bullocks and steers aged from 18 months to 3 years. A heifer is a female which has not produced young, a bullock is a male which has not been used for breeding, and a steer is a castrated male reared for beef production.

Lamb is the flesh obtained from young sheep (up to 1 year old) and mutton is the flesh of mature sheep aged 2–3 years.

Pork is the flesh of breeds of pigs classed as porker pigs aged up to 7 months, and is obtained from animals of either sex.

Animal muscle

The flesh or muscle of animals is composed of tiny fibrils bound together in bundles by strong connective tissues. The cuts of meat which come from muscles which are extensively used tend to be tough e.g. neck and breast of mutton, whereas those from muscles which are little used are tender e.g. loin of lamb and sirloin of beef. Some cuts of meat are tough because they consist of several small muscles and so have a large amount of connective tissue e.g. shin of beef.

Hanging of meat

After slaughter the flesh becomes stiff and hard (*rigor mortis*), and if cooked it would be very tough and tasteless. For this reason meat is hung to develop flavour and tenderness (see Chapter 3, *Post mortem* changes in meat).

Hanging times for the various meats vary according to the animals and the time of year. Meat is hung for a shorter time in the summer and longer in the winter. A guide to the approximate hanging times are:

Beef	10–14 days,
Veal	3–5 days,
Lamb	3–5 days,
Mutton	5–7 days,
Pork	3–5 days.

Recognition of quality in meat

Flesh

Beef should be dark red in colour, flecked with fat to give a marbled appearance, and firm to the touch.

Lamb should be bright red in colour, and firm.

Mutton should be darker than lamb, and firm to the touch.

Veal should be white to pale pink, firm and moist.

Pork should be pale pink in colour, and firm.

Fat

Meat obtains its flavour from the fat, and the carcase should have sufficient fat to cover the flesh without being too heavy or thick. The fat melts during cooking and bastes the joint, keeping it moist.

Beef fat should be creamy white in colour, brittle and firm.

Lamb fat should be white, brittle and flaky.

Pork fat and mutton fat should be white and hard.

Veal fat should be white and fairly firm.

Most of the meat in this country is home-produced. The main imported meats are lamb and mutton (from New Zealand) and veal (from Holland), although some very good veal is being produced at home.

Poultry

Birds classed as poultry are the domestic birds reared for egg production and for their edible flesh. These birds are chickens, turkeys, ducks, geese and guinea fowl.

Chickens

Chickens are graded according to age and weight, and are known to the catering trade by the grades shown in Table 2.1.

Chickens are produced by two main methods: the broiler method, where they are reared in large sheds, and the free range method, where they are kept in large paddocks.

High quality chickens should have firm white flesh and unbroken skin. Young roasting birds have a pliable tip at the base of the breastbone. If this bone is firm, it has ossified, indicating an old bird. The scales on the legs

Table 2.1 Classification of chickens

Grade	Weight	Page
Spring chicken (poussin)	340 g	4–6 weeks
Double spring chicken	450–680 g	6±8 weeks
Small roasting chicken	900–1350 g	8–10 weeks
Medium roasting chicken	1.35–1.8 kg	10–12 weeks
Large roasting chicken	1.8–2.25 kg	12–16 weeks
Boiling fowls	1.8–2.7 kg	12–18 months

should be smooth, and no unpleasant smell or discolouration to the flesh should be apparent.

Chicken may be purchased fresh and drawn, fresh and undrawn, or frozen oven-ready.

Turkeys

With today's methods of rearing and production, turkeys range from small birds of 3 kg to large birds of 14 kg or more. They are available all the year round, with the main market being for the Christmas trade.

The flesh should be white with a mauvish tinge, the breasts firm and full. The legs of prepared birds are generally pulled to remove the coarse tendons from them. Turkeys are purchased fresh and drawn, or frozen over-ready.

Geese

These are larger than ducks, with a darker fatty flesh, and are not in such demand as other poultry. Mainly available at Christmas time.

Guinea fowl

The flesh has a mauvish tinge and should be firm with plump breasts. The legs should have fine scales. The base of the breast bone should be pliable. They are purchased fresh and drawn, or frozen oven-ready.

Most poultry does not require hanging, and may be cooked a day after being killed and prepared. With the exception of ducks and geese, poultry is deficient in fat and is easily digested. A small piece of fat is placed over the breasts to keep them moist during cooking. The birds which do require hanging are guinea fowl and turkeys.

Eggs

The varieties of eggs used in cookery are those from hens, turkeys, ducks, geese, quails and plovers. The last two birds mentioned are protected species in this country. With the exception of hens' eggs they must all be well cooked to ensure that they do not cause Salmonella poisoning. Hens' eggs are the most widely used, and may be cooked by any suitable method.

Eggs are produced by three methods: free range, deep litter and battery.

Hens' eggs are graded according to size and quality. The quality is indicated by the *class*. The top quality is Class A, and the grade sizes which correspond to the weight are as follows:

Grade	Weight
1	more than 70 g
2	65–70 g
3	60–65 g
4	55–60 g
5	50–55 g
6	45–50 g
7	less than 45 g

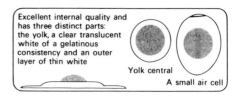

Excellent internal quality and has three distinct parts: the yolk, a clear translucent white of a gelatinous consistency and an outer layer of thin white

Yolk central

A small air cell

Class A eggs should have a clean, slightly rough shell. The air sac should not exceed 6 mm. The white should be very gelatinous, holding the firm yolk in the centre, and there should be no foreign bodies in the white or yolk.

Stale eggs have thin or watery whites, and the yolks become weak and easily broken.

Game

The animals and birds classified as game are the wild varieties which are used for food and are killed by hunting and shooting. The wild birds are classed as feathered game, and the wild animals as ground or furred game.

The main game birds are partridge, pheasant, grouse, quail, capercaille, woodcock, snipe and wild duck (teal, wigeon and mallard). The furred game in this country are wild rabbits, hare and deer.

All game have seasons and must only be taken during their seasons, which are listed in Table 2.2.

Table 2.2 Game and their seasons

Game	Season	Game	Season
Grouse	12 Aug–10 Dec	Mallard	1 Sept–20 Feb
Partridge	1 Sept–31 Jan	Teal	1 Sept–20 Feb
Pheasant	1 Oct–31 Jan	Wigeon	1 Sept–20 Feb
Woodcock	1 Oct–31 Jan	Hare }	1 Aug–Last day
Snipe	12 Aug–31 Jan	Wild rabbit }	of April
Quail	1 Sept–31 Jan	Deer	1 Nov–31 March

Game must be hung to allow the flavour to develop and to tenderise the flesh. Hanging times vary according to weather conditions, but game must never be hung so long that the flesh starts to decompose.

Hares are hung uncleaned, wild rabbits and deer are gutted or paunched immediately after killing, while game birds are hung undrawn and unplucked. The exception is quail, which does not require hanging.

Game is deficient in fat and the flesh may be dry. Therefore it is sometimes marinaded to prevent undue dryness, and the acid in the marinade helps to tenderise the flesh.

Young game birds should have plump breasts and unbroken skin. The beaks should be easily broken, the spurs on the feet should be short and the scales smooth. The webbed feet of water fowl should tear easily.

Young ground game, hares and wild rabbits are distinguished by having sharp claws, ears which tear easily and, with hares, a hare lip which is hardly noticeable. Deer is at its best when 4–5 years old, when the cleft of the hooves are smooth and close, the fat should be bright and clear, and the flesh dark red.

There is always the problem with game that it can never be graded — because of the way it is obtained — and the age can never be determined until it has been killed. The above points will help to distinguish a young bird or animal from an old one.

Animal fats

Fats are oils which become solid at room temperature. There are four animal fats used in cookery: suet, dripping, lard and butter. These are used as shortening agents for doughs and for deep and shallow frying.

Animal fats should have a pleasant smell, with no indication of rancidity.

Suet
This is a hard, brittle, white fat obtained from the kidney regions of animals. Beef suet is the only suet used in cookery, because it has a neutral flavour. It is used for suet pastry, stuffing, mincemeat and Christmas pudding.

Dripping
Dripping is obtained by rendering the raw fat trimming of the meat. Most catering establishments have sufficient meat to make their own dripping. The best dripping is made from rendered beef fat.

Lard
Lard is produced by rendering the fat trimming of pigs, and it has a softer consistency than suet or dripping.

Butter
Butter is obtained by churning milk fat (cream) into a solid mass.

Offal

The term 'offal' refers to the edible internal organs of animals and birds. Also included under the term offal are oxtail, pigs' trotters, calves' heads and pigs' heads.

Offal provides protein, minerals and small quantities of vitamins of the B group. Offal is generally deficient in fat, and easily digested. The different types of offal in general use are the following:

Liver	calf, ox, lamb, pig, poultry
Hearts	lamb, ox
Kidneys	calf, beef, lamb, pig
Sweetbreads	lamb, calf
Brains	calf, lamb
Tongue	ox, lamb
Tripe	ox
Heads	calf, pig
Tails	ox
Trotters	pig
Giblets	poultry, game

Sweetbreads are the thymus glands, from the throat region, and the pancreatic glands, from the heart region.

Tripe is the inner lining of the second and third stomachs of the bullock, heifer or steer.

Giblets of poultry and game are the necks, gizzards and hearts.

Livers
Whole livers, when purchased, are cut. This is because they have been inspected for any growth, cysts or liver flukes which would be harmful to health. The livers of the various animals vary considerably in size, shape, colour and flavour. They should be moist and firm to the touch, but not sticky or giving off an offensive smell.

Kidneys
Lambs' and pigs' kidneys actually are kidney shaped, while ox and calfs' kidneys are oval and made up of nodules. Fresh kidneys should be moist and firm, with no unpleasant smell.

Sweetbreads
These should be pale pink in colour. They are always purchased frozen, because they deteriorate quickly. Once defrosted, they should be blanched and cooked as soon as possible.

Brains
Always purchase very fresh, and never frozen. Fresh brains are creamy in colour, with tiny blood vessels which are removed before cooking.

Tongues
Lambs' tongues are purchased fresh or frozen. They are pink in colour with a rough whitish skin. Ox tongues are much darker in colour, and may be purchased fresh or salted. Fresh tongues should be firm with no unpleasant smell.

Tripe
There are two varieties of tripe: honeycomb and plain. These are purchased ready prepared and should be creamy white, with no unpleasant smell.

Heads

These should be clean and free from hair or fur, and the flesh should be moist, with no unpleasant smell or stickiness. The general appearance should be good.

Oxtail

These should have a good covering of flesh and not be too fatty and thick. The colour should be dark red. They should be moist, not sticky.

Fish

The many varieties of fish are generally classified biologically by the caterer as shown in Table 2.3.

Table 2.3 Classification of fish widely used in catering

Types	Varieties
White	
Round fish	Whiting, cod, hake, haddock, red mullet, monkfish
Flat fish	Dover sole, lemon sole, plaice, halibut, turbot, brill, skate
Oily	
All round	Salmon, salmon trout, herring, eel, mackerel, sardine, anchovy, conger eel, tunny, whitebait
Shellfish	
Crustaceans	Shrimps, prawns, scampi (Dublin Bay prawns), crayfish, lobsters, crawfish
Molluscs	
Bivalve	Oysters, mussels, scallops
Univalve	Whelks, winkles, snails

White fish

The white varieties live on or near the bottom of the sea, and are known as demersals. Flat fish have a flat cross section, and round fish have a round cross section. The oil in white fish is contained in the liver (e.g. cod liver oil), leaving the flesh free of oil and therefore easily digested.

Oily fish

Most of the oily fish live near the surface and are described as pelagic. They are generally found in shoals. The fish contain oil throughout the flesh, which makes them less digestible than white fish.

Fish contain protein and trace elements, while the oily fish also contain vitamins A and D. Fish are generally easily digested.

Unlike meat and game, fish does not require time for *rigor mortis* to pass off and must be eaten as quickly as possible while it is very fresh. Fish deteriorate quickly because of bacteria living in the gut, which multiply rapidly after death. For this reason most fish are gutted soon after being caught. The smell which develops as the fish decomposes is caused by bacteria breaking down the nitrogenous compounds which are present in the flesh.

To determine the freshness of fish we use our senses of sight, smell and touch, and the following points indicate freshness.

(a) The eyes should be prominent and well up in the sockets.
(b) The smell should be fresh.
(c) The flesh should be firm to the touch,
(d) Scales, if visible, should be plentiful and firmly attached.
(e) There should be a sea slime covering the fish.
(f) The general appearance should be good, and any markings should be prominent.
(g) Very fresh fish will be very stiff, and this indicates *rigor mortis* is still in the fish.

Fish may be purchased as whole fish, as fillets or as steaks, fresh or frozen. Some varieties are smoked, such as salmon, mackerel and herrings. The oily fish may be purchased in cans, when they are in oil or tomato sauce. Molluscs and crustaceans are available in bottles or cans in light brine.

Crustaceans
These shellfish have jointed legs and tails, and are able to move by using their limbs.

Molluscs
Molluscs have no visible limbs, and have one or two shells for protection: bivalves have two shells, univalves have one.

Crustaceans. Shrimps and prawns are purchased cooked. A bright appearance and fresh smell indicate freshness. They should be even in size for the variety.

Lobster. These should be purchased live where possible, indicated by the bluish-black shell. The two claws should be attached. Hen lobsters have a broader tail. Cooked lobsters have a bright red shell. They must be heavy for their size, and the tail, when uncurled, should spring back to the curled position, if freshly cooked.

Molluscs (bivalves). Live fish have tightly closed shells, and should be discarded if the shells are open. The smell should be fresh and the shells should be free from barnacles.

Milk

Milk is a white nutritious liquid produced by all female mammals for feeding their young. The milk obtained from cows is most widely used, but milk from asses, camels, goats and ewes may also be used.

The main breeds of cattle which make up the dairy herds in this country are Jerseys, Guernseys, Friesians, Ayrshires and South Devons. Jerseys and Guernseys produce the richest milk with a 4% milk fat (cream), and the Friesians produce the largest quantity of milk per head. Milk produced in the summer is richer than that produced during the winter. This is because the cows eat fresh grass in the summer and hay and fodder in the winter.

Milk has a high nutritional value, containing vitamins A, B, C, D, milk fat, calcium, protein, minerals and lactose. Because of the composition of milk it is an ideal food for bacteria and microorganisms which cause the milk to turn sour or become infected. For this reason, it is essential that all hygiene regulations are strictly observed at all times.

Because milk is readily contaminated, it is heat-treated and graded according to the degree of heat and the method used. These grades are recognised by the colour code of the caps and by visual recognition (see Table 2.4).

Table 2.4 Grades of milk

Grade	Temperature	Colour code	Visual recognition
Pasteurised	71°C for 15 sec	Silver	Good cream line
Homogenised	71°C for 15 sec	Red	No cream line
Sterilised	108–115°C for 20–30 min	Crown cap	No cream line-cream colour
Channel Island	71°C for 15 sec	Gold	Good rich cream line
U.H.T. long life	132°C for 1–2 sec	Wax carton (date stamped)	Nil

Milk must not be diluted with water or any other liquid if it is to be sold as fresh milk, nor must any other form of fat be added other than milk fat. There must be no off or sour aroma, and the flavour must not be tainted. As milk absorbs flavours readily it must always be kept covered.

Milk is widely used in the catering industry as a beverage, with breakfast cereals, in sweet and savoury sauces, ice cream, milk puddings, cold sweets and for poaching certain cuts of fish.

Various methods of preserving milk are explained in Chapter 6.

Cream

Cream, or milk fat, is the mass of tiny fat globules which settle on the surface of the milk when it is allowed to stand. Cream is separated from the milk by centrifugal force. Being lighter than milk, cream is retained in the centrifuge

Table 2.5 Grades of fresh cream

Grade	Legal minimum fat content (%)	Uses
Half cream	12	Coffee (will not whip)
Single cream	18	Sweets, coffee, sauces (will not whip)
Whipping cream	35	Sweets, gateaux, piping
Double cream	48	Sweets, gateaux, forcemeats
Clotted cream	55	Sweets, Devonshire teas, poached fruits

and the milk, being heavier, is spun outwards and is known as skimmed milk. The thickness of the cream depends on the amount of milk fat present in the milk and the breed of cows from which it is obtained. For this reason, cream is graded according to the fat content, which ranges from 10% fat to 55% fat (see Table 2.5). The fat content of fresh cream must be 100% milk fat.

Whipping cream and double cream have sodium alginate added. This is a stabiliser, and gives a smoother texture and appearance as well as improving the keeping qualities.

Synthetic (or imitation) creams are made from an emulsion of milk powder, water and vegetable fats and flavourings. The fat content allows them to be whipped, and they are used for cakes, pastries and sweets.

Self assessment questions

Animal foods
1 Define the following terms: meat, poultry, game, molluscs, crustaceans, white fish, oily fish, offal.
2 Explain how animal muscle is made up.
3 Why is it necessary to allow game and meat to hang?
4 What are the main animal fats, and how are they used in cooking?
5 List the points to be observed in judging the freshness of fish.
6 How are milk and cream graded? State the grades of milk. Why do the various grades of cream differ in thickness?

Part B

Animals as consumers of energy. Introduction to main food animals and their classification. Animal cells and tissues.

The origin and variety of animal foods

Plants, as we saw in Chapter 1, are the producers of energy, while animals are the consumers. The animals which live directly on plant foods are termed herbivores, or primary consumers. Amongst this group are the animals which graze as herds (cattle, sheep and goats) which have been domesticated to provide meat, milk and hides. It also includes deer and game birds hunted as much for sport as for the table. Other herbivores compete with us for nourishment — rodents, snails, birds and the vast army of insects.

The living world can be regarded as a pyramid (see Fig. 2.1). Any area of woodland, grassland, cultivated farmland, lake or river can support a large number of wild or cultivated plants. These in turn provide food for a smaller number of herbivorous animals. This is because energy is lost as it passes from the lower levels of the pyramid to the higher. It is rather like riding a

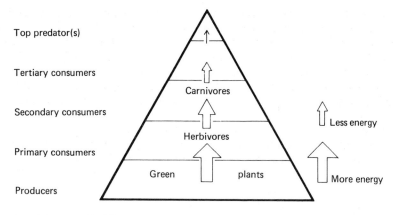

Fig. 2.1   The pyramid of life

bicycle, where all the energy you put in does not appear as useful work, i.e. movement, but is lost as heat in friction.

The animals in the next level of the pyramid which prey upon the herbivores are carnivores or, if like man they eat both types of food, omnivores. There are still less of these secondary consumers. This is one reason why animals such as tigers, lions and bears have rarely been used for food. There are fewer of them, and they are also fiercer and more difficult to domesticate. It is also the reason that animal foods are generally more expensive than plant foods. An acre of land will produce a larger amount of food if planted with wheat than if grazed by cattle. Animals mature more slowly than plants and need more daily care.

In natural conditions there may be four, or even five, levels of the living pyramid. At the top there is a large predatory animal, such as an eagle or jaguar, which needs a large territory to maintain itself and to raise young.

Agricultural conditions modify the pyramid. Plants are grown in monoculture. A large area is planted with one variety of a single species; Arran Banner potatoes or Huntsman wheat. The competing animals and plants are kept down by cultivation and chemical sprays, while the yield is artificially raised by inputs of nitrogen fertilizers.

These shortened pyramids (shown in Fig. 2.2) support the large popula-

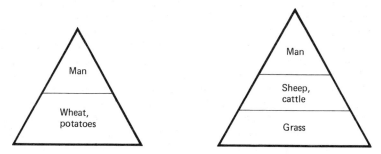

Fig. 2.2   Monocultures have shortened pyramids

tions of our cities. They can only be maintained by skill, care and research. When disease strikes a monoculture, the effect can be devastating — as with potato blight in Ireland in the nineteenth century and coffee leaf rust in Brazil in 1970.

Food animals

Mammals

In theory most of the animal kingdom could provide us with food but, as with plants, only a small proportion of the animals available have been domesticated or hunted for food (a simple classification is given in Table 2.6). Most of these belong to the backboned animals, the vertebrates. Ruminant animals are particularly useful as they can live on grass, a crop which is totally indigestible to man. They owe their ability to derive nourishment from the tough leaves of grass to the bacteria in the rumen, the first section of their specialised stomachs. The bacteria produce enzymes which split the cellulose in leaves to release sugars.

Table 2.6 A simple classification of food animals

Characteristics	Examples		
	VERTEBRATES		
Mammals	*Domesticated*	*Game*	
Hairy skins	Cows	Hares	
Live young	Sheep	Rabbits	
Produce milk	Pigs	Venison	
	Goats		
Birds	*Domesticated*	*Game*	
Feathered	Hens	Pheasants	
Forelimbs adapted to flight	Geese	Grouse	
Lay eggs	Ducks	Partridges	
	Turkeys	Wood pigeons	
		Wild ducks	
Fish			
Cold blooded	Freshwater fish	Trout	
Aquatic		Carp	
Scaly skins		Salmon	
Lay eggs	Sea fish		
	1. Pelagic fish.	Herring	
	Live at or near	Sprat	(oily
	the surface of	Mackerel	fish)
	the water	Tunny	
	2. Dermersal fish.	*Round fish*	
	Live at or near	Cod	
	the sea bottom	Haddock	(white
		Dogfish	fish)
		Whiting	
		Flat fish	
		Plaice	

Table 2.6 — *continued*

Characteristics	Examples		
		Dover sole	(white
		Lemon sole	fish)
		Turbot	
		Halibut	
		Skate	
Reptiles			
Cold blooded	Turtles		
Four legged			
Scaly skins			
Lay eggs			
Amphibia			
Cold blooded	Edible frogs		
Eggs laid in water			
Adults four legged			
	INVERTEBRATES		
Crustaceans			
Skeleton external	Lobsters		
Jointed legs	Crabs		
Aquatic	Crayfish		
Breathe by gills	Shrimps		
	Prawns		
	Scampi		
Molluscs			
Move by means of a	*Univalves*		
fleshy foot	(having one spiral	Whelks	
Most have external shells	shell)	Roman snails	
	Bivalves		
	(enclosed in two	Mussels	
	shells)	Cockles	
		Scallops	
		Oysters	

Rabbits have a similar mechanism in an enlarged part of their intestines called the caecum. Rabbits were managed in warrens in Britain from medieval times to produce an economical source of meat. In fact, it was not until the Second World War that rabbits were considered such a threat to agriculture that they merited a full-scale campaign to reduce their numbers.

Apart from the ruminant animals (cattle, sheep, goats and deer) the other main source of meat is the pig. Pigs are less efficient in converting fibrous plants to human food than ruminants, but they have the advantage of being omnivorous. They can be fed on a wide selection of foods, including those which are unsuitable for man or other domestic animals. Where they are most successful is in turning cereals into flesh. They have a high rate of reproduction. Eleven piglets in a litter is common and the sows may farrow more than twice a year.

Pigs have been the traditional animals to keep on small holdings for subsistance farming. However, they are social animals and lend themselves to large-scale units of 5000 or even 10 000 sows.

A wide variety of products can be made from pork carcases. The meat is particularly suitable for preservation by salting. In the past the fat was also prized for rendering to lard, and some breeds were kept especially for this purpose. Today lard production is less important and leaner pigs are preferred for both pork and bacon.

Birds and reptiles

Birds and their eggs have long been items of the human diet. Chickens are known to have been domesticated in Southeast Asia as early as 1400 B.C., and they were established in Europe before the Romans invaded Britain. Poultry are highly efficient in converting plant energy into human food energy. The modern poultry industry is divided into two distinct areas: battery and deep litter farming produce the eggs, and the broiler industry provides the meat. As a result of intensive production and marketing, poultry is no longer a luxury and is often cheaper than other types of meat. Poultry flesh is more tender, lower in fat and milder in flavour than butcher's meat.

The eggs of birds and their ancestors, the reptiles, are exceptional both for their size and the extent of their food reserves. They supply a high quality protein, as well as fat and the fat-soluble vitamins. If produced hygienically and stored carefully, their nutrients are less prone to decay than other highly nutritious foods. Eggs are one of the most versatile foods in the kitchen. They lighten soufflés, thicken sauces, bind ingredients, and are used for glazing and in the production of mayonnaise.

Fish

Fish occupy the same position in the pyramid of life in water as do birds and mammals on dry land. Life in the water is dependent on light that penetrates the upper layers. This energy is intercepted by the myriad of algae in the surface waters. The cells of this phytoplankton are too small to provide a direct source of food for many fish, but they are grazed by small animals such as shrimps and prawns. These in turn provide food for newly hatched fish. The majority of adult fish are carnivorous, eating smaller fish or other animals. Fish are a very diverse group and have evolved ways of living in all kinds of waters. They are to be found in mountain streams, brackish swamps, on the shallow rocky ledges around coasts and in the sunless depths of the oceans.

Unlike the land vertebrates, fish have been acquired by pursuit rather than by domestication. Various methods of fishing have been developed to match the habitat and behaviour patterns of the species hunted for food. Mackerel, pilchards and sprats swim in large schools feeding on plankton. They are usually caught by drift netting. The nets are towed vertically in the water about 1 m from the surface. They catch the fish by their gills as they attempt to swim through the nets. These fish are described as oily because oil is contained in their flesh and not simply in their livers, as in white fish.

Demersal fish, which live at or near the bottom of the sea, can be caught by trawling, where a ship drags a bag-shaped net, or by seine netting. The commonly used term for demersal fish is white fish. They can be divided into two distinct types by their shape. Cod, haddock, dogfish and whiting are the convential torpedo shape with a round cross section. Flounders, plaice, sole, halibut and skate are fish which have evolved a flat shape to enable them to life half-hidden on the sea bed. They are effectively lying on one side of the usual fish body. The upper side is camouflaged to match the materials on the sea bottom, while the underside is pale. More surprising is the migration of one of the eyes during the early stages of their development so that in the adult both appear on the upper side.

Supplies of fish have in the past been uncertain; being dependent on season and weather, and subject to scarcity and glut. This has been lessened recently by extensive freezing facilities. However, the supplies are now threatened by over-fishing of some species, particularly the herring.

In recent years there has been much progress in the development of fish farming. Trout and salmon are already farmed on a commercial scale, while Dover sole and turbot look promising at the research stage. Hopefully these enterprises may open the way to providing valuable fish protein with less danger to human life and fewer international disputes over wild fish stocks.

From the nutritional point of view, fish flesh supplies high quality protein and a source of the minerals calcium, phosphorus, fluorine and iodine. There is, however, more waste than on carcase meat. Fish deteriorates very rapidly, so that commercial freezing is essential if fish cannot be consumed soon after landing. On the other hand, fish is less likely than butcher's meat to harbour food-poisoning bacteria, because of its cold water origin.

Crustacea and molluscs

The invertebrate animals provide only a small proportion of our food. Of the reptiles, only the turtles have been hunted extensively for their eggs and flesh. The edible frog is the sole culinary representative of the Amphibia, providing a delicacy particularly appreciated in France. The crustaceans and molluscs are the invertebrate groups which supply the greatest amount of human food. Caterers tend to bracket these two biologically dissimilar groups as shellfish. The crustaceans have heavy external skeletons composed of chalky material. They inhabit both fresh and sea water. Their limbs are jointed; some being modified to form feelers, others for feeding or offence, and still others for reproduction and swimming.

The crustaceans are a large and diverse group. Some are minute and form an important part of the plankton providing food for larger animals.

The crustaceans used for human food fall into two main groups; the larger, crabs, lobsters and fresh water crayfish and the smaller, more delicate, prawns, shrimps and scampi.

The molluscs include a number of groups of animals which at first sight appear quite dissimilar. All molluscs have a soft muscular body covered with a thin mantle which, in most cases, secretes a single or pair of shells. They also have a fleshy foot which is used for movement and to probe surfaces for food. These features are most familiar in the land and water snails, which house their soft organs in a single spiral shell. Molluscs such as these are known as univalves, and include the whelks and winkles that are popular at the seaside, and the Roman snail, which is much enjoyed in France.

In another group of molluscs, the bivalves, the soft tissues lie between two tightly hinged shells. This group includes the mussels, scallops, cockles and clams which are eaten on a large scale. These creatures live two entirely different lives. After hatching from eggs, the early stages are spent as tiny larvae floating in the surface waters of the sea. Only later do they settle on the sea bottom and acquire their familiar shells. Adult mussels attach themselves to rocks and obtain their food by filtering microscopic creatures from the water. Bivalves such as the scallop are more mobile, and swim by flapping the two shells.

Oysters, which also belong to this group, have been farmed on a commercial scale for many years. The young oysters are raised in trays or on rafts in shallow coastal waters. In 1965, the faster-growing Pacific oyster was introduced into the U.K. in an attempt to make the industry more profitable. Unfortunately, this species proved to be less popular with the consumers, who found the corrugated oval shells less attractive and the flesh less succulent than those of our native species.

The other main group of molluscs includes the cuttlefish, squid and octopus. These appear quite unrelated to the animals in the previous groups, as they have tentacles around their mouths and their torpedo-like bodies move rapidly through the water by a form of jet propulsion. Internal examination, however, reveals that they have the soft muscular body, the mantle and the shell of the other molluscs. The lightweight shell is inside the animal, not external as in the shellfish. The tentacles and the sharp 'beak' are used to catch their prey, which is mainly shrimps and prawns. The tentacles of some of the larger species are sold as human food in some Mediterranean countries.

Shellfish as a class are good sources of protein, iron and calcium. They also supply the trace elements copper and zinc, which are needed in the diet in minute amounts. Their main role, however, is to add variety and piquancy to meals.

Part A of this chapter described the main animal food commodities and the signs which indicates good quality. Animal foods are more variable and vulnerable in nature, so need even more care in selection, handling and storage than plant foods.

Animal cells

Animal cells (see Fig. 2.3) share many of the characteristics of plant cells but lack the firm cell wall.

Animal tissues

Like plant cells, animal cells also have specialised functions and form tissues. The cells of the voluntary muscles which move the skeleton are long and contractile while those in the upper layers of the skin are flat and protective.

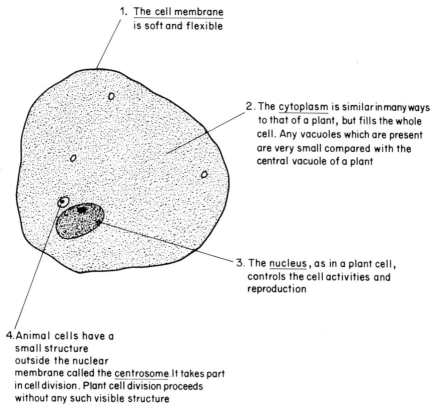

1. The cell membrane
   is soft and flexible

2. The cytoplasm is similar in many ways
   to that of a plant, but fills the whole
   cell. Any vacuoles which are present
   are very small compared with the
   central vacuole of a plant

3. The nucleus, as in a plant cell,
   controls the cell activities and
   reproduction

4. Animal cells have a
   small structure
   outside the nuclear
   membrane called the centrosome. It takes part
   in cell division. Plant cell division proceeds
   without any such visible structure

Fig. 2.3   An animal cell

The tissues which concern the caterer most, are those which provide the meat and fat for cooking. Meat consists of muscle fibres interspersed with connective and fatty tissues. Changes occur in all three components during cooking.

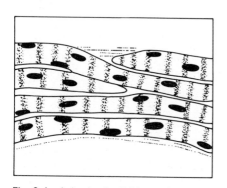
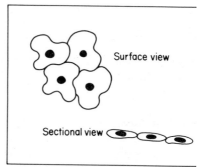

Surface view

Sectional view

Fig. 2.4   Animal cells: (left) muscle cells, (right) skin cells

Muscle fibres

Meat comes mainly from the voluntary muscles of the body. It is composed of fine filaments of contractile proteins in each cell arranged in bundles. Each group of cells is held together by a skin called the *endomysium* (see Fig. 2.5). Groups of bundles are surrounded by a thicker layer of connective tissue, the *perimysium*. The whole muscle is bounded by a strong sheath, the *epimysium*, which is attached to the skeleton by tendons. Muscle fibres differ in diameter, the slender ones are associated with the most tender meat. Fibres tend to thicken as the animal ages.

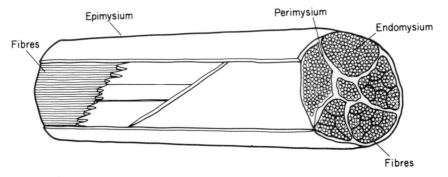

Fig. 2.5 Voluntary muscle fibres

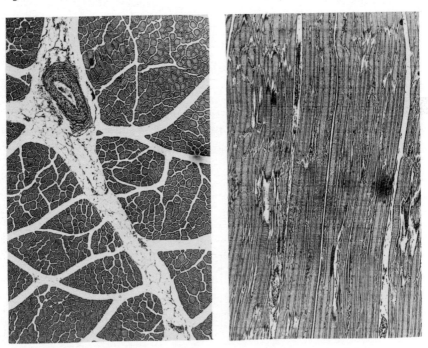

Fig. 2.6 Transverse (left) and longitudinal (right) sections of meat muscle

Connective tissues

Connective tissues are tough binding tissues containing fibres in a gelatinous ground substance (see Fig. 2.7). Two types of fibre occur in these tissues.

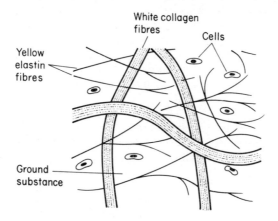

Fig. 2.7   Connective tissue

White fibres which form thick wavy bundles in which many fibres lie parallel to each other. White fibres are made of *collagen* and are strong and flexible, but inelastic. Tendons consist almost entirely of white fibres.

Yellow fibres which are single branching fibres made of elastin and, as the name implies, they can stretch and return to their original length.

Fat tissue

Fat is also present in specially enlarged connective tissue cells forming *adipose* tissue. As an animal is fattened, fat is first laid down under the skin and round organs such as the kidneys. Later, fat is formed between the muscle bundles, forming a marbled pattern.

When meat is cooked, changes occur in all of these constituents. The muscle proteins coagulate, the fat melts and changes occur in the surrounding connective tissues.

3
Food storage

Part A

The storeroom — layout and management. Storage and shelf lives of canned foods, dry goods, frozen and chilled foods, perishable goods and dairy products. Food pests. Questions.

Most catering establishments buy food in bulk from wholesalers because it is cheaper and more convenient. Large quantities can be purchased and are readily available if supplies fail to be delivered or estimated demand is greater than anticipated. The most important factor which governs the quantity of food purchased is the amount of suitable storage space available and the turn-over of certain items of stock. The stock purchased may represent thousands of pounds in cash, and if this stock were to deteriorate during storage it would mean a great loss of food and money. High quality food products are required if high standards of food preparation and presentation are to be achieved and maintained; therefore the correct methods of food storage must be kept to at all times.

The storeroom

Ideally, food stores should be situated on the north side of the building, since this ensures they will be as cool as possible. The general requirements for food storage areas are that they should be cool, dry, well-ventilated and, above all, vermin-proof.

The main fixtures and fittings required are ample shelves for stacking packed goods, and metal storage containers. Large bins mounted on castors are used for bulk cereals and flour. The castors allow for ease of movement during cleaning operations. Cupboards with adjustable shelves are needed for the smaller items; also various airtight containers of a suitable material. A filling system is essential for the storekeeper to keep all records of invoices, credit notes, catalogues, price lists and books for recording goods received, goods returned and goods issued.

Storeroom management

To be efficient the stores must be well organised, tidy and have all stock stacked conveniently and correctly, so as not to cause accidents or damage to other stock by falling off shelves. When replenishing with new stock, the old stock should always be brought forward to use first as this ensures that most of the stock will be used by any sell-by date, best-by date or any other specific date by which the food should be consumed to maintain its quality. Stock should be ordered in good time, so that it is received before the last items are issued.

A high standard of hygiene is essential where foods are stored. A cleaning rota should be devised showing clearly how frequently each area of the store should be cleaned.

Daily cleaning   gangways and floors
Weekly cleaning   shelves, shelf brackets, cupboards
Fortnightly   walls, ceilings, windows

Regular inspection of stock must be carried out, particularly for all cereals, cereal products, dried fruit, cake and soup mixes, to check for signs of attack by mites or weevils.

Many foods are packed and delivered in stout packing cases secured with metal or strong plastic bands, or in wooden packing cases secured with nails. To assist the storeman in opening these, he must have suitable equipment for cutting the bands or removing the nails, and it essential that these tools are stored correctly. All empty boxes and wrappings must be cleared away as soon as possible, and boxes should be broken down if possible and stacked in the refuse area.

It is essential that a wash hand basin, soap and nail brush and towel are available for the stores staff, also a well-stocked first-aid box. Suitable steps must always be available to enable staff to reach stock on the higher shelves, and when lifting or moving large packs the appropriate trolley should be used to prevent any personal injury. Staff must get help when lifting packs which are too heavy to lift with comfort, and any injury sustained should be correctly recorded.

The storeman and his staff must practise a high standard of personal hygiene, keep their overalls or white coats clean and in good repair, and wear suitable shoes, preferably with strengthened toe-caps to prevent any injury to toes if heavy items are dropped or knocked over. A good standard of safety must always be practised to prevent any unnecessary accidents or injury.

All cleaning equipment and materials must be stored in a separate area, well away from the food storeroom so that there is no possibility of the food becoming tainted with soaps, detergents or any other cleaning materials.

Food storage

Foods may be divided in to various groups according to the methods of storage and preservation. These groups are:

Dry goods   canned goods, dried fruit, cereals, nuts, sugar, spices, herbs, beverages, pre-packed cake and soup mixes.

61

Frozen foods	meats, fish, vegetables, complete meals and dishes, ice cream and confectionery items.
Chilled foods	meat, fish, made-up dishes, complete meals.
Perishable foods	meat, fish, dairy products, fresh fruit and vegetables, fats and oils.

Dry goods

Canned foods

Canned food is easy to store but the condition of the stock should be checked at the time of purchase. Any cans with leaking seams, bulging ends or serious rusting should be returned to the supplier who will replace the items or give credit. Cans may deteriorate during storage, so regular inspection is essential. Any blown or rusted cans should be discarded unopened (see Chapter 6).

The storage limit for most canned foods is about one year in a dry cool store, while large cans of meat such as cooked shoulder of ham should be stored in a refrigerator because the temperatures used in canning are not sufficient to kill the spoiling bacteria (see Chapter 6).

Dried fruits

These commodities must be kept in airtight containers in a cool part of the store. If they are allowed to become moist and warm they will go mouldy and be unusable.

Cereals and cereal products

Cereals must be stored in a cool dry atmosphere in airtight containers. Brown varieties of flour, which contain the crushed germ, must be used within 12 weeks because the oil contained in the crushed germ will turn rancid. The varieties and grades of flour are purchased wholesale in 35 kg bags, and are best stored in wheeled metal bins. If they are stored in the sacks, then they must be at least 18 inches (approx. 46 cm) off the ground to comply with food storage regulations. Tapioca and rice, if stored for too long, will lose brightness, while semolina will become webby with age. White varieties of flour have a longer storage life than the brown varieties because they do not contain the germ.

Beverages

Tea, being a dry product, must be kept in airtight containers because any moisture will cause deterioration in flavour and keeping quality. It must be kept well away from foods which have strong flavours, as these may be readily absorbed by the tea. Tea may be purchased in bulk in chests, and these must be kept properly sealed when not in use to prevent the tea from absorbing odours and moisture.

Coffee beans, if roasted, must be kept in sealed dark containers to retain the flavour and freshness. Ground coffee, if not vacuum-packed, must be transferred to suitable containers with tightly-fitting lids, unless delivered in suitable packaging.

Cocoa must be kept in containers with tightly fitting lids.

Herbs and spices

Herbs and spices contain volatile oils, and must therefore be kept in airtight containers, and these must be opaque to prevent light from causing the colour to fade. When the herbs and spices are purchased in retail glass containers they should be kept in a dark cupboard to preserve the colour.

Bottled fruits and vegetables

Glass containers transmit light, which causes the colour to fade from fruits and vegetables. Therefore they must be kept in a dark cupboard, suitably stacked to prevent breakages. It is advisable to check the seals periodically to ensure that they are still airtight.

Dehydrated and dried foods

These foods must be kept in a cool, dry atmosphere in airtight containers, or sealed packets, to prevent the absorbtion of moisture which would cause deterioration.

Although pulses contain a small percentage of moisture, they must be kept dry because if the moisture content becomes too high they will develop mould and be unusable.

Frozen foods

Foods purchased from the manufacturers in the frozen state must be placed immediately on delivery into a deep-freeze at the correct temperature of $-20°C$. The food must not be allowed to defrost or start to defrost, and then be placed in the freezer as any bacteria would have the chance to develop during this period. Frozen goods, if accidentally thawed, should be cooked and used within a short period. However, great care must be taken with ice-cream because this once thawed has to be thrown away.

When freezing your own foods, whether fish, meat, fruit or vegetables, remember that only top quality foods should be used, and these should be properly packed in moisture-proof freezer bags from which all the air has been excluded, and then be blast-frozen. The foods must be date-stamped because frozen foods do not keep their quality indefinately. Foods become freezer-burnt if stored for long periods at too low a temperature. The recommended storage times for classes of frozen foods are the following:

Dairy products	1 month
Beef, lamb	10–12 months
Pork	3–6 months
Sausages	1 month
Shellfish	3–4 months
Fish	3–6 months
Poultry	8–10 months
Vegetables, fruit	10–12 months

A wide range of dishes and complete meals are prepared and frozen for many different catering outlets. The storage instructions of the manufacturer must be strictly followed.

Chilled foods

Fish and meat are the main foods stored by chilling, and these are held at a temperature of 1–2°C. Carcase meat and joints should be hung in a cold room to allow cold air to circulate around the meat. Fish should be placed in single layers with ice to keep them moist in a fish cabinet at a temperature of 1°C.

Any cook–chill dishes must be stored at the recommended temperature (between 0°C and 4°C).

Fresh meats

The best temperature for storing fresh meat is between 4°C and 6°C, as this will prevent the formation of surface slime (bacterial growth). This temperature is only suitable for short-term storage. The humidity of the cold room should be controlled, as this will prevent the surface from browning and becoming dry.

Fresh fish

To prevent fish from deteriorating too quickly, it must be purchased as fresh as possible (ideally 'stiff alive', when the fish is still stiff from *rigor mortis*) and kept as cold as possible until required.

Smoked fish

Smoked fish must be stored in a refrigerator kept for this type of fish only at a temperature of 10°C. The flavour of smoked fish is strong, and is liable to affect other foods stored with or near them. When storing smoked fish, it should be turned regularly to allow the oil to permeate through the flesh to keep it moist.

Perishable foods

Fresh fruits and vegetables

Unlike storage of the foods already discussed fresh fruit and vegetables are living foods and therefore need to breathe to keep them in good condition and preserve their structure, crispness and nutritional content for as long as possible. The temperature required for storing most fruits and vegetables is 4–6°C, with a humidity that will not result in loss of water from the leaves causing them to go limp. A dark area is also required, particularly for green vegetables, to prevent the leaves from turning yellow.

Some fruits, such as peaches and avocado pears, from tropical areas are best stored at a temperature of 10°C, while bananas must not be stored below 13°C. Any unripe fruit may be left at a higher temperature to allow for ripening. If large quantities of fresh fruit and vegetables are being stored they must be checked regularly and any items showing signs of deterioration must be removed to prevent further deterioration of the remaining stock.

Dairy products

Milk in its raw state is a highly perishable commodity. On delivery it must be placed in the cold room at a temperature of 2°C until required. It should be kept in the sterile container in which it is delivered. Yoghurt, and fresh and synthetic creams, must be stored at a temperature of 2°C and the containers must be kept sealed to prevent the milk products from absorbing any strong flavours.

Cheese

Different types of cheese require various methods of storage according to the degree of ripeness when purchased and when they will be required for eating. (For the different types of cheese see Chapter 7).

Whole hard cheeses are best stored in a cool airy room at a temperature of 7–10°C and should be turned regularly to keep the moisture content evenly distributed.

Whole soft varieties should be stored in a cheese room or refrigerated at a temperature of 7–10°C. If they are under-ripe and are required for use sooner than anticipated, they should be stored at a higher temperature to aid ripening. They should be kept in their wrapper until required. The test for ripeness is by light finger pressure; unripe cheeses resist finger pressure, ripe cheeses have a springy texture and over-ripe cheeses retain the finger mark when lightly pressed.

Whole blue cheeses are stored as for soft varieties, but away from mildly flavoured cheeses which might be affected by their strong aroma.

Processed cheeses, if kept in their plastic wrappers or tin foil covering, do not require any special storage other than being kept in a cool dry place. This is because they are cooked products and do not require ripening.

If cheeses are stored in damp conditions they develop unwanted mould growth. If the temperature is too low and the atmosphere too dry, cheese will crack and dry out, while too high a temperature will cause them to sweat and become oily and over-soft.

Storing cut portions of cheese in polythene containers allows them to breathe while preventing them from drying out.

Butter

Butter is generally purchased in bulk by the case, fresh or salted. Because the salted varieties contain a percentage of salt, they have a longer storage life than unsalted butters. The required temperature for unsalted butter is 2°C, while salted butter may be stored at a slightly higher temperature.

Fats and oils

When fats and oils are stored incorrectly they develop off-flavours, known as rancidity. This is caused during storage by keeping them in warm humid conditions or storing them so that they are exposed to air or strong light. The manufacturers of catering fats and oils distribute their products in sealed cans and wrappers which do not transmit strong light. On delivery the oils should be kept in a dry cool store. If small quantities are purchased in bottles they should be placed in a cool dry dark cupboard. Cooking fats and margarine should be placed in the cold room or refrigerator at a temperature of 4–7°C.

Many large catering establishments have separate cold rooms or refrigeration units for their perishable goods, each unit being held at the appropriate temperature for the particular commodity. This is the ideal situation, and ensures that all the perishable foods are held in perfect condition and that there is no chance of cross-contamination of flavours. All refrigeration units must be kept clean, and scraps of food must not be allowed to accumulate anywhere in the stores area.

Food pests

Many foods are subject to attack by various insects and flies which may enter the food store in certain foods or be blown in on the wind. Pests may be attracted to scraps of food left between cracks in floors or walls as a result of poor storeroom hygiene. The more common food pest in catering establishments are grain weevils, pea weevils, biscuit or bread beetles, flour beetles, fruit flies, ants, silverfish and cockroaches.

Grain weevil
These are the commonest species and will attack wheat, maize rice, barley, oats and flour products. Pasta products are also attacked by these pests (see Fig. 3.1).

Pea weevils
These are primary pests of all pulses which may be imported in the product (see Fig. 3.2).

Bread or biscuit beetles
Cake mixes, spices and flour-based products are liable to be attacked by these pests.

Flour beetles
These may be found in cocoa, groundnuts, and sometimes in dried fruit and also varieties of cereal products.

Fruit flies
Fermenting and rotting fruit attacts these flies, as do decaying vegetables and jams.

Flour mites
This is the commonest species of mite, and attacks all cereals and cereal products (see Fig. 3.3). It is much smaller than the grain weevil. Flour mites have been known to affect cheese, along with the cheese mite.

Silverfish
These fast-moving silver-grey insects are quite common in catering establishments, feeding on a variety of foods.

Fig. 3.1 Grain weevil

Fig. 3.2 Pea weevil

Fig. 3.3 Flour mite (greatly enlarged)

Fig. 3.4 Common cockroach

Cockroaches

Cockroaches (see Fig. 3.4) are common in nearly all catering concerns, and flourish under moist warm conditions where a source of food is always available. They eat almost anything, but prefer sweet foods. The two main species are the black beetle and the light-brown beetle.

Ants

Mainly a summer pest attracted by sweet foods, but there are species which have become established in kitchens and bakeries where there is constant heating all the year round.

The insects mentioned so far cause nuisance and can ruin food commodities during storage. They are generally not responsible for diseases contracted by man. Most of these pests can be kept in check if the various points in stores management and the storeroom are always observed.

The pests and rodents which carry serious diseases are rats, mice, blowflies and common houseflies. Rats and mice will be dealt with in Chapter 9.

House flies

House flies (see Fig. 3.5) tend to breed in decomposing food and carry the eggs of parasitic worms, and diseases, which they pick up from refuse heaps. They must never be allowed to settle on foods, and must be eliminated from any area where food is handled.

This is what happens when a fly lands on your food.

Flies can't eat solid food, so to soften it up they vomit on it. Then they stamp the vomit in until it's a liquid, usually stamping in a few germs for good measure. Then when it's good and runny they suck it all back again, probably dropping some excrement at the same time. And then, when they've finished eating, it's your turn.

Cover food. Cover eating and drinking utensils. Cover dustbins.
The Health Education Council

Fig. 3.5   Common house fly

Blowflies

Blowflies or bluebottles attack decomposing animal matter, and lay their eggs on meat, poultry and game. Therefore every effort must be exercised to prevent these flies coming into contact with meat or entering the cold store where meat is kept.

In severe cases of insect infestation, advice may have to be obtained from the Health Department of the local authority on ways to deal with the problem.

68

Food storage

1 Write brief notes on good storeroom management applicable to the catering industry.
2 What are the groups into which food may be divided for storage? Which methods of storage are required for the various groups?
3 List some of the food pests which may be responsible for causing damage to foods during storage, and list the foods which they affect.

Part B

Water in cells, fine structure of cells, autolytic enzymes. Rancidity in fats and oils. Changes in meat during hanging. Questions. The nature of moulds, yeasts and bacteria. Bacterial spore formation and reproduction. Conditions affecting growth of microorganisms. Questions.

In the living world, nothing stands still so when we put animal and plant foods into storage, changes continue to occur in the cells or the products we have obtained from them. Some of these changes are desirable such as the ripening of fruits and the maturing of meat and cheese. In these cases we aim to control the rate at which these changes occur. Other changes such as the development of rancid or mouldy flavours are undesirable and ideal storage conditions are those which prevent or arrest these changes in food.

Control of water in storage conditions

Animal and plant tissues contain a great deal of water and we have seen that their cell walls and membranes allow water to pass in and out freely. Controlling the moisture content of the food store atmosphere is therefore very important. Too little will cause shrivelling in root vegetables and fruit, limpness and wilting in leafy vegetables and tough surfaces in meat. On the other hand high moisture conditions in the store will encourage the growth of microorganisms and must be avoided, particularly when storing soft vulnerable crops such as raspberries and strawberries.

This control of humidity is necessary whatever the temperature of the store. Frozen meat suffers from 'freezer burn' if it is not covered by a moisture-proof film to prevent water vapour subliming from the ice in the meat into the surrounding dry atmosphere. Loss of water in this way produces a hard brown surface on the meat.

Osmotic pressure and cells

The moisture content of tissues also depends on the fluid in v
bathed. Animal and plant cells tend to behave differently i
and sugar solutions. A few simple experiments will demonst.

1. Place a few red blood cells from fresh human or animal bloc
of the following solutions on microscope slides: (a) 0·9% salt solut.
1·8% salt solution and (c) water.
Examine these under the 40 × lens of a microscope. You will find (see Fig
3.6) the cells in (a) stay intact and normal with the red pigment inside the
elastic envelope of the cells. In (b) the envelope is shrivelled, while in (c) the

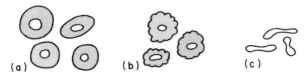

Fig. 3.6   Blood cells: (a) in 0.9% salt solution, (b) in 1.8% salt solution, (c) in water

cells have burst and only the 'ghosts' of the cell membranes remain.
The changes in (b) and (c) are due to *osmosis*. The cell membranes are semi-permeable, i.e. they pass water through freely but are much less permeable to the particles of dissolved salts and sugars.
If the solution bathing a tissue has a greater concentration of solute particles (salt in this case) than the liquid inside the cell, water will pass out the cell until, theoretically at least, the concentrations on both sides of the membrane are equal. So the blood cell envelope shrinks as water is drawn out of the cell into the more-concentrated salt solution.
This process is used in some methods of food preservation. Sugar syrups and brines prevent the growth of microorganisms by drawing out from their cells the water required for their growth.
The blood cells immersed in water burst because an excessive amount of water entered their cells to dilute the salt solutions inside. Their thin membranes could not withstand the excessive pressure.
Changes of this kind can be seen when blanching meats such as veal and rabbit, when the cells burst and the red haemoglobin is released into the water.

2. The behaviour of plant cells in solutions of different osmotic pressure can be studied using a plant tissue with a coloured sap.
Make a cut crossways in the skin of a rhubarb stem. With a pair of forceps pull off a thin layer and place immediately in drops of (a) a 20% salt solution and (b) distilled water on a microscope slide. Cover with a coverslip and examine under a 40 × lens of a microscope.

70

In (a) you will see clearly that the contents of the cell have shrunk as the water left the cell, leaving it plasmolysed with the protoplasm collected into a ball in the centre of the cell (see Fig. 3.7)

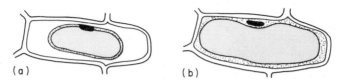

Fig. 3.7   Plant cells: (a) plasmolysed cell in 20% salt solution, (b) normal cell in distilled water.

In (b) you will see that the central vacuole is swollen with water and is pressing the thin layer of cytoplasm against the rigid cell wall. The effect is very similar to pumping air into a soft inner-tube to make a bicycle tyre firm. When cells are swollen with water in this way, they are said to be *turgid*. The crispness of a fresh lettuce is due to the turgidity of its cells. This appetising quality can be retained for some time by placing them in open plastic bags in the crisping drawers of a refrigerator so that this moisture is not lost.

Cell structure and autolysis

The light microscope only reveals a glimpse of the complexity within living protoplasm. Electron microscopy shows the cytoplasm to be a maze of double-membraned compartments or organelles (see Fig. 3.8). Within these organelles a myriad of chemical reactions proceed in an ordered fashion to supply the energy and materials cells need to function.

Each step in the process of synthesis or breakdown is catalysed by an enzyme. Enzymes are proteins, each precisely tailored to the job of ensuring a rapid turnover in one step of the chemical activity of the cell. They enable reactions to proceed in mild conditions which would require high temperatures or harsh conditions in laboratory.

Once the fruit is picked or an animal killed for meat, the lysosomes release their packets of enzymes and the process of destruction begins. Autolysing enzymes thus begin to change the chemical and physical properties of the tissues. Some of these changes are welcomed by the caterer, as in the maturing of meat, but others are regarded as undesirable, as when fruits brown on cutting or become mushy as the pectin between the cell walls is softened.

Oxidative and hydrolytic rancidity in fats and oils

In Chapter 1, Part A we noted that the edible oils and fats (lipids) do not occur as such in nature, but have to be extracted from animal and plant foods. After extraction, they need purifying and often further processing to

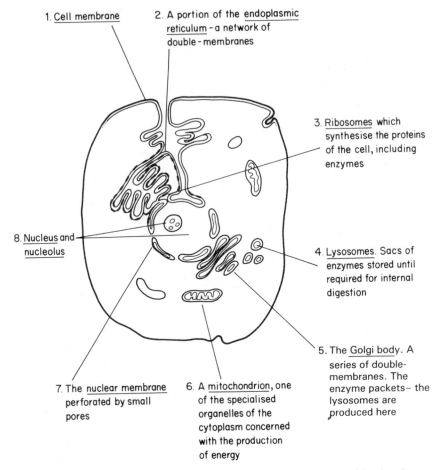

1. Cell membrane

2. A portion of the endoplasmic reticulum – a network of double-membranes

3. Ribosomes which synthesise the proteins of the cell, including enzymes

4. Lysosomes. Sacs of enzymes stored until required for internal digestion

5. The Golgi body. A series of double-membranes. The enzyme packets– the lysosomes are produced here

6. A mitochondrion, one of the specialised organelles of the cytoplasm concerned with the production of energy

7. The nuclear membrane perforated by small pores

8. Nucleus and nucleolus

Fig. 3.8 Diagram of an animal cell showing some of the detail revealed by the electron microscope

make them suitable for frying, shortening, cake-making and other purposes. If the processed lipids are to maintain the qualities intended by the manufacturer, they require careful storage to prevent rancid flavours and odour from developing. Some of the main points about the storage of these foods have been covered in Part A of this chapter.

To understand in more detail the factors which control rancidity in fats, we need to understand the basic chemistry of this group of foods.

Triglycerides

The lipids we use for cooking, butter, lard, margarine and plant oils, consist of molecules called *triglycerides*. Triglycerides are formed by the reaction between a molecule of glycerol and three fatty acid chains. This is shown in diagrammatic form in Fig. 3.9.

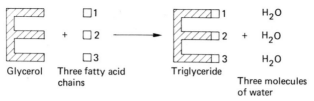

Glycerol Three fatty acid Triglyceride Three molecules
chains   of water

Fig. 3.9   Formation of a triglyceride

Glycerol is familiar to caterers as the syrupy sweet liquid which they use to soften icing. The chemical formula of glycerol is shown in Fig. 3.10. From this we can see it is a compound of the elements carbon, hydrogen and oxygen. It is, in fact, an alcohol and the end of each arm of the 'E' in the simple diagram in Fig. 3.9 is occupied by an OH (or *hydroxyl*) group.

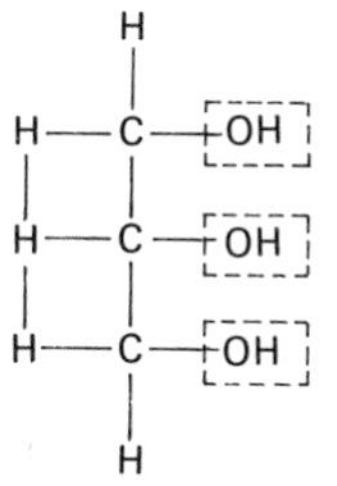

Fig. 3.10   A molecule of glycerol showing the hydroxyl groups

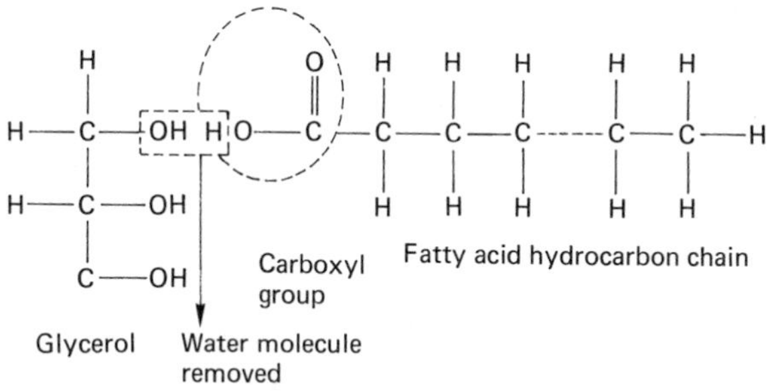

Glycerol   Water molecule removed

Carboxyl group   Fatty acid hydrocarbon chain

Fig. 3.11   Formation of a glyceride

When a triglyceride is formed, each hydroxyl group reacts with a fatty acid so the acid chains become firmly attached to the glycerol molecule and three molecules of water are removed (see Fig. 3.11). In most triglycerides, all the fatty acids are different; in some, two are similar and a few have three similar chains.

Fats and oils are not pure substances like sugars, for instance, where all the molecules are identical in a pure sample. Apart from the different fatty acid chains *within* a single triglyceride, all lipids are mixtures of different triglycerides. The properties of lipids depend on the proportions of the different fatty acids in their triglycerides. The composition of some lipids is shown in Table 3.1.

Fatty acids
Fatty acids consist of chains of carbon and hydrogen atoms with a COOH (or carboxyl) group reacting with one hydroxyl group of a glycerol molecule. Fatty acid chains vary greatly in length from the short chain of four carbon atoms in butyric acid from butter, to long ones of 20 or more, as in arachidomic acid in peanut oil.

Table 3.1   % of common fatty acids in some animal and plant lipids

Lipid	Saturated fatty acids		Unsaturated fatty acids	
	Palmitic	Stearic	Oleic	Linoleic
Animal fats				
Beef	28	19	44	2
Lard	31	7	46	10
Vegetable oils				
Olive	9	2	76	7
Groundnut oil	8	6	47	29
Corn oil	8	2	28	53

Apart from chain length, fatty acids vary in their degree of saturation. Figures 3.12(a) and (b) show parts of the hydrocarbon chains of two fatty acids.

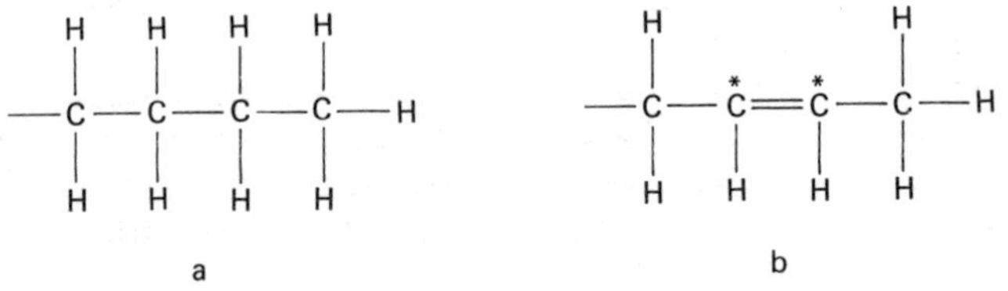

Fig. 1.12   Parts of hydrocarbon chains of two fatty acids

In (a) all the carbon atoms have their full complement of hydrogen atoms, so this fatty acid is *saturated*. In (b) the carbon atom marked with a star lacks a hydrogen atom and consequently a *double bond* is formed. Oleic acid is a fatty acid of this type having one double bond, and so is termed *mono-unsaturated*. Where two or more double bonds occur in a fatty acid chain it is said to be *polyunsaturated*. Most vegetable oils are richer in unsaturated fatty acids than animal fats.

Rancidity

In a fresh fat or oil all the fatty acids are firmly attached to the glycerol in the triglycerides. In a rancid lipid, some of the triglycerides have been split, liberating, amongst other products, short-chain fatty acids which have unpleasant tastes and odours. The most common way this occurs is by oxidation.

Oxidative rancidity

In oxidative rancidity an oxidative chain reaction begins at a double bond of an unsaturated fat, producing a complex mixture of substances, including the unpleasant short-chain fatty acids such as butyric and caproic acid.

A number of factors have been shown to influence the rate at which lipids become rancid. These are: (1) oxygen, (2) temperature, (3) light, (4) traces of rancid fat, (5) traces of copper or iron and (6) an enzyme, lipoxidase.

74

So, to keep fats fresh they should be stored in a refrigerator or cold store away from the light. Some manufacturers wrap butter and other fats in foil to protect them from the light and to restrict access to oxygen. If fats are to be stored in bulk, it is important that the containers be kept scrupulously clean. Traces of rancid fat left from a previous batch rapidly begin a chain-reaction accelerating the development of rancidity in the fresh fat.

The containers should have tightly fitting lids which will not only prevent access of oxygen, but also prevent the fat from absorbing the flavours of any strong-smelling foods stored in the vicinity. When removing fat from the bulk containers metal implements should be avoided. Very small amounts of iron or copper accelerate the rancidity process to a remarkable degree.

Since plant oils contain more unsaturated fatty acids, it might be supposed that they would become rancid more rapidly than animal fats, but the reverse is the case. This is due to the presence of natural *antioxidants* in plant oils. The vitamin E content in plant oils acts in this way, so oils can be stored at room temperature for weeks without developing rancidity.

Manufacturers use similar substances to protect animal fats. They add a compound B.H.A. (butylated hydroxyanisole) to lard to make it as stable as the vegetable shortenings.

Apart from rancidity problems in fats, caterers will sometimes encounter similar problems in fatty foods. Blood contains iron, so can accelerate rancidity under some conditions. It is the cause of unpleasant off-flavours which sometimes arise in frozen raw meat and in sliced cooked meat held in the refrigerator for a few days.

Fat is not restricted to animal foods, so similar problems can arise with vegetables such as peas. Here the enzyme lipoxidase has been at work accelerating oxygen absorption and inducing rancidity. The problem can be remedied by blanching the vegetables to inactivate the enzyme.

Hydrolytic rancidity
Hydrolytic rancidity is less common than the oxidative type. It depends on the presence of fat-splitting enzymes known as *lipases*. These enzymes reverse the process which formed the triglycerides, introducing water into the molecule and splitting the fatty acids away from the glycerol.

The enzymes may come from the fat itself, but more often they are produced by contaminating moulds or bacteria. It is less likely to be a problem where fats are stored hygienically.

Post-mortem changes in meat

'Meat' is the muscle tissue of an animal and consists, as we saw in Chapter 2, of striated muscle fibres, connective tissue sheaths and interspersed fat deposits. You can see the nature of the muscle fibres by taking a few fibres from some stewing steak and teasing them out in some 0·9% salt solution or Ringer's solution. The striped nature of the fibres shows quite clearly under a 40 × objective (see Fig. 3.13).

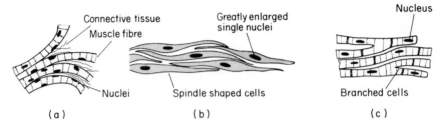

Fig. 3.13   Muscle fibres: a) striated voluntary muscle, b) unstriated involuntary muscle (e.g. gut, blood vessels) and c) cardiac muscle

After an animal has been slaughtered, the muscles stiffen in *rigor mortis*. At this stage it is not meat as we know it, and would be very tough and tasteless if cooked at this stage. It has to be hung so that chemical and biological changes can take place which mature the muscle into meat which will be succulent and tasty when cooked.

Hanging drains most of the blood from the carcase. This is necessary to prevent rapid bacterial contamination. During *rigor mortis* the proteins actin and myosin, which allowed contraction of the muscles when the animal was alive, lock together and form rigid chains of actomysin. This sets up great strains in the fibres, so that when the muscle relaxes after a few days of storage, breaks can be seen in the fibres. At this stage autolytic enzymes take over and soften and tenderise the meat.

At the same time, the tissue is becoming more acid as the glycogen, the energy store of the muscle, is converted into lactic acid. Under normal conditions the pH of the meat drops from about 7·4 to around 5·5 (see p. 91 for details of the pH scale). The lactic acid coagulates the proteins of the meat. This desirable change in the meat is reduced if animals have been excited or distressed before slaughter so that the glycogen in their muscles has been depleted. Meat from such animals develops a purplish-black colour and is often rather sticky in texture.

Low glycogen levels are normal in game animals such as the hare, so a longer ageing process is required to allow the autolytic enzymes to soften the meat. Meat from different species of animals is hung for different lengths of time. Beef, because it has a thick layer of fat to protect it from bacterial decay, is usually hung for 10–20 days. Veal lacks this thick fat layer and pork fat goes rancid quickly, so these are hung for shorter periods.

Changes in meat pigments
Two related pigments are found in animal flesh, *haemoglobin*, the red pigment of the blood, and *myoglobin*, which occurs in the muscles. In the living animal, haemoglobin carries the vital oxygen from the lungs to the tissues, and myoglobin holds it in the muscles until it is needed for muscular contraction.

Haemoglobin
(bluish-red pigment
in venous blood)

Oxyhaemoglobin
(bright red pigment
in arterial blood)

Both pigments consist of two parts: the pigment haem and the protein globin. The haem is identical in the two pigments, while the globins are different. Haemoglobin has four units of haem attached to the globin, while myoglobin has only one.

The structure of haem bears a remarkable resemblance to that of the plant pigment chlorophyll. They differ in the central metal atom, which is iron in the animal pigments and magnesium in chlorophyll. The essential part of the haem molecule can be represented as in Fig. 3.14, with a ring of four nitrogen atoms and a iron atom.

Fig. 3.14   The central part of haeme

Most of the colour of meat is due to myoglobin, since most of the haemoglobin drains away when meat is hung. Hard-working and old tissue is rich in myoglobin, which is why the heart muscle is dark-coloured and beef is more pigmented than veal.

Myoglobin

When meat is cut, the surface layers become bright red. This is due to the reaction of myoglobin with atmospheric oxygen. The meat in the centre of the joint retains the normal purplish-red colour.

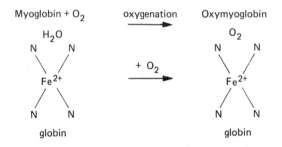

As meat is stored, the myoglobin undergoes a further change to a brownish-red substance called *metmyoglobin*. The central iron oxidises, changing from the Fe^{2+} (or ferrous) to the Fe^{3+} (or ferric) state. Meat normally contains reducing substances, so it only when these substances have been exhausted that the change to brown metmyoglobin occurs.

H$_2$O   OH

N   N   N   N

Fe^{2+} oxidation ⟶ Fe^{3+}

N   N   N   N

Myoglobin (purplish-red)   Metmyoglobin (brownish-red)

The formation of the brown discolouration of meat is accelerated by storage at high temperature (and also freezing), salting and, particularly, bacterial contamination.

When meat is heavily contaminated, further unpleasant changes occur, producing pale brown or even green pigments. These changes can take place quickly in frozen minced meat, which is particularly prone to bacterial multiplication. The changes can be prevented to some extent by the addition of ascorbic acid (vitamin C), which is a reducing agent.

Curing

The characteristic pink colour of bacon, ham and other processed meats is due to the effect of the curing salts on the myoglobin of the meat. Nitrite salts convert the myoglobin into a pink-coloured material called nitroso-myoglobin. When cooked this pigment remains pink and is not subject to change. However, when the meat is cut and exposed to light and air brown discolouration can occur. Supermarkets get round this difficulty by having cut meats packed in film which is not permeable to oxygen.

Myoglobin (purplish-red)   Nitroso-myoglobin (pink)

Self assessment questions

Post mortem changes in meat
1 Why is it necessary to drain the blood from a carcase of meat?
2 What happens to the contractile proteins in the muscles during *rigor mortis*?
3 What part is played by autolytic enzymes in the maturing of meat?
4 What changes occur in the glycogen of muscle during the hanging period?
5 Why is game hung for longer than meat from domestic animals?

6 Why are veal and pork hung for shorter periods than beef?
7 Name the pigment found (a) in red blood cells and (b) in muscles. What is the function of these two pigments in the living animal?
8 What change occurs in the colour of myoglobin (and in meat) when (a) it is oxygenated by exposure to atmospheric oxygen and (b) it is oxidised to metmyoglobin? Which types of storage conditions accelerate change (b)?
9 How is myoglobin affected by curing salts?
10 What changes occur in the colour of cured meat in storage? How can these undesirable changes be prevented?

Microorganisms

Microorganisms are everywhere; on the surface of the foods we store, in the air and on our clothes and skin. The foods which nourish our bodies are equally attractive to the smaller organisms, moulds, yeasts and bacteria.

Fungi
The fungi (singular: fungus) are a group of plants which lack chlorophyll. They are said to be *heterotrophic* since their nutrition is animal-like. Unlike the *autotrophic* green plants which can built up their own energy-rich substances, fungi have to rely on ready-made sources from dead or living tissues or their products.

Fungi vary greatly in size. The fruiting bodies of the larger fungi, the Basidiomycetes, are familiar as mushrooms, toadstools and truffles (see

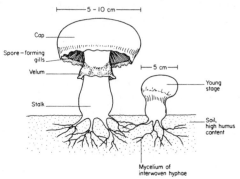

Fig. 3.15 Field mushroom

Fig. 3.15). In this group we have a number which are prized for the distinctive flavours they add to dishes. Others, such as the wet and dry rot fungi, are very destructive to the structural timbers of damp and poorly ventilated buildings.

The smaller fungi, the Ascomycetes, which attack food come in two main categories, moulds and yeasts.

Moulds
We are all familiar with the greenish-blue powdery patches which appear on

over-ripe fruits such as oranges and the fluffy growths on jam or damp bread. If these are examined microscopically they are found to consist of long thin filaments as in Fig. 3.16. If you look carefully at this figure you should be able to pick out two characteristics which indicate that these organisms are plants in spite of their lack of chlorophyll: they branch and have firm cell walls. These filaments are called hyphae, and the whole mass of *hyphae* is known as the *mycelium*. Two types of hyphae can be distinguished, those which grow and branch within the food, the *vegetative* or nutritive hyphae, and those which rise above the food, the *aerial* or *reproductive* hyphae.

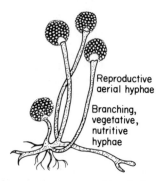

Reproductive aerial hyphae

Branching, vegetative, nutritive hyphae

Fig. 3.16 *Rhizopus nigricans* — a common mould on fruits, vegetables and bread.

Some moulds are capable of attacking the tissues of living plants and animals, and are therefore regarded as *parasites*, while many only attack dead organic material, and are termed *saprophytes*. Moulds attack more readily if the surface of a food is physically damaged, which is one reason for rejecting cut or bruised fruit and vegetables for prolonged storage.

Nutrition of moulds
Since moulds live on the complex food stores of other organisms, the first stage in their nutrition is digestion of these large molecules to simpler, more-soluble products. To accomplish this, the mould exudes enzymes into the surrounding food. When the food has been made sufficiently soluble it is absorbed through the cell wall into the protoplasm of the mould, where it is used for growth and energy production (see Fig. 3.17). So one of the indications that a food has been attacked by moulds is a change in structure. It becomes soft and moist, so the texture of a fruit or vegetable is no longer crisp, while changes also occur in the flavour as sugars, starches and proteins are broken down and the waste products of the mould flavour the food.

Earlier in this chapter we noted that enzymes are specific and designed to attack particular categories of chemical substances. So to be capable of growing on a food a mould must be able to produce enzymes which will solubilise the main constituents of that food. For instance, a mould which attacks bread must have enzymes which will break down the starch and protein which are the main nutrients in that food. Thus, while some moulds can attack a wide variety of foods, many are restricted to one particular class of food, such as fruits or starchy foods.

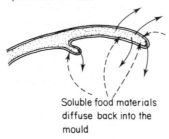

Extra-cellular digestive enzymes
spread into the food

Soluble food materials
diffuse back into the
mould

Fig. 3.17   Nutrition of moulds

Reproduction of moulds

The aerial hyphae of moulds produce vast quantities of *spores*, light bodies which are propelled into the air by the smallest air currents. In some cases, as in *Penicillium* and *Aspergillus* (see Fig. 3.18), the spores are simply nipped

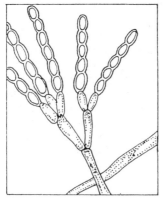
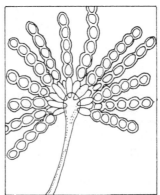

Fig. 3.18   *Pennicillium* and *Aspergillus*

off the tips of the reproductive branches. In others, special structures called *sporangia* develop and release the spores when they are ripe. Most spores are single cells, but a few moulds such as *Fusarium*, a common mould on fruit and vegetables, produce multicellular spores (see Fig. 3.19).

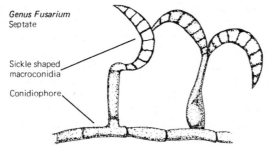

Genus Fusarium
Septate

Sickle shaped
macroconidia

Conidiophore

Fig. 3.19   Multicellular spores of *Fusarium*

Since the spores of moulds are so light, they can stay suspended in the air for long periods. When they alight on a suitable food which contains sufficient moisture they *germinate*, the spore wall splitting to allow the tip of a new hypha to emerge and to grow into the food (see Fig. 3.20).

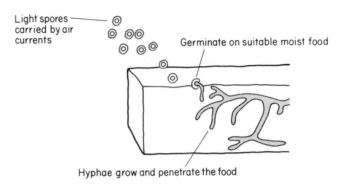

Fig. 3.20 Germination of fungal spores

Since these spores have been produced directly from the hyphae of the parent mould, they are *asexual* spores carrying exactly the same characteristics as the original mould which bore them. Many moulds also produce *sexual* spores. These are produced when the tips of two hyphae fuse together. Although the hyphae are visibly indistinguishable, they are genetically different and are referred to as − and + strains.

The *zygospores* produced as a result of these sexual fusions usually have thick resistant cases which allow them to survive unfavourable conditions (see Fig. 3.21). When they do germinate, the mycelia have characteristics from both parents which allow them to survive if conditions change.

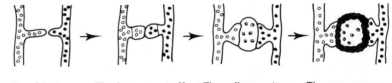

| The tips of the two hyphae grow towards each other | Tips become cut off from rest of hyphae by cross walls | The wall separating them breaks down and the nuclei fuse | The zygospore grows a thick protective wall |

Fig. 3.21 Formation of a zygospore

Yeasts

Yeasts can be seen as small oval or round cells under the 40 × lens of a microscope. Stained preparations under higher magnification (see Fig. 3.22) show that they have a firm cell wall, nucleus, large vacuoles and often droplets of oil or reserve granules of the same carbohydrate found in muscles, glycogen.

82

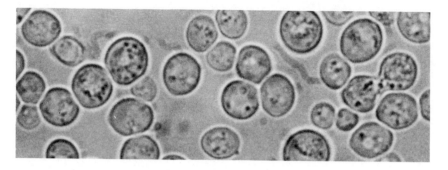

Fig. 3.22 *Saccharomyces cereviseae*

Reproduction of yeasts

Yeasts normally reproduce by budding. A small outgrowth appears on one side of the cell. This grows and then separates from the mother cell (see Fig. 3.23). If conditions are particularly favourable, separation may not take place and a chain of cells (or a 'pseudo-mycelium') is formed.

Some yeasts also have a sexual method of reproduction which involves the formation of one or more *ascospores*.

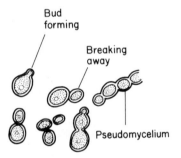

Fig. 3.23 Yeasts multiply by budding

Habitat and nutrition of yeasts

Wild yeasts are found on the surface of fruits and flowers, where they live on the sugary juices of the plant. Yeasts are of importance in catering for two reasons. First, they are spoilage organisms growing in conditions which would be unfavourable to other microbes. *Saccharomyces mellis* ferments high-sugar foods such as honey and syrup; yeasts of the *Pichia* group form skins and off-flavours in beers, while *Candida lipolytica* can spoil butters and margarines.

On the other hand, yeasts have been cultivated from the earliest times to raise bread and to produce alcoholic beverages. This arises out of the fact that, although they grow best in the presence of oxygen, yeasts can also obtain energy by fermentation of sugars under anaerobic (oxygenless) conditions (see p. 90). The carbon dioxide which is produced is used to leaven bread and the other product, alcohol, is the basis of the brewing industries.

Bacteria

Bacteria are also unicellular organisms, but are much smaller than yeasts. Whereas a cell of baker's yeast, *Saccharomyces cerevisiae*, might measure about $10 \times 5 \mu m$*, a cell of a bacterium such as *Staphylococcus aureus* would measure only $0.5 \mu m$. So stained preparations of bacteria under an oil immersion objective giving a magnification of $1000 \times$ will show bacteria, as in Fig. 3.24, only as small spheres, rods or curved shapes.

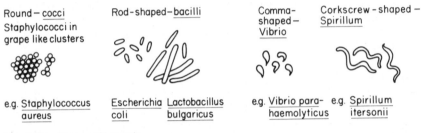

Round – cocci
Staphylococci in
grape like clusters

Rod-shaped–bacilli

Comma-
shaped –
Vibrio

Corkscrew - shaped –
Spirillum

e.g. Staphylococcus
aureus

Escherichia Lactobacillus
coli   bulgaricus

e.g. Vibrio para- e.g. Spirillum
haemolyticus   itersonii

Fig. 3.24   Shapes of bacteria

Further magnification by electron microscopy reveals that bacteria share with plant cells the feature of firm cell walls, but lack the double membrane structures in their protoplasm (see Fig. 3.25). Bacterial cells also lack a discrete nucleus separated from the cytoplasm by a nuclear membrane, having instead nuclear material scattered throughout the cytoplasm. As will be seen from Fig. 3.24, there are only four basic shapes of bacteria, so visual observation is not sufficient to identify these organisms.

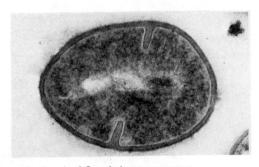

Fig. 3.25   Electron micrograph of *Straphylococcus aureus*

Apart from the structures shown in Fig. 3.26, some bacteria have other features.

*1 μm or micrometre $= 10^{-6}$ m.

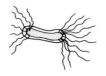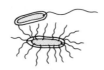

Fig. 3.26   Bacteria with flagella

Flagella
Most bacteria are carried passively in water, air currents or on the skin of animals. A few species are motile; that is, they can move of their own accord. These bacteria possess whip-like structures called *flagella* (singular: flagellum). The number and position of the flagella on the bacterial cell is characteristic of the species, so they can be used for identification purposes (see Fig. 3.26).

Capsules
Some species of bacteria produce capsules — layers of slime on the surface of the cell wall (see Fig. 3.27). Bacteria which produce large amounts of this capsular material cause 'ropiness' in foods. *Bacillus subtilis* can cause this condition in bread, so that a loaf heavily contaminated with this organism will show long slimy threads when it is broken and pulled apart (see Fig. 3.28).

Fig. 3.27   Some bacteria produce capsules

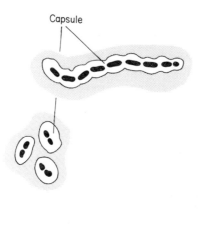

Capsule

Fig. 3.28   Ropy bread

Endospores
Bacteria belonging to the genera *Bacterium* and *Clostridium* produce endospores (see Fig. 3.29). These structures, usually referred to simply as spores,

are small round bodies with thick walls. They are highly resistant to normally lethal agencies such as heat, chemicals and radiation. The food-poisoning organisms *Clostridium botulinum, Clostridium welchii (perfringens)* and a number of food spoilage organisms are sporing organisms. It is important that caterers are aware of this property of some bacteria, as foods which may harbour spores require more severe conditions for sterilisation.

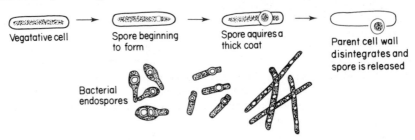

Fig. 3.29   Production of endospores

Reproduction

Most bacteria are capable of extremely fast rates of multiplication given favourable conditions. They reproduce by binary fission, a simple process whereby the mature cell splits into two and the 'daughter' cells then grow to adult size and repeat the process (see Fig. 3.30).

The generation time, the time required to double the number of bacteria can be as little as 10 minutes. With this rate of multiplication one single cell could produce over 4000 descendants in 2 hours!

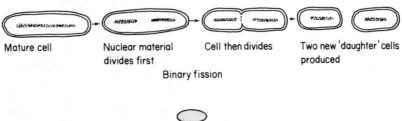

Binary fission

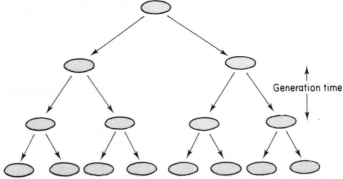

Fig. 3.30   Binary fission and generation time for bacteria

Bacteria and food

Knowledge of the characteristics of bacteria is useful to caterers in three different ways: (1) food production, (2) food poisoning and (3) food spoilage.

Food production

Lactic bacteria are used in the production of cheese, yoghurt and fermented milk drinks. Other species are used to sour beers and wines to make vinegars, and in the manufacture of pickles.

Food poisoning

A number of pathogenic species of bacteria are carried by or grow in food and drink. These cause food illnesses or food poisoning. Caterers need to know the characteristics of these bacteria so that they can protect their clients from these unpleasant illnesses.

Food spoilage

Bacteria, like moulds and yeasts, are involved in food spoilage. They tend to require moister conditions and to be less tolerant of extremes of acidity and alkalinity than fungi, so tend to be most common in moist neutral foods such as meat and milk.

Conditions affecting growth of micro-organisms

Six main factors control the growth of all microorganisms. Knowledge of these factors allows caterers to choose the storage conditions which prevent rapid growth of organisms in their foods. The factors are:

1 time,
2 temperature,
3 food,
4 water,
5 oxygen and
6 pH.

Time

Although bacteria grow rapidly in favourable circumstances, they require time to multiply to amounts which affect the quality of foods. Thus food which is clean and undamaged is likely to last longer than food which is heavily infected prior to storage.

Temperature

Microorganisms vary in their preferred temperatures for growth. We can divide them into three categories:

Mesophiles   — grow best at temperatures around blood heat,
Psychrophiles — grow well at lower temperatures and
Thermophiles   — grow at abnormally high temperatures.

All microbes have a comparatively narrow range of temperatures over which they grow profusely. This is their *optimum* temperature range. As the temperature drops below this range, growth slows down until the *minimum* temperature for that organism is reached and no further growth is possible. Similarly, there is a *maximum* temperature for each species of organism (see Table 3.2).

Table 3.2 Temperature requirements of different classes of food spoilage bacteria

Type of bacterium	Minimum growth temperature (°C)	Optimum growth range (°C)	Maximum growth temperature (°C)
Psychrophiles	0	10–15	20
Mesophiles (pathogens)	10	35–42	45
(saprophytes)	10	18–25	45
Thermophiles	30	45–55	65

Mesophiles This represents the largest group of microorganisms. It can be subdivided into two distinct groups. The disease-causing (pathogenic) organisms of man and other warm-blooded animals whose optimum temperature range lies near to blood heat, and the *saprophytic* bacteria whose optimum is lower. The food-poisoning organisms come within the first category, while the food-spoilage organisms whose natural origin is the soil belong to the latter group.

Psychrophiles Mesophiles cease to grow at around 10°C, although they are merely kept dormant at this temperature and will recommence growth when the temperature is raised. Chilling temperatures (10–15°C) and refrigerator temperatures (0–7°C) will therefore prevent the growth of mesophiles.

Psychrophilic organisms, on the other hand, can not only survive these low temperatures, but actively multiply in them. Those with the lowest optima, sometimes called *psychrotrophs*, will multiply readily at or around 5°C, the temperature of many domestic refrigerators. (Table 3.3 names some of the bacteria, yeasts and moulds which are psychophilic/trophic.) Their natural habitat is the soil or cold marine waters. Many are found on meats and vegetables, and contribute to their breakdown in cool storage. Only one food-poisoning organism falls into this group. *Clostridium botulinum* of the type E found in fish and other marine food from certain parts of the world, has been found to grow and produce its poison in temperatures as low as 3.3°C (see Chapter 8). Freezer temperatures of −18°C or below normally prevent the growth of even psychrotrophs, though in exceptional circumstances some of these hardy organisms can grow at a very reduced rate.

Thermophiles These bacteria have high optimum temperatures, usually 55°C or above. Many of them belong to the genera *Bacillus* and *Clostridium*, so are not only thermophilic, but also spore-bearing. For this reason, thermophiles such as *Bacillus stearothermophilus* and *Clostridium thermosaccharolyticum* are a problem in the canning industry as they cause spoilage of canned goods if they are under-processed (see Chapter 6).

Table 3.3 Some psychrophilic/trophic organisms found in foods

Organisms	Foods
Bacteria	
Pseudomonas spp.	Meat, fish, eggs
Micrococcus spp.	Dairy products
Alcaligenes spp.	Butter, cottage cheese
Moulds	
Cladosporium spp.	Fruit, vegetables
Sporotrichium	Chilled meat
Thamnidium	Chilled meat
Yeasts	
Trichosporon	Chilled beef, beer
Debaryomyces	Cured meats, sausages

Food

Like human beings, microorganisms need sources of energy and a supply of minerals and nitrogenous compounds with which to build and maintain their protoplasm. Some have greater synthetic ability than others, and will grow on simple inorganic media in the laboratory, while others such as the human pathogens have need of organic forms of nitrogen and a battery of vitamins.

Food is the factor over which caterers have least control, since if foods are nutritious for human beings they can also sustain invading microorganisms. Caterers can only try to ensure that foods are clean and as free as possible of spoilage organisms when put into storage, and that they are protected from subsequent contamination.

Water

We have already seen the vital part that water plays in the metabolism and reproduction of microorganisms. However, the fact that water is present in a food does not necessarily mean it is available to contaminating microbes. They require *liquid* water which can pass through their cell membranes into the cytoplasm. Water is unavailable to microorganisms if it is (a) frozen, (b) associated with high concentrations of salt or sugar, or (c) bound to the jelly-like colloids in a food.

(a) Freezing a food is a double protection against the growth of organisms. The low temperature slows down the vital processes, and the water necessary for multiplication is locked up in a solid form.

(b) Earlier in the chapter we noted that cells draw in liquids by osmosis. Brines and syrups which are used in food preservation have high osmotic pressures, and so tend to dehydrate microorganisms and prevent their growth.

(c) Some food ingredients, particularly proteins and starches, are present not in true solution but in the forms of colloids, and their particles often have water strongly bound to them. This water is not available for growth of microorganisms.

How much water is available in a food can be expressed on a water activity scale (A_W). On this scale, pure water has an A_W of 1.0. So, in pure water all the water is available to microorganisms. However, no microorganisms can grow in pure water due to the total lack of nutrients to support their activity. As all foods contain dissolved substances, and often water-retaining colloids, their A_w values are always less than 1.0. The more of these substances contained in the food or solution, the lower the A_w value, so that a strong brine solution used for food preservation might have an A_w as low as 0.6, which would prevent all normal organisms from growing.

However, microorganisms differ in their water requirements. Amongst the normal spoilage organisms, bacteria have the highest requirement for water, yeasts somewhat less, while the moulds can withstand drier conditions (see Table 3.4).

Table 3.4   Moisture requirements of food spoilage organisms

Type of organism	Minimum A_w for growth
Most bacteria	0.91
Most yeasts	0.88
Most moulds	0.80
Halophilic bacteria	0.75
Osmophilic moulds	0.65
Osmophilic yeasts	0.60

Most fresh foods have an A_w of more than 0.99, and so provide suitable conditions for all types of organisms as regards the need for water. To make them less inviting for microbes, foods have to be dried, frozen or immersed in high salt or sugar solutions.

Even with these precautions some specialised organisms may spoil foods. *Halophilic* organisms, such as the bacteria of the genus *Halobacterium*, can grow in salted fish and meats.

Others, such as the *osmophilic* yeasts *Lygosaccharomyces rouxii*, can grow in as much as 60% sugar solutions, and so can spoil syrups and honey.

Oxygen

The majority of microorganisms respire *aerobically*. Oxygen is used to release the energy from foods such as sugars and, in the process, carbon dioxide and water are formed:

$$\text{sugar} + \text{oxygen} \rightarrow \text{carbon dioxide} + \text{water} + \text{energy} \qquad 1$$

Anaerobic respiration (or fermentation) is an alternative method of energy production which does not involve the use of oxygen. It is a less efficient method as it only releases part of the available energy in a food:

$$\text{sugar} \rightarrow \text{carbon dioxide} + \text{alcohol} + \text{less energy} \qquad 2$$
$$\text{(or other product)}$$

Equations 1 and 2 are only summaries of these energy-releasing processes, showing the initial and final products. The energy is released gradually within the cells by a long chain of chemical reactions, each aided by a specific enzyme.

We can divide microorganisms into four groups according to their respiratory requirements.

1 *Aerobic organisms.* These require the presence of free oxygen in the atmosphere around them.
   Examples: Bacteria of the genus *Bacillus* and most moulds.
2 *Obligate anaerobes.* These grow well only in the absence of free oxygen. They are encouraged by reducing conditions in foods produced by certain sulphur-containing amino acids in meats, and also by ascorbic acid and reducing sugars found in fruits.
   Examples: Bacteria of the genus *Clostridium.*
3 *Facultative anaerobes.* These organisms grow best aerobically, but can also release energy in the absence of oxygen.
   Examples: Many species of yeast belong to this group.
4 *Microaerophiles.* These are a small group of bacteria which require a definite but small amount of oxygen.
   Examples: Bacteria of the genus *Lactobacillus.*

Foods differ in their ability to provide oxidising or reducing conditions for microbial growth. Most plant foods provide oxidising conditions, so tend to be spoiled by the bacteria and moulds which respire aerobically. Matured meat, on the other hand, contains sulphur groups (—SH) in its proteins which are reducing, so solid cuts of meat are inviting to anaerobic bacteria, particularly if vacuum-packed to exclude air.

pH

Another factor which affects the growth of microbes is the acidity or alkalinity of the food. This quality is expressed numerically by the pH scale. Solutions which have pH values below 7 are acidic, those greater than 8 are alkaline, and neutrality occurs at pH 7.

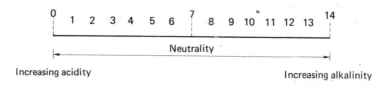

Most microorganisms are *neutrophiles*, preferring to grow in foods which are within the pH range 6.6–7.5. This group includes the majority of the food-spoilage bacteria and all the food-poisoning organisms. Moulds and yeasts, on the other hand, can tolerate a wide range of pH values.

Some specialised microorganisms can tolerate acid conditions. They are known as *acidophiles*, and are responsible for the spoilage of acid foods, wines and vinegars.

If you examine the pH values of different classes of foods in Table 3.5 you will find that meat, fish, shellfish and dairy products all come into the range of 'neutral' or 'low acid foods', having pH values of 5.5 or above. This makes these foods the most vulnerable to bacterial spoilage, and gives them the capacity to support the growth of food-poisoning organisms.

Table 3.5 pH values of some foods.
Group I. Neutral or low acid foods (pH 5.3 and above)

Food	pH	Food	pH
Meats		*Dairy products*	
Freshly killed beef	7.4	Milk	6.4
Beef, matured	5.6	Butter	6.2
Ham	6.0	Cheese (Cheddar)	5.9
Chicken	6.3		
Mutton	5.4		
Fish and seafood		*Vegetables*	
Salmon	6.2	Asparagus	5.9
White fish	5.5	Sprouts	6.3
Crab	7.0	Cauliflower	5.6
Oyster	4.8–6.3	Potatoes	5.3–5.8
		Sweetcorn	7.3

Group II. Medium acid foods (pH 5.3–4.5)

Food	pH
Turnips	5.2
Carrots	5.0
Beetroot	4.3

Group III. Acid foods (pH 4.5–3.7)

Food	pH
Bananas	4.6
Tomatoes	4.2
Pears	3.9
Cherries	3.8

Group IV. High acid foods (pH 3.7 or less)

Food	pH
Limes	1.9
Grapefruit	3.0
Oranges	3.6–4.3
Grapes	3.4–4.5
Apples	2.9–3.3

Most vegetables come within the pH range 4.0–6.0. They also tend to be attacked more frequently by bacteria than by fungi.

Fruits tend to be more acidic than vegetables, and to be spoiled by yeasts and moulds. There is, however, quite a wide range of acidity amongst fruits. Melons, bananas, tomatoes and pears are examples of fruits which are only slightly more acidic than vegetables, while gooseberries, grapefruit, lemons and limes represent the lower end of the pH scale.

Knowledge of the pH values of food is valuable in two areas of catering: in storing and in preserving food.

The low acidity foods, as we have seen, include the highly nutritious high-protein foods such as meat and milk. They provide all the necessary conditions for microbial growth, yet have little natural acidity for protection. Therefore these foods require the most stringent storage conditions. On the other hand, acidic fruits such as lemons and liquids such as vinegar will keep well for long periods without special care.

In Chapter 6 we shall also see the importance of pH values in the preservation of foods. Low acidity foods require more-intensive treatment to ensure safety than do the naturally protected acidic foods.

Self assessment questions

Microorganisms

1 How is the nutrition of a mould different from that of a higher plant?
2 How do moulds digest complex foods?
3 List the changes which occur in fruits and vegetables which have been attacked by moulds.
4 How do moulds spread from one food to another?
5 How do yeasts reproduce?
6 In what ways are the contents of bacterial cells different from those of yeasts and higher plants?
7 State whether the descriptions of the function of the spore below indicate (a) a bacterial spore or (b) a fungal spore:
   (1) light spore for reproduction and distribution of the species,
   (2) spore with resistant coat to withstand adverse conditions.
8 What is meant by (a) binary fission and (b) the generation time?
9 List the six factors which control the growth of microorganisms.
10 List the main ways in which bacteria are associated with food.
11 Which class of organisms (pschrophiles, mesophiles and thermophiles) has (a) the highest and (b) the lowest optimum growth temperature?
12 Explain briefly why (a) freezing, (b) salting and (c) drying prevent growth of microorganisms.
13 Which of the specialised types of foods listed are likely to provide suitable growth conditions for obligate anaerobes? Fruits, large joints of meat, vegetables, vacuum-packed foods and cereal products.
14 Which specialised types of organisms are likely to cause spoilage in (a) salted foods and (b) jams and honeys?
15 Which of the following classes of foods are most vulnerable to bacterial spoilage? Foods of pH: (a) 5.3 and above, (b) 5.3–4.5, (c) 4.5–3.7 and (d) 3.7 and below.

4

Cooking food

Part A

Methods of heat transfer — conduction, convection and radiation. Methods of cooking. Cooking equipment — stoves, ovens, boilers, grills, roasting spits and deep fryers. Metals for cooking utensils. Fuels — electricity and gas, reading meters. Questions.

Food is cooked to make it more palatable and more digestible, and to prevent the growth of food-spoilage and food-poisoning bacteria. During cooking the appearance of the food is altered according to the method used. To cook food, heat is transferred from its source — which may be gas, electricity or steam — to the food by radiation, convection or conduction.

Cooking by conduction

Conduction involves the direct transfer of heat energy from one particle of matter to another. Conduction takes place more readily in solids than in liquids, and is very ineffective in gases. Metals are good conductors, while non-metals are poor in transferring heat in this way.

When food is heated or cooked by conduction, the heat is transferred from the energy source to the cooking vessel and thence to the food, which is in direct contact with the surface. Shallow frying is the only common method of cooking where heat is transferred by conduction alone.

Cooking by convection

Convection takes place in liquids and gases. These media expand when heated, and so become less dense. A heated gas or liquid rises and is replaced at the bottom of the container by the heavier cooler liquid or gas. In this way a convection current is set up which transfers the heat rapidly until the whole has reached the desired temperature. This will be 100°C for boiling water, or the required temperature for baking or roasting in the oven.

Cooking by radiation

Radiant heat is given off from the source, and is in direct contact with the surface of the food, which heats up very quickly.

Methods of cooking

The main methods of cooking food are roasting, shallow frying, baking, grilling, deep frying, braising, boiling, steaming, poaching, pot-roasting and spit-roasting.

Roasting
Heat transfer is by a combination of convection and conduction. Heat is carried around the oven by convection currents. The surface of the food absorbs heat from the air and the hot fat. The heat is then transferred slowly to the centre of the joint by conduction.

Baking
Convection and conduction are employed as in roasting, but no liquids are employed.

Grilling
Foods cooked by grilling are placed over or under the direct heat source, and are cooked by radiation. If the food is fairly thick, then only the surface is cooked by radiation, and further cooking takes place by conduction.

Deep frying
The oil or fat is heated by convection, and when the required temperature is reached the food is placed in the oil and cooked by conduction.

Braising
The oven is heated by convection, the braising pan by conduction and the liquid by convection. The food is cooked by conduction.

Boiling
In boiling in water or stock, the heat transference is similar to deep frying.

Steaming
Cooking by steam can be carried out using equipment which steams at atmospheric pressure or when steam is under pressure (5–15 psi). Cooking by steam at atmospheric pressure is done by placing the food in live steam circulated by convection. The steam surrounding the food condenses, releasing latent heat. This is transferred to the food, which is then cooked by conduction.

In cooking by steam under pressure, the same methods of heat transfer are involved, but the steam reaches a much higher temperature, resulting in the food being cooked much more quickly.

Poaching
Poaching is similar to boiling, but the temperature is kept below 100°C.

Pot-roasting
This method is similar to braising, but the heat is transferred by convection of air rather than liquid.

Spit-roasting
Spit-roasted foods are exposed to radiant heat which cooks the surface. Further cooking takes place as a result of conduction.

These methods of cooking are shown diagrammatically in Fig. 4.1.

Cooking equipment

Various items of cooking equipment are shown in Fig. 4.2.

Stoves
The two main types of cooking stoves used in catering establishments are the solid top stove and the open or single burner stove, both of these are fired by gas. Electric stoves have sealed heated plates.

Solid top stoves transfer heat from the hot top to the cooking vessel by conduction. These stoves take some time to heat up sufficiently to transfer the heat, but once heated the gas can be reduced as the heat will be retained by the top. Because the burner is in the centre, this is the hottest part of the stove, the outside will be cooler. This enables food to be cooked quickly in the centre of the stove and simmered in the outer area. These stoves can be used to cook a number of dishes at different temperatures using just one burner. They are uneconomical if only one or two saucepans are to be used at one time.

Single burner or open stoves heat up and cook more quickly because the gas flame is in direct contact with the saucepan. Open gas stoves give instant heat or reduced heat when required, but only one saucepan can be used on each burner.

Electric stove plates are heated by elements by conduction, as with solid top stoves. They take time to heat up before heat is transferred to the cooking vessel, but if the heat is reduced towards the end of cooking there should be enough heat retained in the plate to finish the process.

Ovens
Ovens are heated by convection, and the air circulates until the required temperature is reached. This is controlled by a thermostat or regulo. Ovens take 15–20 minutes to reach the required temperature.

Forced air convection ovens are fan-assisted to circulate the heated air throughout the oven to ensure an even temperature.

Microwave ovens
Foods cooked by conventional methods use heat transfer by convection, conduction and radiation, but microwave ovens operate by a different mechanism. The source of energy used is high-frequency electromagnetic

96

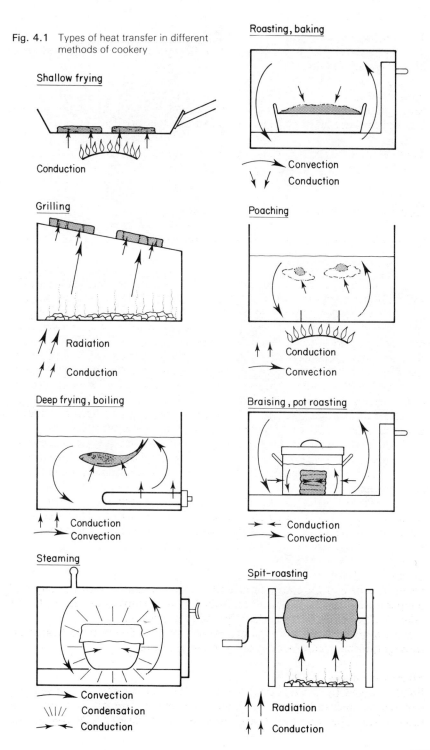

Fig. 4.1 Types of heat transfer in different methods of cookery

Shallow frying

Conduction

Grilling

↗↗ Radiation

↗↗ Conduction

Deep frying, boiling

↑ ↑ Conduction
⟶ Convection

Steaming

⟶ Convection
\\|// Condensation
→← Conduction

Roasting, baking

⟶ Convection
↓↓ Conduction

Poaching

↑↑ Conduction
⟶ Convection

Braising, pot roasting

→← Conduction
⟶ Convection

Spit-roasting

⇑⇑ Radiation
↑↑ Conduction

97

Fig. 4.2 Cooking equipment

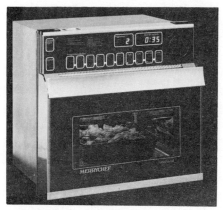

waves (microwaves) produced by a magnetron inside the oven. These waves do not create heat within the oven or transfer heat to the food. The food is cooked by directing the microwaves onto it. The waves agitate the molecules of water in the food very rapidly. This creates heat by friction and the water is converted to steam which heats or cooks the food. Microwaves do not colour food, if colour is required the food can be coloured by conventional methods.

Micro-air ovens

These ovens cook by both microwaves and convected heat. The food is cooked by molecular agitation and the browning is caused by convected heat.

Steam boilers

These are items of equipment heated by steam enclosed in a surrounding jacket (see Fig. 4.3), and are used for soups and other liquids. Best results are obtained when the boiler is working to its fullest capacity, preventing burning above the liquid level.

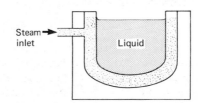

Fig. 4.3 Cross section of a steam boiler

Steam ovens and steamers

Foods can be cooked by steam at various pressures. The steam may be supplied from a main supply or generated in the appliance itself by heating a water bath at the bottom of the steamer. The average working pressure is 15 psi. Steam circulates by convection and condenses on the food releasing latent heat. Further cooking is by conduction.

Grills

Grills may be heated using radiation from gas or charcoal beneath the grill bars. Gas requires at least 15 minutes to heat up, and charcoal grills need to be lit at least 1 hour before use, to allow the embers to glow without smoking.

The salamander type grill has radiant heat projected from above.

Contact grills have electrically heated surfaces. The food is sandwiched between them so that both heated surfaces are in contact with the food. Cooking takes place simultaneously on both sides, reducing the cooking time by half.

Roasting spits

Modern spits are electrically powered and heated by gas or electricity. The food to be spit-roasted is impaled on a rod or large skewer, and is secured in position by two adjustable clips. The food is cooked by radiant heat.

Deep fryers

In many catering establishments the deep fryer is the most essential piece of cooking equipment, particularly in fast-food operations. Fryers today are heated by gas or electricity and are thermostatically controlled. The most recent development is that fryers incorporate computers which not only control the temperature of the oil, but also the cooking times of the different types and varieties of food. These computers can be programmed to the individual requirements of establishments.

Many models of fryers incorporate a cool zone below the heating element. The oil in this area does not reach the high temperature required for frying. Any food particles dropping into the cool zone do not become burnt, which would spoil the oil or food.

Iron fritures are placed on the stove and are still used where small quantities of deep-fried foods are required.

Metals used for commercial cooking vessels

Cast aluminium

Cast aluminium is a widely used metal for saucepans, stockpots, braising pans and trays. Aluminium items are not so expensive as those made of other metals. The metal is a good conductor of heat providing the bottoms are ground flat to give good contact with the stove. Aluminium pans are hard-wearing, but may need to be reshaped after a period of long and continual use.

Aluminium can discolour white stews, sauces and soups. Wooden implements should be used to stir light coloured dishes in aluminium pans. The use of metal utensils will cause the aluminium to colour the sauces or stews grey.

Cooking vessels are available in various gauges of metal, and only heavy gauge aluminium is suitable for commercial use.

Stainless steel

Stainless steel is not widely used in catering establishments for cooking vessels because of the high cost and its poor conduction of heat. Hot spots are created in the metal, which causes burning. Stainless steel is used extensively for basins, trays, mandolines, hot plates, service counters and coffee stills.

Copper

Copper is the most widely used metal for saucepans, baking trays, sugar boilers and fish kettles. It is a good conductor of heat, heats up quickly and evenly, and cools down rapidly.

With the exception of sugar boilers and copper bowls, all other vessels must be lined with a coating of tin. When this wears off, the vessels must be re-tinned. Tinned copper items must not be left on the stove with nothing in, as the tin lining will melt and form a rough surface. Sugar boilers are not tinned because the temperatures used in cooking sugar are much higher than the melting point of tin. Copper bowls are left untinned because they are used for whipping egg whites rather than cooking. They can be easily cleaned with lemon and salt to remove all grease, to enable the whites to be whipped successfully. Copper vessels must always be kept clean, otherwise a verdigris of copper carbonate forms.

The advantages of copper vessels are that they can be repaired and reshaped easily, they cook evenly, are hard-wearing and very serviceable.

The disadvantages are the high initial cost of purchase and the cost of regular re-tinning. They require cleaning frequently to keep them clean and bright. Larger vessels are heavier than comparable aluminium ones.

Wrought iron
Frying pans, roasting trays, baking sheets and fritures are made from wrought iron. It is a heavy material and will stand up to hard usage. The roasting trays and baking sheets sometimes buckle in the oven, which can result in uneven cooking. When wrought iron equipment has been cleaned it should be lightly greased to prevent it going rusty.

Fuels

The main fuels used for cooking are electricity and gas. Both should be used economically as they are expensive. Undue heat loss from appliances will be a drain on profits, as well as making the kitchen hotter than is necessary.

Electricity
Electricity is indispensable in any catering establishment because it is essential for operating dishwashers, refrigeration units, food processors, floor-cleaning machines and many other pieces of equipment.

Electrical power for cooking represents a large proportion of the overheads of a catering establishment, so careful use is essential.

Economical use of power must begin when electrical equipment is purchased. Careful analysis of the workload of the kitchen is essential so that the equipment is of the correct type and size.

Daily work schedules should be planned so that the best use is made of heat in ovens and on stoves. Large ovens should not be used to cook small batches of food. As far as possible, items needing the same cooking time should be cooked together so that ovens are not opened needlessly.

The best use is made of heat on cooking plates when the pans are of the appropriate size, neither too small nor too large. Electric cooking plates need switching on some time before use, but retain heat, so they can be turned down before the cooking is finished.

Mixers and bowls are needed in a variety of sizes so that it is not necessary to use unduly large equipment to mix small amounts of food.

It is useful to know the wattage of electrical equipment, particularly when there may be a choice of equipment to perform a task. This information is given on the baseplate of the appliance, together with the appropriate voltage for the appliance.

The wattage indicates the power of the appliance and the loading on the mains supply. Electricity bills give power consumption in units (kilowatt-hours). This means that a single-bar fire rated 1000 W (1 kW) uses one unit of electricity per hour. A 100 W lamp consumes a unit in 1000/100 = 10 hours, while a 10 kW oven uses a unit in 1000/10 000 hours, i.e. every 6 minutes. From these examples it can be seen that the greatest economies can be made by using heating equipment carefully.

If power bills seem unduly large, periodic checks on the meter readings can be useful. Where there is a choice of heating equipment, running alternative devices for measured periods and checking their consumption can be a guide to the best use of power in the kitchen (see later in this chapter for how to read electricity and gas meters).

Advantages
Clean and easy to use.
Additional power points can be added to the circuit easily.
In the event of a power failure the supply can easily be connected to a generator if available.
When used for baking, good even results are obtained.

Disadvantages
Expensive to produce.
Cooking plates take time to heat up.
It is not always visual.
It is subject to power failure or breakdown.
The cooking vessels must have flat bases if proper contact with the hot plate is required.

Reading an electricity meter
The readings are taken from left to right. The figures recorded are those that the pointer has just passed, or the number which the pointer is at. When the pointer is between 0 and 9, record the 9; between 0 and 1, record the 0. See Fig. 4.4.

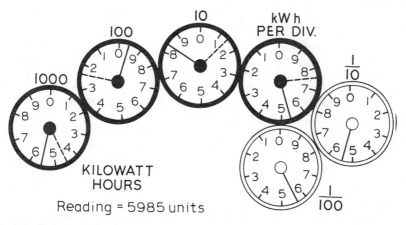

Fig. 4.4 Dials on an electric meter

Calculating an electricity bill

To calculate the amount of power used, record the present meter reading and subtract the previous reading. To calculate the cost, multiply the number of units used by the cost per unit.

The dials in Fig. 4.4 read as follows:

————	Current reading	5985
----------	Previous reading	− 4217
	Units used	1768
	Cost per unit	5.5 pence

Cost of electricity used 1768 × 5.5 pence = 9724.0 pence
= £97.40

Gas

Natural (or North Sea) gas is now widely used throughout the U.K. The range of gas cooking equipment is similar to those using electricity.

Calor gas (or bottled gas) is widely used by caterers who specialise in outdoor catering functions, and the gas equipment is designed to work efficiently from this portable supply. Bottled gas is also used, but in much smaller containers, to fuel the table cooking lamp used in restaurant work. Calor gas is cheaper for outside catering functions, because electricity would have to be supplied by a generator.

Advantages
Instant heat as and when required.
The range of heat is very flexible, with a visual flame.
It is economical.
Special cooking vessels are not required.

Disadvantages
Some heat is lost in to the kitchen.
It is subject to ignition problems.
Flash back may occur when lighting.
Regular servicing is necessary to maintain efficiency.

Natural gas is odourless, and has been given the smell of coal gas so that people can detect any gas escapes or leaks. If you suspect a gas leak, turn off the appliance or supply and notify the Gas Board immediately.

Reading a gas meter
The readings are taken as for an electricity meter (see above).

Calculating a gas bill
The difference between the present reading and the previous reading is the amount of gas used, in cubic feet (cu. ft). To find the number of therms used, multiply the amount used in cu. ft by the calorific value and divide by 1000. Multiply the therms by the cost per therm to arrive at the cost of the gas used.

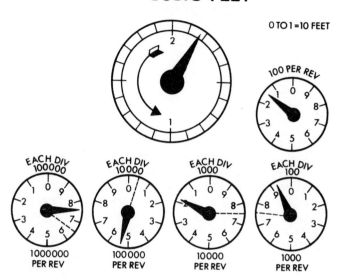

CUBIC FEET

0 TO 1 = 10 FEET

100 PER REV

EACH DIV 100000
EACH DIV 10000
EACH DIV 1000
EACH DIV 100

1000000 PER REV

100000 PER REV

10000 PER REV

1000 PER REV

Fig. 4.5   Dials on a gas meter

The dials in Fig. 4.5 read as follows:

●—	Current reading	7519 cu. ft
--------	Previous reading	6077 cu. ft
	Gas consumption	——
		1442 cu. ft

Calorific value = 1032

Number of therms used $= \dfrac{1032 \times 1442}{1000}$

= 1488.144

Cost per therm = 33 pence

Cost of gas consumed $= £\dfrac{1488.144}{100} \times 33$

= £491.09

Self assessment questions

Cooking of food

1 State the various forms of heat transfer utilised when cooking food. Which method of heat transfer is used in the following methods of cookery? (a) Deep frying, (b) baking, (c) grilling, (d) steaming, (e) braising, (f) boiling.

2 List the various metals used for commercial cooking vessels, and state the advantage and disadvantages of each.

3 Calculate the gas/electricity consumption of your own home over a given period using the formula in the example.

4 Briefly describe the following: (a) cool zone, (b) salamander, (c) contact grill, (d) under-fired grill, (e) microwave oven.

Part B

Effects of cooking on foods. Sugars — inversion, caramelisation. Crystalline and non-crystalline sugar products. Starches — gelatinisation, thickening properties, uses of common starches. Eggs — composition, properties of egg proteins (coagulation, egg white foam, emulsification). Questions. Effect of cooking on fibres and colour of meat, poultry and fish. Frying oils — smoke and flash points. Vegetables — changes in colour on cooking. Questions. Effect of cooking on the nutrient value of meat, fish, eggs, fruit and vegetables, cereals. Questions.

Sugars

Sugars belong to the group of foods known as *carbohydrates*. The molecules of these substances contain the elements carbon, hydrogen and oxygen in the proportions as shown below:

$$\text{Carbon} \underset{\text{Oxygen}\quad 1}{\overset{\text{Hydrogen}\quad 2}{\Big\langle}} \left.\vphantom{\begin{array}{c}2\\ \\1\end{array}}\right\} \text{ as in water}$$

A simple classification of the common carbohydrates is given in Table 4.1.

The chemistry of these substances is considered in Chapter 5 in connection with nutrition. In this chapter we are concerned with how these substances behave in cooking.

Sugar cookery
The main sugar used in cooking is sucrose:

It is a disaccharide formed from the monosaccharide sugars glucose and fructose linked together chemically. It is sold, as we saw in Chapter 1, in different degrees of refinement from dark sugars to white, in various crystal sizes and in the pulverished state for icing cakes.

Sugar solutions are used for many different purposes. Syrups are used to soak babas and savarins, pulled sugar is converted into baskets and other

Table 4.1 Classification of common carbohydrates

Common name	Chemical name	Examples	Food sources
Simple sugars 1 sugar unit	Monosaccharides	Glucose	Fruit, honey
		Fructose	Fruit, honey
		Galactose	Not free; part of the lactose molecule
Double sugars 2 sugar units	Disaccharides	Sucrose	Sugar cane and beet
		Maltose	Malt (germinated barley)
		Lactose	Milk
Long-chained carbohydrates	Polysaccharides	Starches	Bread, potatoes, cereals
Many sugar units		Dextrins	Derived from starch
		Cellulose	Roughage in fruit and vegetables
		Pectin	The jam-setting substances
		Pectic substances	from plant cell walls

decorative shapes, and caramel provides the bitter flavour to complement crème caramel. Skill and precision are required to produce all these, and many other, products from one main ingredient.

Three main processes are concerned in making sugar confectionery: (a) inversion, (b) caramelisation and (c) crystallisation.

Inversion
When sucrose is boiled in the presence of an acid, hydrolysis takes place, splitting the disaccharide into its constituent monosaccharides. The process is called *inversion*, and the mixture of equal parts of glucose and fructose is called *invert sugar*.

$$C_{12}H_{22}O_{11} + H_2O \xrightarrow{\text{Acid}} C_6H_{12}O_6 + C_6H_{12}O_6$$

Sucrose   Glucose   Fructose

Invert sugar

This process can be initiated in sugar solutions by boiling with acids (such as citric acid from lemons) or by using cream of tartar (which is an acid salt). Alternatively, chefs may use ready-made invert sugars in the form of 'confectioner's glucose'. This is a complex mixture of dextrins and many types of sugars, obtained by the breakdown of corn starch.

Caramelisation
The burnt sugar flavour we call caramel is produced by heating sugar at high temperatures with the minimum amount of water.

Caramel is formed by a complex chain of reactions in which sucrose is first inverted and then the monosaccharide sugars are further decomposed to acidic anhydrides. These polymerise (join together) to form a solid network of caramel.

Crystallisation

When a concentrated solution of sucrose is cooled slowly, large crystals appear. Such crystals would impart an unpleasant gritty texture to confectionery, so various techniques have evolved to reduce crystal size or to avoid crystals forming altogether.

In general, sugar products can be divided into two classes:

| non-crystalline | these are boiled at high temperatures and have a low moisture content; |
| crystalline | these are boiled at lower temperatures and have higher moisture content. |

Non-crystalline products Hard crack, pulled sugar and spun sugar are examples of this type of confectionery which contain no crystals and are hard and glassy in appearance. The effect required is achieved by a high boiling temperature (more than 140°C, 284°F) and low moisture content. The hot sugar is cooled very rapidly, before crystallisation can begin.

Crystalline products With these products the aim is to produce a large number of microcrystals rather than a smaller number of large crystals. The different methods available can be illustrated by various ways fondant can be produced.

(i) *By beating.* A skilled chef can produce a fondant from sucrose alone. The concentrated sugar solution is heated to 115°C to saturate it, then cooled to about 40°C and beaten vigorously to obtain microcrystals. This method requires great care. The smallest particle of dust or sugar falling into the cooling sugar solution would cause premature formation of large crystals.

(ii) *By inversion.* It is easier to make good fondant by adding cream of tartar before beating the sugar. This inverts the sucrose, releasing glucose and fructose. This mixture of sugars crystallises more slowly than sucrose, so it is easier to obtain the microcrystals which make light-coloured mouldable fondant.

(iii) *By using commercial fondant sugar.* Most caterers make use of commercially-made fondant sugar. This is made by boiling sucrose with 'confectioner's glucose', which is already inverted. The syrup is then cooled by running it on a water-cooled drum until it reaches 38°C (100°F), when it is beaten to produce smooth fondant.

Jam making

Inversion and inhibition of crystallisation are also important in jam making. The essential ingredients of jams are sugar, fruit acids and pectic substances. When the sugar and fruit are boiled together the acid inverts between 23% and 40% of the sugar. It also reacts with the pectin and sugar to form a semi-solid network which traps water within it. This is the gel which is formed when the jam sets. Because the sugar has been partially inverted it does not crystallise out during storage.

Other sugars

Although sucrose is the main sugar used in cooking, there are other sugars present in foods. All sugars are sweet, but their degree of sweetness varies, as can be seen in Table 4.2. From this table you can see that fructose is the sweetest of the sugars listed, so any cooking process which inverts sucrose increases the sweetness of the product.

Table 4.2 Sweetness scores of sugars compared with sucrose (100)

Fructose	170	Glucose	70
Invert sugar	130	Maltose	30
Sucrose	100	Lactose	15

Starches

Most plants lay down the bulk of their energy reserves in the form of starch. The initial products of photosynthesis are sugars, but these are bulky so they are condensed to form long starch chains.

Starches are formed and stored in cell organelles, called *leucoplasts*, as densely packed granules. The grains are characteristic in shape (see Fig. 4.6), so an expert can identify the source of a starch by microscopic examination.

The starch within the grains is present in two forms — straight and branched chains. Both break down to glucose, but the units are associated in different ways in the different forms. The long straight chains of *amylose* represent 20–30% of the total starch in most grains. The remainder consists of the branched form *amylopectin* (for further details see Chapter 5).

Starches are very versatile products. They contribute to the structure of cakes and breads, thicken sauces and soups, and produce blancmange-type puddings. All kitchens keep a stock of different flours and purified starches for these purposes. Each flour and starch has chemical and physical properties which allow it to satisfy the chef's specifications for a particular culinary purpose.

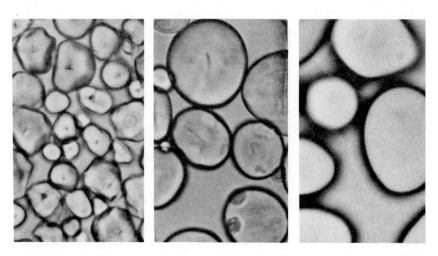

Fig. 4.6 Starch grains

109

Effects of cooking starches

Cooking starchy foods in water gelatinises the starch. In their natural state the amylose and amylopectin chains are neatly packaged inside the grains, and are held in those positions by chemical bonds. Water has to penetrate the grains and break the bonds before the starch chains can be released.

The stages of gelatinisation can be followed by slowly warming a dilute suspension of starch in a water bath. Figure 4.7 shows the sequence of the events which follow. You will note that no change occurs until about 60°C, when the water gradually penetrates the grains and releases the bonds, so the starch chains fan out. As the temperature rises the grains begin to swell visibily. The largest grains generally swell first, followed by the smaller ones. As the grains continue to swell, the cloudy starch suspension clears and thickens. The increased viscosity is due to the difficulty the swollen grains encounter when moving past each other. The whole process of swelling the grains and forming the viscous starch paste is termed *gelatinisation*.

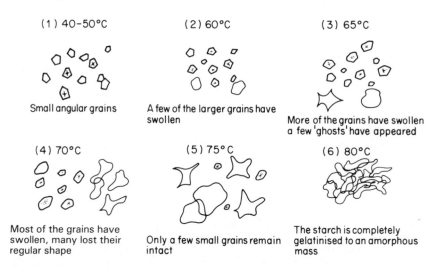

(1) 40-50°C	(2) 60°C	(3) 65°C
Small angular grains	A few of the larger grains have swollen	More of the grains have swollen a few 'ghosts' have appeared

(4) 70°C	(5) 75°C	(6) 80°C
Most of the grains have swollen, many lost their regular shape	Only a few small grains remain intact	The starch is completely gelatinised to an amorphous mass

Fig. 4.7   Stages in the gelatinisation of rice starch

The initial temperature for enlargement and the range over which successive grains swell are characteristic of the type of starch. The gelatinisation range is one of the properties of a starch which fits it for one culinary purpose rather than another (see Table 4.3). Further heating of a hot paste will allow the grains to continue swelling, providing there is sufficient water present. Around 90–100°C the grains reach their maximum size, and then collapse. As a result the paste becomes thinner. However, when it cools it thickens again.

Most cooked starches will form a *gel* when left to cool undisturbed. The long chains of the starch, which have been freed from the grains, associate to form a three-dimensional network, trapping water within the spaces. How permanent the solid shape of the gel will be depends on the proportion of

110

Table 4.3 The properties and uses of the common starches

Properties	Uses
Potato starch (fecule de pomme de terre)	
Initial gelatinization temperature (I.G.T.) low (58°C). Clear, highly viscous paste formed. Little tendancy to gel. Neutral in flavour	Used to thicken soups which would curdle at a high temperature
Tapioca (cassava)	
Low I.G.T. (52°C). Produces an exceptionally clear paste	The liquor from the cooked starch is used to thicken consommé. 'Pearl' tapioca is used for puddings. 'Flake' tapioca is used for garnishing
Rice (crème de riz)	
I.G.T. higher (68°C). Clear pastes are formed more quickly than with potato starch. The gels are opaque and very tender	The starch is used for thickening soups. *Short grain* (Carolina rice) is used for puddings *Long grain* rice is used in savoury rice dishes
Cornflour	
I.G.T. 62°C. Forms cloudy pastes. Gels very stiff but tend to retrograde particularly when frozen and thawed	Thickening sauces. *Disadvantages—* lumps form easily, may crack if used for glazing
Arrowroot	
Forms clear pastes	Thickening lemon sauce (clear). Glaze for fruit flans.
Waxy rice flour	
A natural flour with high freeze–thaw stability	White sauces and starch thickened puddings in cook–freeze operations
Starch phosphates	
Chemically modified starches with high freeze–thaw stability	White sauce formulation in cook–freeze operations
Pregelatinized starches	
The starch has been cooked and then dried. Forms a thick paste in cold milk	Instant pudding mixes

amylose in the starch. The straight chains of amylose touch and form new bonds at intervals without difficulty. The branches of the amylopectin chains get in the way and prevent a firm network from forming. Starches containing large amounts of amylose will gel at low concentrations, while waxy starches which contain large amounts of amylopectin can only be gelled at very high concentrations.

Because starches and flours from different origins vary greatly in gelatinisation range, gel formation and clarity of pastes, kitchens keep a variety of these products for different purposes. Table 4.3 shows the properties and uses of the common starches.

Factors affecting starch gels

Sauces, puddings and other dishes contain ingredients which modify the behaviour of starch gels.

Sugar

Sugar slows down the process of gelatinisation by competing with the grains for the available water. The greater the amount of sugar in the product, the more delicate the gel formed. The sugar prevents water from being bound to the starch network, and instead forms a sticky syrup within the gel.

Acids

The addition of acids to starch pastes, as in lemon pie fillings, also causes problems. The acid can break the starch chains, so that the gel becomes thinner. For this reason it is advisable to add the lemon juice after the paste has thickened.

Fat

The first step in thickening many sauces is to form a roux, i.e. to work the flour or starch into fat over a gentle heat. The fat adds flavour and texture to the sauce, but its main function is to ensure that the starch grains suspend individually, and so prevent lumps forming on the addition of hot liquid.

Proteins

You will perhaps have noticed that flours and purified starches do not behave in a similar manner. For instance, sauces and gels produced from corn starch will be different from those made with cornflour. This is because the protein in flours and those added to dishes in the form of egg, meat juices, milk or gelatin modify the behaviour of a starch to a marked extent.

Dry proteins absorb a considerable quantity of water, so wheat flours containing 10% protein make suitable pastes for batters, while pure wheat starch does not. Proteins also improve the freeze–thaw stability of starch pastes (see below) since they help to bind water inside the gels.

Retrogradation

When starch gels are stored, changes occur which cause the starch network to contract and squeeze out some of the water normally held within. This makes the gel opaque and spongy. It has been a serious problem with starch-thickened dishes in cook–freeze operations.

This difficulty has been overcome by changing the type of starch used. Amongst the natural starches, waxy rice flour was found to have most freeze–thaw stability. However, chemically modified starches have been produced (see Table 4.3) which are even more suitable for the purpose.

Eggs

Eggs are used in a wide variety of dishes. Their uses depend on three main properties.

1 The white can be beaten into thin elastic films which hold air, as in meringues and soufflés.
2 The egg proteins coagulate, forming custards, scrambled eggs and the binding agent in rissoles.
3 Eggs (particularly the yolks) contain emulsifying agents: used in salad dressings, sauces and choux paste.

Composition of hens' eggs
The composition of hens' eggs is given in Table 4.4.

Table 4.4   Composition of hens' eggs

	Total weight (%)	Water (%)	Protein (%)	Fat (%)
Whole egg	100	65	12	11
White	58	88	11	Trace
Yolk	31	48	18	33

The white
This is a dispersion of nine proteins in a watery medium. The two *albumins, ovalbumin* and *conalbumin*, make up 70% of the protein. These are fibrous proteins which contribute to the structure of baked products such as cakes. *Ovomucin* is only a small part of the white, but helps to make the 'thick white' of egg more solid than the rest of the white. Lysozyme is one of the globular proteins. It protects the egg by lysing (splitting open) bacteria.

The yolk
The yolk is a complex dispersion of lipids and proteins. Many of the proteins are loosely combined with the lipids to form *lipoproteins*. These substances are the cause of the 'gummy' quality of frozen egg yolks. Some of the lipoproteins contain lecithin, and these are responsible for most of the emulsifying ability of egg yolks.

Egg yolks also contain cholesterol, a substance which is required for the manufacture of vitamin D and some hormones. Recently there has been concern that Western diets contain excessive levels of this substance, leading to hardening of the arteries in middle-aged people (see Chapter 5).

Proteins
Many of the culinary properties of egg depend on their proteinous nature. A brief summary of protein structure is given below.

Proteins are polymers of amino acids. There are about 20 different amino acids which occur in foods. These are linked together in an infinite variety of ways to form all the individual proteins which make up living organisms.

The general structural formula for an amino acid is shown in Fig. 4.8. You will recognise COOH as the carboxyl group which also occurs in lipids, as described in Chapter 3. The group in the circle is an *amino* group, which gives the acid its name. It contains the element nitrogen, making proteins different from the carbohydrates and lipids studied so far.

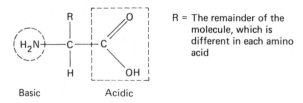

R = The remainder of the molecule, which is different in each amino acid

Basic   Acidic

Fig. 4.8 General structural formula of an amino acid

Amino acids in proteins are linked together by *peptide bonds*. The carboxyl group of one amino acid reacts with the amino group of another, forming a bond by eliminating one molecule of water (Fig. 4.9).

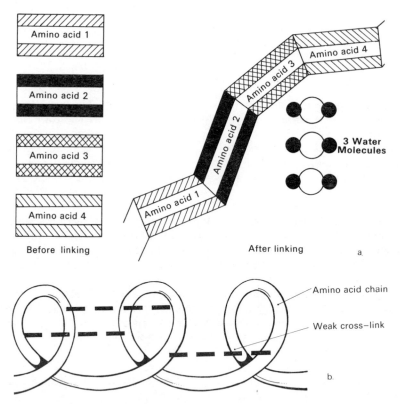

Fig. 4.9 Formation of a peptide bond

Proteins are more complex polymers than starches. In starch, the chains, whether straight or branches, are formed by repetition of only one basic unit, glucose. Proteins have 20 or more different amino acids which can be assembled into many thousands of different protein arrangements.

The chains of amino acids in a protein fold to form molecular threads. The precise mode of folding depends on the amino acids present, and is stabilised by chemical bonds formed between the side-groups of the chains. In addition, the threads themselves fold to form either rounded shapes, as in globular proteins such as lysozyme, or fibres, as in fibrous proteins such as keratin, elastin and myosin.

Thus, the three-dimensional shape of proteins is complex and unique to individual proteins. Cooking operations involving heating, beating or the addition of salt or sugar have marked effects on the structure of the proteins which make up eggs, and so modify their properties.

Heating
Heating coagulates proteins. The clear liquid of the white of egg becomes solid and opaque when heated. The yolk also solidifies, but this requires a higher temperature.

Eggs cooked in the shell Only high grade eggs should be used for these dishes. The degree of solidity obtained depends on the temperature and time of cooking (see Table 4.5).

Table 4.5 Eggs cooked in the shell

Type of egg	Characteristics	Minutes at 100°C
Breakfast egg	White just solid, yolk liquid	3
Oeufs mollet	White solid enough to peel from shell, yolk soft	5
Hard-boiled	Uniformly hard cooked egg	10 (cool rapidly to prevent green ring forming around the yolk)

Poaching eggs Vinegar and salt are added to the water, which should be boiling when the eggs are broken into it. The outer part of the white coagulates quickly and the temperature can be lowered after this stage. The vinegar and salt assist the rapid coagulation of the white, while the yolk stays fluid due to its higher coagulation temperature.

Omelets and scrambled eggs These dishes involve mixing the white and yolk, and the addition of other ingredients (see Table 4.6).

Table 4.6 Omelets and scrambled eggs

Description	Comments
Plain omelet Eggs are broken, seasoned and beaten to mix white and yolk, then cooked rapidly at a high temperature in a shallow heavy pan	The high temperature and mixing coagulates the egg into a thin foamy layer which should still be moist in the centre
Scrambled eggs Eggs are beaten with milk, seasoned and stirred over a gentle heat	The milk creates a more tender product. Stirring during cooking breaks up the coagulum into a creamy texture

Custards Custards are sweetened products made from eggs and milk. Their consistency varies from the solid to the liquid, according to the proportions of ingredients used and the method of cooking.

Baked custard. A baked custard is a gel. It is produced by cooking the mixture slowly, so it just solidifies and does not curdle. The gentle heat first changes the arrangement of the egg protein fibres, which then aggregate to form the solid structure, the gel. The sugar in the custard raises the temperature at which the gel is formed to above 80–84°C. When this temperature has been reached, cooking must stop, otherwise curdling will occur.

Custard sauce. A greater amount of sugar is employed, which makes a softer gel. Stirring also prevents many of the protein fibres from associating, so producing a more pourable product.

Egg white foams

When egg white is beaten, the protein unfolds so that the chains come to lie with their long axes parallel to the surface. The protein films stretch and dry as beating continues, so they can enclose a great deal of air.

Changes in colour and texture occur as the white is beaten. The pale yellow colour turns to an opaque white as smaller bubbles are formed, and the surface changes from a moist glistening to a dry dull one. Various factors can affect the formation and stability of egg white foams:

1 The foam reaches maximum stability after a certain amount of beating. Further beating breaks the foam and causes drip.
2 The addition of acids or cream of tartar (an acid salt) increases the stability of foams.
3 The addition of sugar early in the beating process delays the necessary changes in the protein and increases the amount of hand-beating required to produce a peak. When using an electric beater the stability point is reached very quickly, so it is an advantage to add the sugar as soon as beating commences, so there is no danger of over-beating.
4 Salt causes drip in lightly beaten whites, but not in those beaten for longer periods.
5 Very small amounts of fat or yolk interfere with foam formation, hence the need for care in separating yolks from whites.
6 Old eggs with watery whites produce poor foams.

Egg white foams are the basis of meringues, soufflés and a number of related products. Meringues are sugary froths of egg albumen which solidify when dried out by gentle heat.

Emulsification

Eggs, particularly the yolks, are used as emulsifiers in many culinary products. In all these dishes there is a watery component and a fatty one which normally will not mix. The function of the emulsifying agent is to enable small droplets of the oil or water to stay suspended in the other medium.

Salad dressings These are good examples of oil-in-water emulsions. In a well-made salad dressing the oil is dispersed as minute droplets in the water medium, which contains the vinegar and flavourings (see Fig. 4.10).

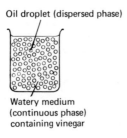

Oil droplet (dispersed phase)

Watery medium
(continuous phase)
containing vinegar

Fig. 4.10   Oil-in-water emulsion

The natural tendency of the oil droplets is to coalesce, so that larger and larger droplets form and the oil separates completely. This tendency can be prevented by adding a substance whose molecules are double-ended. One end has an affinity with the watery continuous phase and the other is repelled by the water but attracted to the oil.

The emulsifier forms a single layer of molecules round each oil droplet, preventing separation of the two phases (see Fig. 4.11).

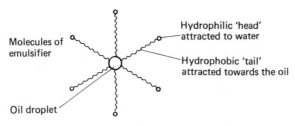

Molecules of emulsifier

Hydrophilic 'head' attracted to water

Hydrophobic 'tail' attracted towards the oil

Oil droplet

Fig. 4.11   Emulsifier molecules surrounding an oil drop

Salad dressings are of two types — temporary and permanent. Vinaigrette is a temporary emulsion. The mustard and garlic only partially stabilise the oil/water dispersion, so it has to be reshaken before use. Mayonnaise, on the other hand, is a permanent emulsion produced from 65% or more of good quality oil and egg yolk. The yolk provides lecithin which acts as the emulsifier.

Thickening sauces Warm emulsified sauces such as Hollandaise and Béarnaise are given their creamy rich texture by emulsifying warm whisked egg yolks and melted butter. Great care is required to produce a smooth emulsion. The temperature must be kept below 55°C, otherwise the egg proteins will begin to coagulate. The butter must be added cautiously and the mixing sufficient to produce emulsification but not so vigorous that the protective film around the droplets is broken.

The velvety texture of velouté soups is achieved by the addition of an emulsion of egg yolks and cream (liaison) just before service.

Cake making The emulsifying and foaming properties of eggs come into play in cake making. The eggs emulsify the fat so that it blends into the other ingredients. Beating the mixture foams the eggs, and the structure coagulates in the heat of baking.

Choux paste In this paste the high concentration of eggs and the protein of the flour provide the necessary emulsification and the light open structure. The fat, water and salt (and sometimes sugar) are boiled. Then sieved flour is added and stirred over the heat with a wooden spoon until it leaves the side of the pan. The mixture is cooled and the eggs are added one at a time. Then the whole is beaten until smooth and shiny.

Self assessment questions

Changes on cooking sugars, starches and eggs
 1 What conditions are necessary to invert sucrose?
 2 Which sugars are produced by the inversion of sucrose?
 3 Which culinary product is made by heating sugar to a high temperature with only a small amount of water present?
 4 If a sugar solution is boiled to 140°C or above, will it make a crystalline or non-crystalline product?
 5 Why is it difficult to make a good fondant using only sugar solutions?
 6 What part is played by inversion in jam making?
 7 Are amylose starch chains straight or branched?
 8 What is meant by gelatinisation of starches?
 9 How is a gel formed?
10 How is the ability of a starch affected by the content of (a) amylose and (b) amylopectin?
11 Select the most suitable starch or flour from the list at the end for the following culinary purposes. Explain how their gelatinization properties fit them for their kitchen use in: (a) thickening consommé, (b) thickening soups which curdle at high temperatures, (c) glazing fruit flans and (d) making sauces for cook–freeze operations.
    Potato, tapioca, rice, cornflour, arrowroot, starch phosphates.
12 What changes occur in most starches if they are frozen and then thawed?
13 What changes occur in a protein food when it is heated?
14 Why are salt and vinegar added to the water used for poaching eggs?
15 What precautions have to be taken to produce a soft gel in baked custards?
16 What happens when an egg white foam is over-beaten?
17 What effect has the addition of (a) salt and (b) sugar on beaten egg white foams?
18 Draw and label a diagram to show the molecules of an emulsifying agent stabilizing an oil in water suspension.
19 Which emulsifying agent(s) are present in (a) vinaigrette and (b) mayonnaise?
20 Why must Hollandaise and Béarnaise sauce be prepared at temperatures below 55°C?
21 List the properties of egg proteins which are important in cake making.

Meat

Cooking methods

Cooking methods can be divided into moist and dry methods, according to the atmosphere surrounding the meat. Roasting, grilling, frying and microwave cooking are dry methods, while steaming, pressure cooking, stewing and pot-roasting are moist methods. Traditionally, moist methods have been applied to the tougher cuts containing greater amounts of connective tissue, and dry methods to tender cuts with less connective tissue. The thinking behind such practices was that water was necessary to hydrolyse the collagen in the connective tissue to gelatin. Research has shown, however, that the meat itself contains sufficient moisture for this purpose.

In general it can be said that tender cuts do not benefit by slow moist cooking, but tougher cuts can be cooked by dry methods providing the cooking temperature is low.

Roasting

The most obvious changes which occur when roasting a joint of beef are:

1 the meat shrinks,
2 juices are exuded and
3 the colour changes from red to brown.

If a meat thermometer is inserted into the joint the end point for different degrees of cooking can be determined.

Beef is:

rare	at 60°C	(140°F),
medium done	at 71°C	(160°F) and
well done	at 77°C	(171°F).

The end point can be reached either with a high temperature for a short time or a low temperature for a long time. The latter produces more-tender joints in cheaper cuts. It is the rate of penetration rather than the cooking temperature which influences the tenderness of the meat.

Changes occur in the muscle proteins at as low a temperature as 40°C (104°F), but little tendering occurs until an internal temperature between 50°C and 60°C is reached; usually around 57°C. This is the collagen shrink point. At this temperature the helical shape of the collagen molecules breaks down and the joint shrinks. Beef cooked to an end point of 60°C is tender and retains the maximum amount of the juices, and so yields the greatest number of slices.

However, many people prefer their beef cooked to a higher end point. As the internal temperature of the meat rises to between 60°C and 70°C the muscle fibres shrink further, and there is a greater loss of moisture from the meat. At around 75°C the collagen hydrolyses to form gelatin but the yellow elastin fibres are unaffected. The gelatin moisturises the meat and emulsifies the fat that cooking has melted and released from the adipose tissue. Fat makes meat taste juicier, as it stimulates saliva production. Cheaper cuts are often more tender if cooked until well done, providing heat penetration has been gradual. The higher end point temperature has allowed the connective tissue to be softened to gelatin and the fat to be well dispersed.

Colour changes
The change in the colour of meat during cooking is due to the combined effect of heating and oxidisation. Heating denatures the protein part of myoglobin, and the iron becomes oxidised so that a haemichrome is formed which produces the tan colour.

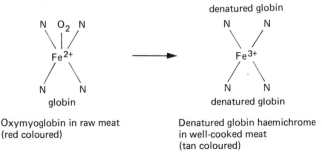

Oxymyoglobin in raw meat
(red coloured)

Denatured globin haemichrome
in well-cooked meat
(tan coloured)

The brown colour of the outside of meat is also due to the effect of heat on sugars in the meat, and to the reaction of meat sugars with amino acids (Maillard reaction).

Moist methods of cooking
Similar changes to those described above occur in meat cooked by moist methods, but the losses into the surrounding fluids are much greater. The collagen is fully converted into gelatin, but the elastin in the yellow fibres is little changed. Heating in moist methods must be slow and gradual, otherwise hardening occurs if the fluids are allowed to boil.

Poultry

Poultry have two distinct types of flesh. The white meat contains no myoglobin; it is more tender, but dries readily in cooking. The dark meat contains myoglobin; it is tougher but more juicy.

Cooking methods

Chicken
Chicken is usually roasted breast uppermost at an oven temperature of 149°C (300°F). However, it is equally tender and well-flavoured when cooked by deep frying, rotary spit or microwave oven. Young birds should be cooked just until the legs do not produce red juice which pricked. Further cooking makes the breast meat dry. Older birds need longer periods to convert their larger content of connective tissue to gelatin. The typical flavour of chicken develops during the cooking of the proteins. It is mainly due to the amino acids cysteine and glycine and a tripeptide, glutathione.

Turkeys

Roasting at 149–163°C (300–325°F) is recommended to an end point of at least 85°C (185°F) in the thigh muscles. With larger birds, the lower end of the cooking temperature range should be used. They should be tested in the breast as well as the legs, to ensure the end point has been reached throughout the bird.

Fish

Unlike meat, the flesh of fish contains little connective tissue, so is liable to fall apart on cooking. White fish, such as cod and haddock, also have a low fat content (less than 5%). Fish should be cooked just to the point at which the protein coagulates. Further cooking makes the flesh dry and crumbly.

Frying oils

The friture is standard equipment in commercial kitchens. Deep frying, properly controlled, seals the juices in a food and produces a crisp product with a characteristic flavour.

Smoke points

Plant oils are generally preferred for deep frying for the following reasons:

1 They have a high thermal capacity, so foods can be heated to high temperatures within a short time. Water is driven off in the process, so food heated in fresh oil is crisp and appetising.
2 They have a high smoke point (see Table 4.7).
3 Oils are not generally strongly flavoured, so do not change the taste of a food. Olive oil is an exception. It is used when its characteristic flavour enhances the dish.
4 Plant oils are economical if used correctly. Olive oil is an exception: it is more expensive, and so is used when its special properties are an advantage.
5 When an oil is heated to a temperature of around 230–260°C, a blue smoke arises. This is a sign that the triglycerides are breaking down. The heating cracks the fatty acid chains, so that volatile hydrocarbons and short-chained fatty acids (which have unpleasant odours) are produced. On heating, the glycerol produces acrolein (acraldehyde) which causes the blue haze and is an irritant to the eyes and throat (see Fig. 4.12).

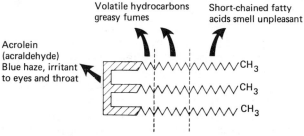

Fig. 4.12   Heating oil to a high temperature splits the triglycerides

When oils smoke it is a sign that they have reached the maximum safe temperature. Further heating is hazardous, as they will soon reach the *flash point*, when the vapours are liable to catch fire.

When using a fresh batch of oil, foods will fry satisfactorily between 180°C and 200°C, well below the smoke point (see Table 4.7). As the oil is re-used, however, the smoke point lowers. This is due to the gradual breakdown of the triglycerides. Eventually the smoke point falls below the temperature at which the food can be fried crisply. At the same time the breakdown products darken the oil and add unpleasant flavours.

Table 4.7   Specification of some animal and plant lipids

Lipid	Flash point (°C)	(°F)	Smoke point (°C)	(°F)	Melting point (°C)	(°F)	Recommended frying temperature (°C)	(°F)
Olive oil	285	545	168	335	0–10	32–50	177	350
Pure dripping	302	575	168	335	(49)	120	171–182	340–360
Maize oil	324	615	224	435	<0	<32	182	360
Pure vegetable fat	296	605	221	430	29–38	85–100	182–187	340–370

Figures courtesy of British Edible Oils Limited.

Frying oil can be kept in good condition for long periods if a few simple rules are followed.

1 Do not heat fresh oil above 200°C.
2 Renew approximately 1/5 of the volume of the oil after each use instead of waiting until most of the oil has been used.
3 Strain food remnants from the oil and keep the friture as clean as possible. Burnt pieces of food encourage rapid breakdown in the oil.
4 Dry foods before frying. Water helps to lower the temperature of the oil, causes 'spitting' and assists the breakdown of oils.

Modern equipment is designed to maintain the quality of cooking oils by having built-in filters to remove moisture and fatty acids, and a cool zone which separates the food particles from the frying area. With the latest computerised fryers, the quality of the oil can be monitored and the time, temperatures and degree of crispness for different products can be automatically controlled.

Colour changes in fruits and vegetables

Fruits and vegetables are valued for their colours as well as their nutrient content. A knowledge of the nature of the coloured materials in foods and how they alter when subjected to changes in temperature, pH and other conditions is helpful to the caterer trying to preserve the attractive appearance of cooked foods.

The pigments in fruits and vegetables can be separated into three main groups: chlorophylls, carotenoids and flavonoids.

Chlorophylls

Chlorophylls *a* and *b* are the green photosynthetic pigments in the chloroplasts of leafy vegetables and unripe fruits. Chlorophylls are complex molecules very similar in structure to the haem in haemoglobin, except that the plant pigment has a central magnesium atom where the blood pigment contains iron. A phytyl group is attached to the main porphyrin ring of the molecule giving chlorophyll fat-soluble properties. The two chlorophylls differ in the other side-group. The *a* form has a methyl group (CH_3) and the *b* an aldehyde group (CHO). Chlorophyll *a* is a blue-green colour, while *b* is a yellow-green. In fresh vegetables there are usually three parts of chlorophyll *a* to one part of *b*.

When vegetables are pickled in mild acids the central magnesium atom is replaced by two hydrogen atoms. The substances formed, phaeophytins, are drab-coloured compared with the fresh green of chlorophyll. Phaeophytin *a* is a grey-green and pheophytin *b* is a dull yellowish-green. A similar reaction occurs when vegetables are over-cooked, as the prolonged cooking releases organic acids from the cells. Canning also changes the colours of vegetables, as heating must be thorough to ensure sterilisation. Canned peas, for instance would become an unpleasant grey colour if a dye were not used to counteract this effect.

When green vegetables are cooked in large batches a compromise has to be made between appearance and nutrient value. It is better to aim at a product which looks and tastes pleasant than to seek for maximum retention of the vitamin C content (see page 126). Since the change to phaeophytin is due to the action of acids, the effect can be diluted if not neutralised by using rather more water than the minimum needed for cooking purposes. The effect will be greater if the water is slightly alkaline, as it is in many parts of the country. As some of the acids formed are volatile, cooking without a lid on the pan often improves the colour.

Another change which occurs when cooking spinach and some other leafy vegetables (not peas or beans) is due to an enzyme, chlorophyllase, which splits off the phytyl group. This allows the chlorophyllides which are formed to dissolve in the cooking water. The enzyme will withstand temperatures up to 77°C, but is destroyed by boiling. So bringing the vegetable to the boil rapidly prevents undue loss of colour into the cooking water.

Carotenoids

These are fat-soluble pigments varying in colour from yellow to red. The yellow-orange colours of oranges, peaches, carrots and swedes belong to this class. Red forms of this type of pigment occur in the skins of tomatoes and the flesh of water melons. Carotenoids are also present in the chloroplasts of plants, though their colours are masked by chlorophyll.

Some of the carotenoids, notably β-carotene, are converted into retinol (vitamin A). Six micrograms of β-carotene are required to produce one microgram of retinol. For this reason the vitamin A activity of foods is expressed as 'retinol equivalents' to take account of both sources of the vitamin.

Carotenoids are little affected by cooking since they are virtually insoluble in water. However, the colour is affected by oxidation (as happens when carrots are dried). Blanching prior to heat treatment minimises this loss of colour.

Flavenoids

Flavenoids are water-soluble and are present in the cell sap of the central vacuoles of plant cells.

Anthocyanins, which belong to this group, range in colour from red to blue. They are responsible for the colour in the skins of radishes, red potatoes and egg plants. They are also found in fruits such as blackberries and cherries, in the leaves of red cabbage and in beetroot.

Anthocyanins behave like laboratory pH indicators. Red cabbage is bright red when pickled in vinegar. At neutrality it is a purple colour, while as alkalinity increases it turns first grey and then green. This type of reaction is reversible, change of pH restores the original colour. Irreversible fading occurs when anthocyanins are heated to high temperatures in canning. Some of these pigments are more heat-sensitive than others. The anthocyanin is strawberries deteriorates to such an extent after heat processing that the shelf life of the product is exceptionally short. Anthocyanins also cause other problems in canning since they attack iron and tin, causing pitting. For this reason fruits containing these pigments are processed in enamel-lined cans.

Anthoxanthins (flavones) are pale yellow pigments. They occur in vegetables such as onions and potatoes. Their colour tends to become more pronounced on cooking, particularly in alkaline conditions. They can react with any iron present in cooking water to produce brownish salts which discolour white vegetables. A little acid in the cooking water will prevent this, but may affect the firmness of the vegetable.

Enzymic browning

Many fruits and vegetables develop unsightly colour changes when cut and exposed to the air; potatoes blacken and apples turn an unpleasant brown colour. This discoloration is due to oxidation of phenolic compounds in the fruit or vegetable accelerated by enzymes known as polyphenol oxidases.

Browning can be prevented by excluding the oxygen or by inactivating the enzymes. The most common methods are:

1 plunging the cut fruit or vegetable into water (preferably water which has been freshly boiled and cooled);
2 sprinkling the cut surfaces with salt or sugar to draw out a protective film of liquid from the food;
3 blanching to destroy the enzyme;
4 adding salt or an acid such as lemon juice to inhibit enzyme activity;
5 the use of antioxidants such as vitamin C to prevent browning during commercial preservation.

Self assessment questions

Changes on cooking meat, fish and vegetables
1 Which type of connective tissue fibres are made of elastin?
2 Which type of energy reserve is found in adipose tissue?
3 Which substance is formed when collagen is cooked gently in moist conditions?
4 Name two moist methods of cooking and two dry methods.
5 What happens to (a) a joint of meat and (b) collagen molecules when beef is cooked to 'shrink point'?
6 How is meat improved when gelatin is released in cooking?
7 Name three chemical reactions which contribute to the development of a brown colour in meat during cooking.
8 Name two ways in which the white flesh of poultry differs from the dark meat.
9 What is the main difference between meat and the flesh of fish?
10 What changes occur in the chlorophylls of green leaves when they are pickled or overcooked?
11 Why are green vegetables generally cooked in uncovered pans?
12 How can loss of colour be avoided when cooking spinach?
13 Explain why (a) the orange colour in carrots is little affected by boiling and (b) is adversely affected by drying. How can the effect in (b) be minimised?
14 Which conditions (a) turn anthocyanins a bright red colour and (b) cause their colour to fade?
15 How are the yellow pigments in onions affected by cooking?

The effect of cooking on the nutrient value of food

Meat
If meat is cooked carefully to produce a tender product, the nutritive value of the protein changes little. The mineral content (iron, calcium, phosphorus) is also little affected by cooking, though a proportion will be washed into the drippings. In moist methods the broth will contain a large proportion of both the minerals and the B group of vitamins. If the drippings are used to make gravy or the broth consumed with the meat, as in a stew, the loss of minerals will be negligible.

Greater loss occurs in the B vitamins, since thiamine, pyridoxine, folic acid and pantothenic acid are all heat-sensitive as well as water-soluble. The greatest losses are in thiamine. Roughly 20% of the thiamine in raw meat is lost when meat is cooked and kept hot. The thiamine is best retained in fast cooking methods such as frying or grilling.

Fish
The flesh of fish does not require ageing as in meat. It should be eaten as fresh as possible, as it deteriorates rapidly. If cooked correctly, less shrinkage occurs than in meat, so losses of minerals are smaller. Fish eaten with the

bones are particularly good sources of calcium and phosphorus. Sea fish are an important source of iodine in the diet.

Fatty fish are good sources of vitamins A and D, which are little affected by cooking. Up to half of the thiamine content of fish may be lost in cooking.

Eggs

The high biological value of egg protein is little affected by cooking. Over-cooking can, however, make dishes such as scrambled eggs and baked custards unappetising, as contraction of the proteins makes them rubbery and causes fluids to be expressed.

The yolk contains 12g fat/100g. This content is doubled when eggs are fried. There is also a significant content of cholesterol, which has led to advice to limit eggs in the diet of middle-aged people. The yolk contains iron, but not in readily available form. Uptake of the mineral can be enhanced by including a source of vitamin C in meals containing eggs. Iron also causes a problem in the presentation of hard-boiled eggs, as it is concerned in the formation of grey-green rings around the yolk. The reaction between iron and sulphur occurs when the white is at an alkaline pH. The problem can be minimised by using fresh eggs (which are less alkaline), cooking for the minimum time and cooling immediately in cold running water.

There is a loss of between 5% and 15% of thiamine and riboflavin in most cooking methods. One of the B vitamins, biotin, is only available after cooking, as in the raw state it is firmly bound to the protein avidin.

Fruit and vegetables

Vitamin C is the nutrient most abused in commercial cookery. It is difficult to retain since it is water-soluble and is destroyed by heat and oxidation. Losses can occur at every stage from purchase to consumption.

(i) *Buying vitamin C.* Careful selection of fruit and vegetables is essential, as the vitamin is lost in any bruised or wilted produce. In healthy intact cells vitamin C is separated from an enzyme, ascorbic oxidase. When cells are damaged the enzyme oxidises the vitamin to the inactive form.

(ii) *Preparation.* Peeling, chopping, grating or cutting the fruit or vegetable in any way exposes broken cells to oxygen and reduces the vitamin content. Preparation should be done as close to the time of cooking as possible, or in some cases the vegetable can be cooked whole. When cutting, steel knives and mincers should be used since traces of iron, copper and zinc act as catalysts, speeding the destruction of the vitamin.

(iii) *Cooking.* The vitamin is retained best by non-watery methods (e.g. stir-fry) or by rapid methods involving the minimum amount of water, such as steaming or low pressure cooking (5psi). When boiling vegetables the best retention of vitamin C activity is obtained by using the minimum amount of lightly salted water and adding freshly shredded vegetables to already boiling water. Bicarbonate of soda added to keep the green colour reduces the vitamin C content of vegetables.

(iv) *Holding.* Vitamin C is lost when food is kept warm prior to service. Up to half of the vitamin content may be lost in 45 minutes, so if possible vegetables should be cooked to order.

Caterers will realise from the above information that little vitamin C will be retained in vegetables cooked under normal commercial conditions. Where the vitamin C content of a meal is of importance, it is better offered in the form of fresh fruit or juice, or carefully prepared salad vegetables.

Cereals and phytic acid

Phytic acid occurs in the bran of cereals, dried pulses and some nuts (almonds, brazils, coconuts). It can occur as both soluble and insoluble salts. When in combination with calcium and magnesium, an insoluble salt, phytin, is produced. Phytin precipitates in the stomach and intestine making the minerals calcium, magnesium and phosphorus in the food unavailable to the body.

The problem can be overcome as regards wholemeal bread by adding extra yeast and using a long-rise method. Yeast possesses an enzyme which hydrolyses phytin so that the minerals become available.

Some dried pulses are difficult to soften in cooking, while others become tender easily. Those which soften readily contain more soluble potassium phytate than the pulses which remain hard. The soluble phytate prevents calcium or magnesium ions in the cooking water from forming tough insoluble pectic substances in the cell walls of the beans or peas.

Self assessment questions

Effect of cooking on nutrient value of food
1 Which of the following vitamins is likely to be found in the drippings from a cooked joint of meat?
   Ascorbic acid, thiamine, riboflavin, cholecalciferol, retinol.
2 Why should baked custards be cooked at a low temperature?
3 How do the green rings form around the yolks of hard boiled eggs? How can this discolouration be prevented?
4 Explain how you would prevent loss of vitamin C in fruits and vegetables:
   (a) while buying and storing,
   (b) during preparation,
   (c) while cooking and
   (d) when holding food prior to service.
5 Which foods contain salts of phytic acid? What effect may these substances have on the nutrient value of these foods?
6 What is meant by (a) the smoke point, (b) the flash point of a cooking oil?
7 What changes occur in the triglycerides of a lipid when it reaches smoke point?
8 What happens to the smoke point of an oil when it is reheated many times?
9 How can frying oils be kept in good order through many heatings?

5
Eating to live

Part A

Food fuels, energy values of foods, BMR, energy balance, body building, protein needs. Functions of major and trace elements, vitamins and deficiency diseases. Multiple-choice questions. Digestion, structure of the alimentary canal, digestion of carbohydrates, proteins, fats. Questions. Nutritional needs of babies, children, adolescents, adults, vegetarians, slimmers, the elderly, pregnant women and nursing mothers. Questions.

Why do we need food?

When we have fasted for some time, we feel tired and unable to do 'work'. Our bodies are like machines, they require fuel for movement and physical activity. However, unlike cars and other machines, human bodies use up fuel even when they appear to be inactive. When we are resting or asleep, our lungs, heart, digestive and other organs still continue to function.

So we require energy for keeping the body 'ticking over'. This is called *basal metabolic* energy. In addition, we also need energy for work and leisure activities: for walking, running, lifting objects or playing games.

Food fuels

Starches, sugars and fats are the main food fuels, though proteins can also be 'burnt' to provide energy. The energy value of a food is measured in *calories* or *joules*.

A calorie is the amount of energy needed to raise the temperature of 1 gram of water by 1 degree Celsius (Centigrade). It is a very small unit, so we generally use the larger unit, the *kilocalorie* in food energy calculations:

1000 calories = 1 kilocalorie (kcal).

In modern books and tables, energy values are given in joules or kilojoules:

1 calorie = 4.2 joules.
1 kilocalorie = 4.2 kilojoules.

Fats are the most concentrated sources of energy in our diet as can be seen from the following figures:

1 g carbohydrate (starches, sugars) provides 16 kJ or 3.75 kcal,
1 g fat provides 37 kJ or 9 kcal,
1 g protein provides 17 kJ or 4 kcal.

The *Manual of Nutrition* provides tables giving the energy values of foods.

Using this information it is easy to work out the *calorific* value of a dish or whole meal. An example is shown in Table 5.1.

Table 5.1 To calculate the energy value of a rice pudding

Code No.	Food	Energy per oz (kcal)	Amount used	Energy in food (kcal)
3	Whole, liquid milk	18	20 fl. oz = 1 pint	360
126	Rice	102	2 oz	204
51	Sugar	112	2 oz	224
			Total energy in pudding	788

If you wanted to know how much energy you would get from a portion of the pudding, you would have to decide how many portions it would provide. If you decided it would serve four people, then the energy value per portion would be 788/4 = 197 kcal.

Table 5.2 Energy value of a portion of scrambled eggs

Code no.	Food	Energy per 100 g (kcal)	Amount used	Energy in food (kcal)
41	Eggs, fresh	147	1 medium egg = 50 g	
3	Milk, liquid	65	25 g	
119	White bread	233	1 large slice = 50 g	_____
			Total in portion =	

Find out the energy value of a portion of scrambled egg on toast. Use the tables for 100 g on p. 245 to get used to working in metric units.
If you wanted to know the energy value in kilojoules you could multiply your answer by 4.2, or you could use the kilojoule values in the *Manual of Nutrition*. Doing exercises such as this can be very useful when planning meals for slimmers. We have noted that our food fuels must provide:
1 basal metabolic energy to maintain essential body services, and
2 work energy to provide for activities in work and leisure.
It may surprise you to learn that for most people the first category is larger than the second, i.e. they need more energy to keep the body going than for their work and play.

Basal Metabolic Rate
If we measure the heat energy produced by a person who is resting in comfortably warm conditions after an overnight fast we can find their Basal Metabolic Rate (B.M.R.).
The size of the B.M.R. depends on the following factors:
1 The size and sex of the person. The greater the amount of heat-producing tissue (muscles, liver) the larger the B.M.R. So a man will have a larger B.M.R. than a woman of the same age and weight, as he has more muscle and less fatty tissue in his body.

2 The surface area. The greater the surface area, the higher the metabolic rate. Premature babies have high surface areas in comparison with their volume and so have to be protected from undue heat loss.

3 Age. Young children have the highest B.M.R. This need for maintenance energy falls as we get older, with a drop of 5% for each decade. So elderly people can maintain their bodies with much less fuel than young children need for this purpose.

Thermic effect of food

It might be supposed that the amount of energy needed could be estimated by adding the basal metabolic energy to the work energy. However, when the body is supplied with food the heat output is increased. This is called the *thermic effect* of food. So we must add 5–7% more energy to the calculation given above to allow for this heat loss.

Work energy

The amount of energy needed also depends on how strenuous your work and leisure activities are, and for how long you engage in them. Obviously, a coal-miner will expend more energy than a clerk in his daily work.

Growing energy

Making new tissue requires energy as well as materials. So children, pregnant women and nursing mothers need extra energy for this purpose.

So now we can list all the energy requirements of the body:

1 Basal metabolic energy — for maintenance of basic bodily activity.
2 Work energy — for work and leisure activities.
3 Thermic effect of food — heat wasted in awakening the metabolism.
4 Growth energy — energy needed to form tissues or secretions (e.g. milk).

Energy balance

In most adults the appetite controls the energy needs effectively. Food intake is increased when work is strenuous and when the weather is cold, and decreased when less energy is needed. In other words the energy intake is balanced with output, and body weight stays constant.

However, some people find this balance difficult to achieve and tend to become overweight.

Body building

While the human body behaves broadly as a machine in oxidising food fuels to provide energy, it is very different in other ways. A car which could make, assemble and maintain its own parts would be a dream come true. Yet a human being begins life as a fertilised egg less than the size of a pin-head and may grow to an adult weighing 70 kg or more. During growth all the millions of cells have to be assembled into the appropriate tissues and organs, each precisely adapted to its function. To accomplish this feat, the diet must contain the necessary nutrients to build the substances needed.

Proteins

Proteins are the main nutrients needed to sustain growth and repair of tissues. As we saw in Chapter 4, proteins differ from carbohydrates and fats in containing the extra element nitrogen. So while all three of the major nutrient groups can provide energy, only the proteins support cell production.

As we saw in Chapter 4, proteins are large molecules composed of chains of amino acids. Each protein has a special pattern of amino acids, making it suitable for its particular purpose in the body. The proteins of each species of animal and plant are different, so when we eat the muscle proteins of beef the amino acid chains have to be broken down in digestion and reassembled to make human proteins.

The human diet usually contains both animal and plant protein. Most people recognise meat, offal, cheese, eggs and milk as good sources of protein, but in fact around 25% of our proteins come from cereals and about 10% from vegetables.

Of the 20 different amino acids needed to make human proteins eight are termed *essential* amino acids (see Table 5.3). The essential amino acids have to be supplied ready-made in the diet. The remainder can be made from simple nitrogenous compounds.

Table 5.3 Amino acids

Essential amino acids	Some common non-essential amino acids
Leucine	Alanine
Isoleucine	Arginine
Lysine	Aspartic acid
Methionine	Cysteine
Threonine	Glutamic acid
Tryptophan	Glycine
Valine	Proline
Histidine (essential for	Serine
young children)	Tyrosine

As animals are more closely related to man than are plants, animal foods contain more of the essential amino acids needed to build our proteins. However, it is very easy to combine small amounts of animal proteins with cheaper plant proteins to achieve diets which provide all the essential and non-essential amino acids needed. With more care, the necessary amino acids can be obtained from a purely vegetarian diet.

As animals mature slowly, meat and animal products are expensive. Increasingly in the future we shall be looking for additional sources of protein to meet the needs of a rising human population.

Already caterers are using textured vegetable protein (T.V.P.) to extend and cheapen meat dishes. In the future microorganisms, which have very rapid growth rates, may be used as sources of food proteins.

Protein needs
As growth is related to protein intake, children need more protein in relation to their size than adults. Women also need a high protein intake when they are pregnant or breast-feeding. People recovering from accidents, burns or prolonged illness need extra protein to replace tissues which have been lost or damaged.

Slimmers should be careful not to cut their protein intake too drastically when they reduce their general food consumption. A glance at food tables will highlight the 'empty calorie' foods which contain little apart from energy and can be cut out without lowering the nutritional value of the diet.

While carbohydrates, proteins and fat form the major constituents of the diet, two other groups of nutrients are needed to maintain good health — the minerals and vitamins. Apart from these nutrients we also need fibre to give bulk to the diet and water to dissolve food materials and to maintain the fluid balance of our tissues.

Dietary fibre
Some foods contain a large amount of material which cannot be digested. This roughage or fibre is essential to provide bulk in the diet. Fibre makes the faeces, the waste products of digestion, soft and bulky so they are easily moved along the gut. Lack of dietary fibre can lead to constipation and a more serious condition known as diverticulitis. In this disease the strain on the intestine wall causes it to form balloon-like pouches.

The main sources of fibre in the diet are fruits, vegetables and the bran of cereals.

Minerals
At least 15 elements are known to be essential to man, and five more are needed by other animals and may also be necessary in small amounts in human nutrition. Eight of these elements are needed in relatively large amounts (0.02 to 5 g/day) so are termed major minerals while the remainder are needed in smaller quantities and are termed trace elements (see Table 5.4).

Table 5.5 shows the functions of all the major minerals and some trace elements.

Table 5.4   Essential minerals

Major elements	Trace elements	
Calcium	Fluorine	Molybdenum
Phosphorus	Iodine	Selenium
Magnesium	Zinc	Silicon
Sodium	Copper	Nickel
Potassium	Manganese	Tin
Chlorine	Cobalt	Vanadium
Iron	Chromium	
Sulphur		

Table 5.5 Functions of the major elements and some trace elements in the human body

Element	Functions	Deficiency diseases	Sources	Notes
Calcium	Forms a compound with phosphorus which strengthens *bones and teeth*. Essential for muscular contraction, nerve transmission and blood clotting	Too little calcium in the skeleton of children causes stunted growth and rickets. In women, repeated pregnancies can cause loss of calcium from the bones (osteomalacia). Lack of vitamin D to absorb the calcium is the usual cause of these diseases	Milk, cheese, fish eaten with the bones, bread	White flour in Britain is fortified with 1.25 g calcium per kilogram. Calcium absorption from food is reduced by phytic acid, a substance found in the outer layer of cereals
Phosphorus	Forms calcium phosphate or apatite in the bones and teeth. Present in some fatty substances, proteins, nucleic acids and in compounds concerned with energy production and storage	Dietary deficiency unknown in man	Widespread in foods: yeast extract, bread, cheese, nuts, processed foods.	
Magnesium	Present in the bones and teeth. Necessary for normal function of nerves and muscles. Plays a part in enzyme reactions transferring energy	Deficiency is rare. Occurs in diseases causing severe diarrhoea. Alcoholics may also suffer from magnesium deficiency	Constituent of chlorophyll, so widespread in vegetables. Aslo in yeast extract and nuts	
Sulphur	Present in the amino acids methionine and cysteine	None	Meat, offal, green vegetables	
Sodium and chlorine	Found in the plasma of the blood and in other body fluids. Salt and water requirements are normally kept in balance by the kidneys and sweat glands	Excessive sweating (as in very hot working conditions) can cause muscular cramps	Table salt, processed and preserved foods, bacon, kippers, meat products	Young infants cannot tolerate salted foods. Excessive intake is thought to be associated with high blood pressure in adults

133

Element	Functions	Deficiency diseases	Sources	Notes
Potassium	Found mainly in the cells and body fluids. Associated with sodium in nerve transmission and muscular contraction	Heart failure can occur from severe deficiency of the element in hunger diseases such as Kwashiorkor	Vegetables, meat milk, fruit juices	
Iron	Necessary for the production of haemoglobin, the oxygen-carrying pigment in the blood, and for the muscle protein, myoglobin	Lack of iron in the blood causes anaemia, in which the person is pale, tired and breathless	Meat, liver, kidney, cocoa powder, watercress	Iron is better absorbed from animal sources than from plants. Vitamin C assists the absorption of the mineral
Iodine	Necessary for the formation of the thyroid hormones which control growth and development	Swelling of the thyroid gland, simple goitre, occurs when drinking waters do not contain sufficient iodine	Water, seafoods, 'iodised' table salt	Some green vegetables contain substances which reduce absorption of the element
Fluorine	Hardens the tooth enamel. Also present in bones	Lack of fluoride in water supplies is not the cause of dental decay, but concentrations of 1 mg/l of fluoride in water helps to protect against dental caries	Drinking water, tea, sea foods and fish. Many toothpastes have fluoride	Some municipal authorities add fluoride to their water supplies

Table 5.6 Notes on the vitamins

Vitamin	Deficiency disease	Sources	Notes
		FAT-SOLUBLE VITAMINS	
A (retinol)	'Night blindness', inability to see in dim light. Eye lesions or complete blindness may occur. The vitamin maintains the mucous membranes of the body, so lack can cause death from respiratory or intestinal disease	Dairy products, liver, oily fish. β-Carotene in carrots and green vegetables	Retinol is only found in animal foods. The carotenes found in yellow and green plants can be converted into retinol in the intestinal lining. Retinol is stored in the liver. The vitamin is required in minute amounts. It is toxic if taken in excess.
D (cholecalciferol)	Vitamin D controls the calcification of the bones and teeth. Lack of the vitamin in children causes rickets, in which the leg bones are soft and 'bow' under the weight of the body. The bones are painful and break easily. Older people suffer from osteomalacia — loss of calcium from the bones	The best dietary sources are eggs, liver and oily fish. The vitamin can be made in the body by the action of sunlight on a fatty substance under the skin	Margarines, breakfast cereals and baby foods are enriched with another form of the vitamin, ergocalciferol. Excessive intakes of vitamin D can cause calcium deposits in the kidneys
E (alpha-tocopherol)	Deficiency is very rare in man. Recent research suggests the vitamin protects the trace metal selenium in an enzyme	The germ of cereals, plant oils (except olive oil), eggs	In rats lack of this vitamin causes sterility, but this effect has not been observed in man or other species
K (phylloquinone)	Vitamin K is concerned in blood clotting. Deficiency prolongs the time needed for the blood to clot	Found in green vegetables, cereals, peas and many other foods	The vitamin is synthesised by bacteria in the intestines

Vitamin	Function / Deficiency	Sources	Notes
B₁ (thiamine)	Thiamine is associated with the release of energy from carbohydrates. Beri-beri is the deficiency disease which occurs when the diet is of polished rice, which is high in carbohydrate but low in thiamine. The disease affects the muscles and nervous system	Whole grains, yeast, pork, green vegetables	In Britain, white flour is fortified with thiamine to at least 0.24 mg/100 g. This replaces the thiamine lost in milling. Thiamine is easily lost in cooking as it is water-soluble and destroyed by heat (particularly in alkaline conditions)
B₂ (riboflavin)	Deficiency of this vitamin is rare. Symptoms include cracked and sore lips, the tongue becomes a magenta colour	Milk, cheese, eggs, meat, yeast, tea	Riboflavin is destroyed by ultraviolet light. As milk is the main source of the vitamin, it is important not to leave milk exposed to sunlight
Nicotinic acid (also known as Niacin in U.S.A.)	Deficiency causes Pellagra, a condition in which the skin becomes dark and scaly when exposed to light. Diarrhoea, depression and partial paralysis may occur in severe cases. The vitamin is an essential part of a number of coenzymes associated with energy cycles	Meat, bread, flour, breakfast cereals, milk, vegetables, cheese and eggs, are rich in tryptophan (see notes)	Pellagra is a disease of people who live largely on a diet of maize. The nicotinic acid in maize is in a bound form. It can be released by treating the cereal with alkali as in the preparation of tortillas. The amino acid tryptophan is converted into nicotinic acid in the body. Nicotinic acid is heat-stable and is only lost in cooking through its water solubility
B₆ (pyridoxine)	Depression, irritability and anaemia are some of the symptoms of pyridoxine deficiency. Infants may have convulsions if fed on milk formulas deficient in this vitamin	Meat, liver, eggs, vegetables, whole grains	The vitamin is involved in amino acid metabolism, including the formation of nicotinic acid and also of haemoglobin. Deficiency may be a side-effect of some drugs. Pyridoxine is water-soluble and heat-sensitive

Vitamin		Sources	
B$_{12}$ (cyanocobalamin)	Severe dietary deficiency causes pernicious anaemia. This type of anaemia cannot be cured by giving extra iron. The disease also affects the nervous system	Only animal foods such as meat, eggs, fish and cheese contain the vitamin	B$_{12}$ does not occur in plant foods so vegans (strict vegetarians) run a risk of developing pernicious anaemia. More often the disease is due to lack of the necessary factor in the stomach which allows the vitamin to be absorbed in the ileum. Cyanocobalamin contains the trace element cobalt
Folic acid	Deficiency causes an anaemia which can occur in pregnant women, elderly people and infants	Green vegetables, fish, liver, bananas	Folic acid is linked with B$_{12}$ in the production of healthy blood cells. The vitamin is heat-sensitive
Pantothenic acid	Deficiency is unknown in man. The vitamin is associated with the release of energy from fats and carbohydrates	Animal products and cereals	
Biotin	Deficiency is unknown in man	Offal, egg yolk	Biotin is also associated with fat utilisation. The vitamin is made by bacteria in the large intestine
C (ascorbic acid)	Vitamin C is needed to form healthy connective tissue. Deficiency leads to bleeding from the mouth and gums. Severe deficiency causes scurvy, in which the gums become swollen and spongy and the teeth become loose. The vitamin assists the absorption of iron from the intestine	Citrus fruits, blackcurrants, strawberries, cauliflower, sprouts. Potatoes provide the bulk of the vitamin in the diet, as they are eaten in large quantities	The vitamin is destroyed by oxidation when fruits and vegetables are cut or shredded. Excessive temperatures, long cooking times and large amounts of cooking water all reduce the vitamin C in cooked foods. Addition of alkalis (bicarbonate of soda) destroyes vitamin C, while acids (vinegar) protect it

Vitamins

Minerals mostly occur in inorganic form, as they are derived from rocks of various kinds. Vitamins, on the other hand, are *organic* substances. They are essential for body processes, yet are needed only in minute amounts in the diet. They were the last group of nutrients to be discovered. Their roles became apparent when it was found possible to cure the symptoms of deficiency diseases by feeding patients with particular foods. For instance, citrus fruits prevented scurvy, the unpleasant disease suffered by sailors on long voyages.

When first discovered, the chemical compositions of the vitamins were unknown, so they were distinguished by letters of the alphabet. These letters are still useful in grouping the vitamins into two major groups:

water-soluble vitamins B group, C,

fat-soluble vitamins A, D, E, K.

The main functions, deficiency diseases and food sources are shown in Table 5.6.

Self assessment questions

Why do we need food?

1 Define a 'kilocalorie'.
2 Express 50 kilocalories in kilojoules.
3 List the four main ways energy is used in the body.
4 Which element is present in proteins but absent from carbohydrates and fats?
5 What is meant by an essential amino acid?
6 How many essential amino acids are needed in the diets of adults?
7 Name two groups of people who need more protein (in relation to their size) than the average adult.
8 Name the major elements needed in the diet.
9 What is meant by a deficiency disease?
10 Name the water-soluble vitamins. Which vitamins are fat-soluble?

Multiple-choice questions

1 The main minerals needed to strengthen bones and teeth are:
    (a) iron and magnesium
    (b) sodium and potassium
    (c) calcium and phosphorus
    (d) sulphur and iodine
2 The vitamin which assists the hardening of bones and teeth is:
    (a) vitamin A
    (b) vitamin B
    (c) vitamin C
    (d) vitamin D
3 Lack of iron in the diet causes:
    (a) goitre
    (b) anaemia
    (c) scurvy
    (d) rickets

4   The vitamin which assists the absorption of iron from plant sources is:
   (a) vitamin A
   (b) vitamin B
   (c) vitamin C
   (d) vitamin D
5   The group of foods which contain large amounts of the elements sodium and chlorine are:
   (a) bacon, kippers, preserved meats
   (b) bread, rice, flour
   (c) potatoes, beans, peas
   (d) oranges, apples, pears
6   The thyroid hormones cannot be formed without the element:
   (a) magnesium
   (b) potassium
   (c) fluorine
   (d) iodine
7   The body converts β-carotene from plants into:
   (a) vitamin A
   (b) vitamin B
   (c) vitamin C
   (d) vitamin D
8   The vitamin which is made by the action of sunlight on fatty substances under the skin is:
   (a) vitamin A
   (b) vitamin B
   (c) vitamin C
   (d) vitamin D
9   The vitamins most easily lost in cooking are:
   (a) vitamin A
   (b) vitamin D
   (c) vitamin C and the B group
   (d) vitamins E and K
10   A diet high in carbohydrate but low in thiamine is likely to lead to:
   (a) scurvy
   (b) beri-beri
   (c) pellagra
   (d) anaemia
11   Vitamin B_{12} is most likely to be lacking in the diet of:
   (a) Moslems
   (b) Jews
   (c) lacto-vegetarians
   (d) vegans
12   Riboflavin is found in:
   (a) cod liver oil, olive oil, groundnut oil
   (b) sugar, honey, jam
   (c) lard, margarine, butter
   (d) milk, cheese, meat
13   Pellagra is due to a lack of:

    (a) thiamine
    (b) riboflavin
    (c) nicotinic acid
    (d) ascorbic acid
14 The cooking method which would best conserve the vitamin C in vegetables is:
    (a) cooking in large amounts of water in an open pan
    (b) cooking and keeping hot for 30 minutes before serving
    (c) cooking in water with bicarbonate of soda added
    (d) stir-frying and serving immediately
15 The vitamins associated with the production of healthy blood cells are:
    (a) biotin and pantothenic acid
    (b) folic acid and vitamin B_{12}
    (c) ascorbic acid and nicotinic acid
    (d) thiamine and vitamin K

How is food digested?

Digestion is the process which makes our food available for energy production, tissue repair and growth. Most foods are solid and are composed of large complex molecules. Digestion is the means of converting solid complex foods into simple soluble substances which can pass from the gut into the bloodstream.

As food passes down the gut or *alimentary canal*, it meets a series of juices secreted by glands. These liquids contain enzymes which accelerate the necessary chemical reactions and allow them to proceed at body temperature and in comparatively mild conditions.

The outline plan of digestion is very simple. It consists of three processes:
1 grinding and softening in the mouth,
2 mixing and liquefying in the stomach and
3 simplifying molecules in the stomach and intestines.

Grinding and softening
Digestion begins when food is chewed and mixed with saliva in the mouth. Human beings have a general-purpose set of teeth as they are omnivores, eating both plant and animal food. The front teeth, the *incisors*, bite off the food, while the *premolars* and *molars* at the back grind it to a paste. Between these teeth there are four pointed *canine* teeth, which are comparatively short in man, and are intended for tearing meat.

The food is softened and lubricated by the secretion from the three sets of *salivary glands*. These lie below the lower jaw and near the ears. Anyone who has suffered from mumps will know exactly where they are! The aroma and taste of well-cooked food makes our mouths 'water' as the salivary glands produce more of this secretion in response to these stimuli.

When the food has been chewed it is formed into a ball or 'bolus' by the tongue, and swallowed. It has to pass over the top of the *trachea* (windpipe)

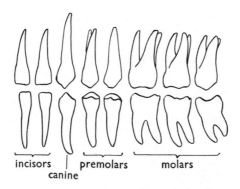

incisors | premolars molars
canine

to reach the *oesophagus*, or gullet. The trachea is guarded by a flap called the *epiglottis* which prevents food from passing into the lungs. If you are unwise enough to try to talk and eat at the same time, the flap opens and the food slips past. You then cough automatically to remove the food before harm is done.

Mixing and liquefying

Food passes down the oesophagus by waves of muscular contraction called *peristalsis*. This is why it is possible to eat standing on your head, if you are so minded!

Further softening and liquefying occurs in the stomach. The stomach is a bag, guarded at either end by circular muscles (*sphincters*) which retain the food until it is liquefied and partially digested. Three sets of muscles in the wall of the stomach allow it to perform a cocktail-shaker action so that the food is thoroughly mixed with the gastric juice. When the food is sufficiently liquefied, the pyloric sphincter opens and allows it to pass into the first part of the small intestine. How long food stays in the stomach will depend on the nature of the meal. A watery drink will pass straight through but a heavy meal, particularly if it contains much fat, will remain 4 hours or longer in the stomach.

Simplification

Simplification of food molecules occurs as a result of a succession of chemical reactions which take place as the food passes down the alimentary canal. Each reaction is catalysed by its own enzyme.

As a large number of digestive reactions take place at the same time in some parts of the gut, it is easy to get lost in the details. It will help if we look at the chemical breakdown of each major food category before dealing with the enzymes which are associated with them.

Carbohydrates

All carbohydrates (sugars and starches) are digested eventually to simple monosaccharide sugars such as glucose and fructose. Starches are very large molecules consisting of straight and branched chains of glucose units (see Chapter 4). Their digestion is accomplished by a series of enzymic reactions

141

which split them into successively shorter chains and finally to the simple sugars as shown diagramatically in Fig. 5.1.

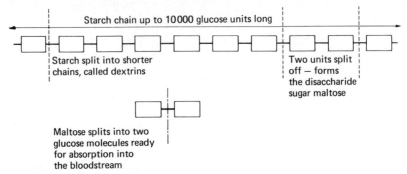

Fig. 5.1 Digestion of starches

Proteins

In the same way, proteins are broken into progressively shorter units until finally the constituent amino acids are freed (see Fig. 5.2).

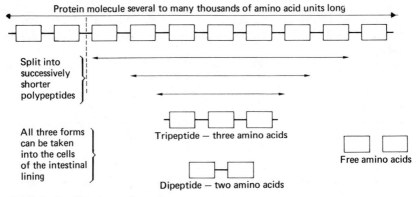

Fig. 5.2 Breaking down of protein

Lipids (fats and oils)

The fats and oils as we saw in Chapter 3 consist of triglycerides. These are simplified by splitting off the fatty acids from the glycerol as shown in Fig. 5.3.

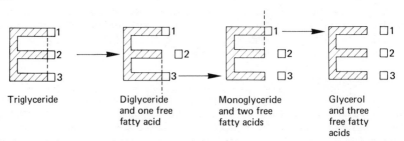

Fig. 5.3 Simplification of triglycerides

142

Stages of digestion

Figure 5.4 shows the stages of digestion in different parts of the gut. You can follow the digestion of particular categories of foods by taking the paths indicated in the key (see also the diagram of the alimentary tract in Fig. 5.5).

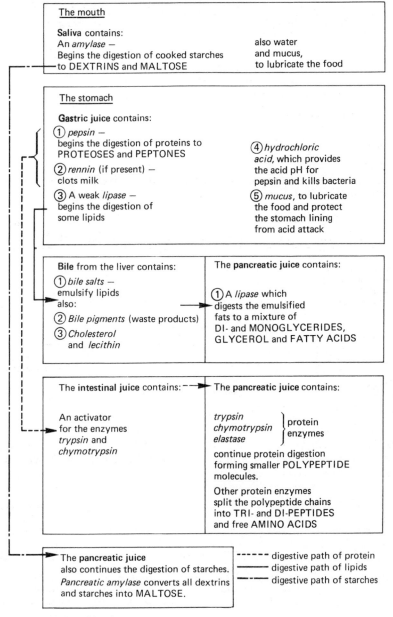

The mouth

Saliva contains:
An *amylase* —
Begins the digestion of cooked starches to DEXTRINS and MALTOSE

also water and mucus, to lubricate the food

The stomach

Gastric juice contains:
① *pepsin* —
begins the digestion of proteins to PROTEOSES and PEPTONES

② *rennin* (if present) —
clots milk

③ A weak *lipase* —
begins the digestion of some lipids

④ *hydrochloric acid*, which provides the acid pH for pepsin and kills bacteria

⑤ *mucus*, to lubricate the food and protect the stomach lining from acid attack

Bile from the liver contains:
① *bile salts* —
emulsify lipids
also:
② *Bile pigments* (waste products)
③ *Cholesterol* and *lecithin*

The pancreatic juice contains:

① A *lipase* which digests the emulsified fats to a mixture of DI- and MONOGLYCERIDES, GLYCEROL and FATTY ACIDS

The intestinal juice contains:

An activator for the enzymes *trypsin* and *chymotrypsin*

The pancreatic juice contains:

trypsin *chymotrypsin* *elastase* } protein enzymes

continue protein digestion forming smaller POLYPEPTIDE molecules.

Other protein enzymes split the polypeptide chains into TRI- and DI-PEPTIDES and free AMINO ACIDS

The pancreatic juice also continues the digestion of starches.
Pancreatic amylase converts all dextrins and starches into MALTOSE.

------ digestive path of protein
——— digestive path of lipids
—·— digestive path of starches

Fig. 5.4   Digestion of foods

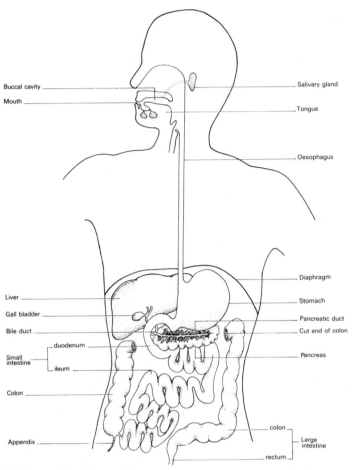

Labels on diagram:

Buccal cavity
Mouth
Salivary gland
Tongue
Oesophagus
Diaphragm
Liver
Stomach
Gall bladder
Pancreatic duct
Bile duct
Cut end of colon
duodenum
Small intestine
ileum
Pancreas
Colon
colon
Appendix
Large intestine
rectum

Fig. 5.5 Diagram of the alimentary tract

The mouth

Saliva contains an *amylase* which begins the digestion of cooked starches. Usually digestion is only partial, as food is not retained in the mouth for long periods. Some of the starch may be converted into dextrins and some may be split as far as maltose.

The stomach

The gastric juice in the stomach begins the digestion of proteins to shorter peptide chains called *proteoses* and *peptones*. The enzyme *pepsin* is responsible for this action. Pepsin works best at an acid pH, and this is provided by the secretion of hydrochloric acid by the oxyntic glands in the stomach wall.

Calves and other young mammals produce another protein enzyme, *rennin*, which clots milk and makes it more digestible. It is doubtful, however, if rennin ever occurs in human gastric juices.

The stomach also produces a weak *lipase* which begins the digestion of some lipids.

Digestion in the small intestine
The small intestine is a long tube, about 3 metres in length. It is 'small' because it is only 2–4 cm in diameter, compared with the large intestine which measures about 6 cm across. The first short section, the *duodenum*, is close to the lower part of the stomach. Here the food meets *bile* from the liver and secretions from the *pancreas* (see Fig. 5.5).

The bile
Bile is made in the liver, and then stored temporarily in a small sac called the *gall bladder*. Bile travels through the *bile duct* into the duodenum when food passes from the stomach into the intestine. Bile contains *bile salts* which act as detergents, emulsifying the fats so that they are easily digested by *lipase* from the pancreas. These secretions are alkaline so they neutralise the acidic stomach juices.

The pancreatic juice
You will note from Fig. 5.4 that the pancreas produces a large number of enzymes which affect all three of the major food categories.

1 The lipase in this juice attacks the triglycerides of the emulsified fats and oils, producing a complex mixture of di- and monoglycerides with some free fatty acids and glycerol.
2 The pancreatic juice contains three protein enzymes which break the internal peptide links of the protein chains at different points. Together, they break proteins down to progressively smaller polypeptides. Two of these enzymes, *trypsin* and *chymotrypsin*, are secreted in an inactive form and have to be activated by *enterokinase*, a substance produced by the wall of the intestine.

    Further protein enzymes in the juice split polypeptides into tri- and di-peptides and free amino acids which are small enough to be absorbed into the cells lining the intestine.
3 The third component of the juice is pancreatic amylase, which splits all dextrins and starches down to maltose.

Final digestion in the small intestine
By the time the food has passed through the middle section of the small intestine (the *jejunum*) into the final section (the *ileum*) all the starchy foods have been digested to maltose. In this form it is taken in with other sugars to the cells of the intestinal lining. Here the final split occurs to produce the following monosaccharide sugars:

maltose   two glucose molecules,
lactose   glucose and galactose,
sucrose   glucose and fructose.

The proteins, as we saw earlier, have been scaled down to tri- and di-peptides and some free amino acids. The final breakdown releasing all the amino acids takes place within the cells of the intestinal lining.

Meanwhile the fats have formed micelles — tiny groups of molecules of monoglycerides, fatty acids and glycerol emulsified by the bile from the liver. The fatty products from the micelles pass into the cells, while the bile salts remain with the fluids in the intestine.

Absorption of the digested food products

By this time the food has been digested to small molecules, but it is not available for use until it reaches the fluids which bathe the tissues — the lymph and blood. This is accomplished through the *villi*, the numerous finger-like structures which project into the intestine. You can observe them in tripe, they give it a furry appearance (see Figs. 5.6 and 5.7). The villi greatly increase the surface available in the intestine to absorb food materials.

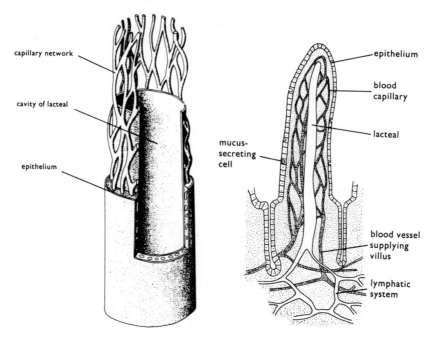

Fig. 5.6   Stereogram of villus structure   Fig. 5.7   Vertical section through villus

The path to the liver

You will see from Figs 5.6 and 7 that each villus has a network of capillaries. These small blood vessels join together to form the *hepatic portal* vein. The sugars and amino acids from the intestine pass into this circulation and are taken to the liver. Here they enter the spongy network of blood capillaries of the major chemical laboratory of the body.

The large intestine

We must leave the work of the liver until later, so that we can follow the path of the remaining food which has entered the large intestine. This consists of the 5-10% of the diet which is indigestible, together with a great deal of water. The indigestible matter is mainly plant fibre (cellulose, lignin and some pectin). Although these substances cannot be absorbed they play an important role in providing bulk in the diet, and so preventing constipation. The water is largely absorbed back into the bloodstream, so the food residues pass out of the large intestine in the form of semi-solid *faeces*. These enter the anal canal of the *rectum* periodically prior to defaecation.

The work of the liver

Previously, we followed the route of the amino acids and sugars to the liver. We will now consider how these substances are processed in that organ.

Amino acids Some of the amino acids are needed for growth and repair of tissues and pass directly into the bloodstream. Other amino acids in excess of immediate needs require processing.

Amino acids consist of two parts (1) the amino part (NH_2 group(s)) and (2) an organic acid. By splitting these two portions apart (*deamination*), chemical juggling can produce the non-essential amino acids needed by the body by transferring the amino group from one organic acid to another (see Fig. 5.8).

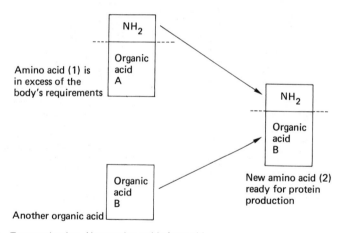

Fig. 5.8   Transamination. New amino acids from old

In this country adults eat more protein than is needed for repair of tissue, so many amino acids are split and the organic acids used for energy production. Amino acids are also split to supply energy under starvation conditions when the energy needs of the body are paramount and the supply of carbohydrates and fats is insufficient.

The amino portion of the amino acid is poisonous, so it is converted into a less dangerous material, *urea*, which is excreted by the kidney (see Fig. 5.9).

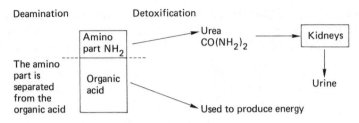

Fig. 5.9   Deamination and detoxification of an amino acid

Sugars The sugars which have been absorbed from the intestine may pass into the general blood circulation to provide the tissues with energy. If the sugar level in the blood is already high they are converted into animal starch (or *glycogen*) so that they can be stored in the liver until needed. The delicate balance between sugar in use for energy production, in passage round the body and in the reserve store in the liver is maintained by *hormones*. One of the most important hormones engaged in this balancing act is *insulin*, produced by specialised groups of cells in the pancreas. If this hormone is lacking, sugar *diabetes* occurs, a disorder in which the tissues fail to absorb and process sugar normally. As a result sugar accumulates in the blood and is excreted in the urine.

Fats You will remember we had reached the stage in the story of fat digestion when the di- and monoglycerides, glycerol and fatty acids had entered the cells lining the intestine. Here, these products are assembled into the triglycerides typical of human fats. They then are provided with a protein coating and form droplets called *chylomicrons*. In this form the droplets pass into the central tube called a *lacteal* in each villus and make their way into the lymphatic system of the body. This system is complementary to the blood circulation. It carries food materials to the tissues and removes waste products. The two systems interconnect in the chest so the fat droplets eventually enter the blood circulation.

   The primary function of fats is to provide a concentrated source of energy. Any fat surplus to this requirement is stored in depots under the skin or round the internal organs, providing insulation and protective padding for delicate tissues.

Self assessment questions

Food digestion
  1 Why do most foods need digesting?
  2 Name the three main processes involved in digestion.
  3 Which enzyme is present in saliva?
  4 Name the main enzyme present in the stomach. Which class of food is attacked by this enzyme? Is the gastric juice acid or alkaline?
  5 Where is bile made? How are fats affected by the bile when it reaches the duodenum?

6 Complete the following summaries of the action of the pancreatic enzymes:

fats + oils $\xrightarrow{\text{lipase}}$

proteins, peptones + proteoses $\xrightarrow[\text{enzymes}]{\text{protein}}$

starches + dextrins $\xrightarrow{\text{amylase}}$

7 Complete the table below in your workbook to show the simple sugars produced by digestion of the disaccharide sugars:

Disaccharide	Monosaccharides
Maltose	
Lactose	Glucose + galactose
Sucrose	

8 Name the final breakdown products of (a) proteins and (b) fats.
9 Which part of the alimentary canal absorbs most of the water from the digested food?
10 Route (1)   blood vessels $\longrightarrow$ hepatic portal vein $\longrightarrow$ liver
                    of the villi
    Route (2)   lacteals of $\longrightarrow$ lymph system $\longrightarrow$ liver
                    the villi

Write the number of the route taken by the final breakdown products of (a) fats, (b) proteins and (c) carbohydrates.
11 Name two constituents of food which *cannot* be digested.
12 What is meant by (a) deamination and (b) detoxification of amino acids in the liver?
13 Name the polysaccharide which forms the temporary store of energy in the liver and muscles.
14 Which hormone maintains the sugar balance of the body?
15 Describe three different functions performed by fats in the body.

How much food do we need?

The need for caterers to consider the nutritional value of the food they provide will vary with the type of work undertaken. Clients come to a restaurant or hotel to enjoy meals in pleasant surroundings, rather than for 'nutrition'. Whether it is a banquet to satisfy the discerning palates of gastronomes or quick snacks for travellers, caterers will be guided by their knowledge of their clients as to the quality and quantity of food to provide. However, many caterers work in circumstances where they provide the total nutrition for sick people, or for the young or elderly in residential homes. Here, they have a direct influence on the health and growth of their clients, and need to take a quantitative view of the nutritional value of the meals provided.

Although age, sex, height and weight are the major factors influencing the quantity of the various nutrients needed by the body, there are considerable differences between individuals. These differences are taken care of by the individual's appetite and preferences. Caterers have to consider nutritional need in terms of *groups* of people — children, adolescents, adults and the elderly.

The Department of Health and Social Security tables of Recommended Daily Allowances of Nutrients (R.D.A.s) p. 253 are useful guides when planning diets for such groups. The R.D.A. of each nutrient has been worked out statistically to be sufficient or more than sufficient for healthy people within the group concerned. We will consider the special needs of a number of groups in relation to the Recommended Daily Allowances.

Babies
In comparison with their body weights, babies need large amounts of energy, protein and calcium since they are growing rapidly and forming bones and teeth. Breast milk is the ideal food for them, as it contains all the necessary nutrients in an easily assimilated form. Amounts of iron and copper are low in milk, but these minerals are provided by the stores built up in the liver before birth.

When babies are bottle-fed, the cows' milk needs modifying as the proportion of nutrients is different from those in human milk (see Table 5.7).

Cows' milk has more protein and calcium, but is lower in vitamins C and A. Bottle-fed babies are given extra vitamin C in the form of orange or hip juice.

Table 5.7 Content (per 100 g) of human and cows' milk

	Protein (g)	Fat (g)	Energy (kcal)	Vit. C (mg)	Iron (mg)	Ca (mg)	Vit. A (mg)	Vit. D (mg)
Human milk	1.3	4	70	4	0.07	35	60	0.03
Cows' milk	3.5	4	70	1	0.1	120	44	0.05

When the age of 4 months (or a weight of 6 kg) is reached the milk diet needs supplementing with broths which supply the iron necessary for blood formation. From 6 months of age, cereals and puréed fruits and vegetables can be introduced into the diet. These help to introduce new tastes and supply extra energy, vitamins and minerals. These supplements should contain little or no salt or sugar. An infant's kidneys cannot eliminate salts as an adult's can, and extra sugar may make babies overweight.

Children
Young children have a high requirement for energy and protein, as they are very active and growing rapidly. Up to 5 years of age the R.D.A. for energy is about 100 kcal for each kilogram of body weight compared with 40 kcal per kilogram for an adult. This high need for energy gradually falls off until by

15–18 years of age they need much the same amount of energy as adults in proportion to their body weights.

High energy foods
(over 200 kcal/100 g food)
Butter, margarine,
bread, sugar,
rice, jam.

High protein food
(over 10 g/100 g food)
Cheese, meat, fish
sausages, liver,
baked beans.

Use the tables on p. 245 and fill in your workbook three more examples of each of these types of food.

At birth a baby needs three times as much protein per kilogram of body weight as an adult does. This need gradually falls, until at 8 years of age it is only twice the adult ratio.

For strong bones and teeth, and healthy blood, children need an adequate supply of minerals, particularly calcium, phosphorus and iron.

High calcium foods
(over 100 mg calcium/100 g food)
Milk, yoghurt,
cheese, bread,
rice pudding.

Write down some other examples of foods rich in calcium.

Phosphorus is widespread in many different foods, so it is unlikely that any normal diet would be lacking this mineral.

Eating habits are established in childhood, so the caterer who provides varied meals with the correct nutritional value is helping to establish a healthy approach to food in the future. This applies particularly to the energy content of the diet. The portions of food in Table 5.8 all supply 200 kcal, which is approximately one-tenth of the R.D.A. for energy for an 8-year-old. A glance at the figures reveals that the sugar provides only energy, while the equivalent portions of bread, oatmeal and cornflakes also contain significant amounts of protein, calcium, iron and B vitamins. Encouraging children to take more of their energy needs in the form of cereal foods rather than as between-meal sugary snacks will improve their nutrition as well as protecting their teeth against decay.

Table 5.8 Percentage of R.D.A. of nutrients of 8 year old boy provided by 200 kcal portions of foods.

Food	200 kcal portion (g)	Protein (g)	Calcium (mg)	Iron (mg)	Thiamine (mg)	Riboflavin (mg)	Nicotinic acid (mg)
White sugar	50	0	0	0	0	0	0
White bread	86	13.6	14.3	15.0	18.75	2.5	17.2
Oatmeal (fortified)	50	12.6	4.6	20.5	31.0	5.0	12.7
Cornflakes	54	9.3	0.3	36.0	121.0	86.0	100.0

Fresh fruits and vegetables are important in the diet of both young and old because they supply vitamin C (ascorbic acid). You will remember that this vitamin protects against infection, helps heal wounds and assists with the absorption of iron. But are all fruits and vegetables equally valuable as sources of vitamin C? Table 5.9 gives the ascorbic acid content of a selection of fruits and vegetables. Look up the remaining values in the tables in the Appendix and complete the table in your workbook.

Table 5.9 Ascorbic acid content of some fruits and vegetables

Fruit	Ascorbic acid (mg/100 g food)	Vegetable	Ascorbic acid (mg/100 g food)
Oranges	50	Cauliflowers	60
Lemons		Runner beans	20
Apples	5	Baked beans	
Pears		Carrots	
Blackcurrants	200	Potatoes, boiled	
Grapefruit		Sprouts, raw	90
Bananas		Sprouts, boiled	

The R.D.A. for ascorbic acid is 20 mg for young children and 30 mg for adolescents and adults. From the table we can see that:

1 Citrus fruits are rich sources of ascorbic acid, while some native fruits contain little vitamin C;

2 Vegetables such as cauliflower and sprouts are useful sources of the vitamin in winter, when fruit may be expensive and
3 Potatoes contain only a small amount of ascorbic acid even when new. However, we all eat large amounts of potatoes, so the total amount of the vitamin provided by this staple vegetable is by no means unimportant.

Adolescents

Adolescent boys have large appetites, so the main problem for parents and caterers is providing satisfying meals if the budget is limited.

Girls, at this age, have a tendency to become overweight. For this reason, the R.D.A. for energy is not increased between 11 and 17 years of age, as it is for boys. Caterers can help by providing buffet meals with a variety of salads for calorie-conscious girls.

Anaemia is another problem occurring in teenaged girls. Their diet does not always provide sufficient iron to compensate for iron lost in menstruation. Iron is not always easily assimilated, even if present in sufficient quantity in the diet. Most iron in the British diet comes from meat, bread, cereals and vegetables: meat and offal contain organic iron which is readily absorbed, and plant sources contain inorganic iron which is less available to the body. Absorption of inorganic iron can be improved by the addition of vitamin C. Bread is fortified with extra iron, so it is an important source of the mineral in the diet.

The R.D.A. of iron for adolescent girls is at least 12 mg. A little calculation will show that knowledge and planning are needed to ensure their amount of iron is available in the diet from day to day.

Example: How much liver would provide 4 mg iron? (approximately one-third of this R.D.A.)

100 g of fried liver contains 9 mg iron

x g of liver contains 4 mg iron

$$x = \frac{4}{9} \times 100 \times 44 \text{ g liver (about } 1\tfrac{1}{2} \text{ oz.)}$$

Table 5.10 shows the portions of common foods providing the R.D.A. of iron. Calculate the remaining value from the information given and complete the table.

Table 5.10   Portions of common foods providing the R.D.A. of iron

Code no.	Food	mg iron per 100 g food	Portion providing 4 mg iron (g)
119	Bread, white	1.7	235
124	Flour, white	2.2	181
77	Potatoes, boiled	0.5	800
61	Cabbage, boiled	.4	1000
17	Beef, stewing (cooked)	3	
130	Cocoa powder	7	175

Adults

Adult diets should provide:

> sufficient energy to fuel the individual's needs and
> enough proteins, vitamins and minerals to maintain vigorous health.

The majority of the adult diet problems in this country can be classified as diseases of affluence. This does not mean the individuals are necessarily wealthy, but that they tend to consume more of some nutrients than is good for them.

Overweight

Many adults are concerned about weight increase, particularly in middle age. They are aware that diseases such as coronary heart disease and diabetes are associated with obesity. People put on weight for many reasons. Some of these are discussed below.

1 Eating is habit-forming. The size and number of meals consumed tends to be fixed in youth, when body needs are high. Some people do not adjust to falling energy needs over the years.
2 Ignorance of calorific values. Carbohydrates and fats are generally regarded as high energy foods, and weight-watchers reduce their consumption of these nutrients. However, they often fail to consider the total energy content of their diet and ignore the proteins and alcohol which are also 'fattening' if taken in excess.
3 Modern occupations. Travel, work and leisure involve less physical effort than in previous generations. On the other hand, modern life can be stressful and food is the traditional comforter.

Caterers can assist their weight-watching clients by providing a low calorie alternative in each course so that these clients can enjoy dining out without the embarrassment of refusing dishes.

Excessive salt consumption

Processed and convenience foods play an increasing role in our diet today. In many ways these foods are of excellent nutritional quality. However, most contain a large proportion of salt or sugar as preservative. Sugar, as we have previously mentioned, increases the calorific value of a food without adding any additional nutrients.

Recently, concern has been expressed by the medical profession that persistently high salt intakes may be associated with the increasing number of middle-aged people suffering with hypertension (high blood pressure).

Natural foods contain little salt. The sodium chloride in our diet comes from the salt added for flavouring, and increasingly from preserved foods. An average intake of sodium is 1000–2000 mg per day. If processed foods play a large role in the diet it is easy to exceed a reasonable daily sodium level, as can be seen from the Table 5.11.

High saturated fat consumption

An increasing number of men over 40 years old are suffering from coronary

Table 5.11   Sodium content of some foods

High sodium foods, (500–2000 mg/100 g)		Low sodium foods (0–20 mg/100 g)
Corned beef	1380	Flour	2.7
Ham, lean, boiled	2100	Apples, eating	2.0
Bacon, back, fried	2790	Broad beans, boiled	19.6
Kippers, baked	990	Macaroni, boiled	7.9
Sausages, pork, fried	999	Lettuce	3.1
Baked beans	591	Walnuts	2.7

Values from *Composition of Foods* by R. A. McCance and E. M. Widdowson.

heart disease in Britain and other Western countries. The condition is due to fatty deposits in the arteries supplying the heart muscle. As the flow of blood is impeded conditions favour the formation of blood clots which starve the heart muscle of oxygen and nutrients causing heart attacks. The precise reasons why this condition is becoming more common have yet to be determined, but there is strong evidence to suggest that a high consumption of saturated fat is one factor. Men with high cholesterol blood levels have been shown on average to have a greater risk of suffering from this condition than those with a lower level. Cholesterol is a lipoprotein which is manufactured in the body. Diets containing a large amount of fat (40% or more) tend to raise the blood cholesterol level. This is particularly so if most of the fat is of the saturated type as found mainly in animal fats. People with high cholesterol levels have been able to lower them by changing the lipid content of their diet to plant oils and margarines high in polyunsaturated fatty acids.

Cuisine moderne and nouvelle cuisine
Haute cuisine tends to be lavish in the use of butter, eggs and meat with a high cholesterol content; however a number of high class chefs are responding to the wishes of clients who prefer lighter meals. They have developed methods of cookery which replace the elaborate dishes of the past with lighter dishes which have their natural flavours enhanced by sauces rather smothered by them. Less fat and sugar is used in the cooking and sauces are thickened with cornflour rather than with the traditional roux base. Fresh vegetables are served without butter; while butter and cream for finishing dishes has been reduced or omitted completely. Portions are smaller and garnishes have been simplified. The dense, heavy pâtes of the past have given way to lighter mixtures while pâtes of fish are gaining popularity. New combinations of aromas and flavours are being introduced by using fresh herbs.

Nouvelle cuisine also caters for weight-watching clients. It differs from Cuisine moderne in that it does use cream, butter and fat, but in moderation.

Vegetarians
Recent years have seen an increased interest in vegetarian cookery. Caterers need to be aware of this interest and be able to respond to clients who prefer this type of food.

155

People adopt vegetarian diets for a number of reasons. They may simply not like meat or they may have humanitarian or religious scruples about the slaughter of animals for food.

Vegetarian diets have a number of advantages for the sedentary urban dweller. They tend to have a lower energy value and a higher content of dietary fibre than mixed diets. As they are likely to contain more fresh fruit and vegetables, they are high in vitamin C. Eating crisp vegetables promotes better dental health than the sugary refined diets common among city people. As meat tends to be one of the most expensive items of the diet vegetarian cookery can be more economical providing natural foods are used rather than proprietary 'health foods'.

Lacto-vegetarians

Lacto-vegetarians do not eat meat, but are happy to consume animal products such as eggs and dairy foods. Cooking for them presents little difficulty as eggs, cheese, nuts and pulses provide the basis of a wide variety of main dishes of high nutritional value. The diet only differs from more conventional ones by being more bulky and of lower calorific value.

Vegans

Vegans are strict vegetarians who eat no animal products. With these restrictions a detailed knowledge of nutrition is needed to produce a well-balanced and appetising diet. Individual plant proteins lack some essential amino acids, so a wide variety of sources must be provided so that they complement each other (see p. 179) and together provide the full range of amino acids necessary for human proteins.

Vitamin B_{12}, riboflavin, vitamin D_3 (cholecaliferol), calcium and iron are all lacking or supplied only in small quantities in a vegan diet (see p. 180).

Slimmers

Producing an alternative weight-watchers' menu is a challenge to the ingenuity of the caterer. It must obviously have an energy value less than the R.D.A. for the group concerned so that excess fat stores are gradually mobilised and burnt off. About 1000 kcal less than the R.D.A. would be a reasonable value to aim for in the case of adults.

At the same time meals must be appetising and provide enough bulk so that people do not feel constantly hungry. It is important that sufficient protein is still retained and the minerals and vitamins are still in adequate amounts.

The general rules are:

less carbohydrate (particularly sugar) and alcohol,
less fat,
enough protein and
more fruit and vegetables (which provide minerals, vitamins and the bulky fibre).

The method of cooking can make a great deal of difference to the energy value. Fried potatoes have over three times the energy value of baked or boiled potatoes. A rich salad dressing might contribute 100 kcal per table-spoonful, while a simple dressing — with perhaps yoghurt as the base — might rate about one-third of this value. An enterprising caterer can find many ways to produce interesting meals which help slimmers to stay on the straight and narrow!

Elderly people

A good diet can prolong good health into old age. Many elderly people come into residential homes showing signs of nutritional deficiencies, and regain an interest in life when given a good diet.

In general their needs are similar to those of younger adults, except they need less energy. As with slimmers, it is important that proteins, minerals and vitamins are not cut down at the same time as the energy-giving foods. Meals need to be attractively flavoured because elderly people often have little sense of smell so food can seem unappetizing if it is not well seasoned.

Bones become fragile in old age; there is a tendency for them to decalcify (osteomalacia) and in elderly women there can be actual loss of the bone itself (osteoporosis). Accordingly, it is important that their diet contains sufficient calcium and vitamin D (which allows the mineral to be maintained in the bones). The actual amounts of vitamin D required are very small. They are measured in micrograms (μg): 1000 μg = 1 mg.

Vitamin D is confined to fatty foods: dairy products, eggs and oily fish. About 2.5 mg of vitamin D daily would be an adequate amount for an elderly person. Table 5.12 gives a number of good sources of the vitamin.

Table 5.12 Sources of vitamin D

Food	μg vitamin D/100 g	Portion size (g)	Vitamin D in portion (μg)
Margarine	8	25	2
Eggs	1.5	50	0.75
Sardines	8	25	2
Tinned salmon	13	100	13
Herring	22	125	27.5

Pregnant women and nursing mothers

During her pregnancy a woman needs extra energy and nutrients to support the growth of her infant and the surrounding tissues which provide protection and nourishment. In addition, she must be able to accumulate stores which will sustain her through the demands of breast-feeding the infant later. Table 5.13 shows the increases in the R.D.A.s necessary to keep the mother and baby healthy.

1 In the last three months of pregnancy the appetite increases in response to the need for extra energy for the growth process.
2 A pregnant women needs extra milk, cheese, eggs or meat in her diet to provide the proteins to support the growth of tissues in the developing infant.

157

Table 5.13 R.D.A.s during pregnancy

	1	2	3	4	5	6	6	6	7
Group	Energy (kcal)	Protein (g)	Calcium (mg)	Vit. D (µg)	Iron (mg)	Thiamine (mg)	Riboflavin (mg)	Nicotinic acid equiv.* (mg)	Ascorbic acid (mg)
Non-pregnant women	2150	54	500	—	12	0.9	1.3	15	—
Pregnant women	2400	60	1200	10	13	1.0	1.6	18	500
Nursing mothers	2750	69	1200	10	15	1.1	1.8	21	600

* Nicotinic acid can be provided as the acid itself or as the amino acid tryptophan, which can be converted into nicotinic acid. Tables therefore express both of these sources as nicotinic acid equivalents.

Selected from D.H.S.S. 1979 Tables of Recommend Daily Amounts of Nutrients for Population Groups.

3 The demands for calcium are very high both during pregnancy, when the infants bones and teeth are developing, and during breast-feeding, when calcium is needed for the milk.
4 Vitamin D is needed with the calcium to ensure that the mineral is laid down in the skeleton. It can be supplied by the diet, as we saw in connection with elderly people, or as fish liver oil capsules.
5 It is common practice to supply pregnant women with iron tablets to supplement the supplies from meat and other sources in the diet.
6 Extra B vitamins are needed in the diet during pregnancy. In particular, the need for folic acid is greater than usual as it is required in the formation of red blood cells. Liver and kidney are particularly rich in folic acid and also supply the remaining B vitamins and iron.
7 The R.D.A. for vitamin C is doubled in pregnancy. Extra fruit in the diet is one way of providing the vitamin, or it can be taken in the form of orange or blackcurrant drinks.

Self assessment questions

Amount of food required
1 Explain what is meant by the R.D.A.s of nutrients.
2 Do the R.D.A.s refer to the needs of groups or of individuals?
3 Name three examples of foods rich in the following nutrients: energy, calcium, protein, iron, vitamin C.
4 From the tables in the Appendix, find two examples of food or drink which supply energy but no other nutrient.
5 What dangers are associated with excessive intake of salt in (a) infants and (b) adults? Which types of foods add the greatest amount of sodium to the diet?
6 Which disease is associated with high blood cholesterol levels? Which types of fats are believed to be associated with high blood cholerestrol values?
7 Which vitamins and minerals are likely to be in inadequate amounts in vegan diets?
8 List the guidelines for preparing slimmers' diets.
9 What points should be borne in mind when preparing menus for elderly people?
10 List the nutrients which are particularly important in the diets of pregnant and nursing mothers.

Part B

Chemistry of carbohydrates. Questions. Chemistry of lipids — types and production of margarine. Questions. Calculations of calorific values of dishes and meals. Slimmers' diets. Exercises. Proteins — biological value, complementation, protein values of dishes. Questions.

The chemistry of the major food categories

Carbohydrates

Carbohydrates occur in cereals, fruits, tubers and roots. They can be represented by the general formula $C_n(H_2O)_n$; that is for every carbon atom their molecules have the same number of oxygen and twice as many hydrogen atoms. Carbohydrates can be divided into two main groups: sugars, having one or few units, and polysaccharides, which consist of many units.

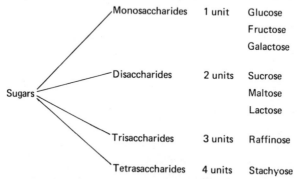

	Monosaccharides	1 unit	Glucose
			Fructose
			Galactose
	Disaccharides	2 units	Sucrose
Sugars			Maltose
			Lactose
	Trisaccharides	3 units	Raffinose
	Tetrasaccharides	4 units	Stachyose

The main food polysaccharides can be divided into two groups: those formed from one repeating sugar unit and those formed from chains of other substances, such as sugar acids.

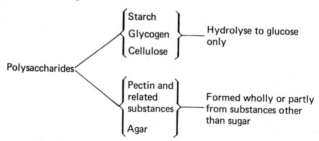

Polysaccharides:
- Starch, Glycogen, Cellulose — Hydrolyse to glucose only
- Pectin and related substances, Agar — Formed wholly or partly from substances other than sugar

Sugars

All sugars share three characteristics: they dissolve readily in water, taste sweet and form crystals.

Monosaccharides Most of the monosaccharides in foods are *hexose* sugars, having six carbon atoms in their molecules. They all have the general formula $C_6H_{12}O_6$. The carbon skeleton of these sugars is shown below. For identification the carbon atoms are numbered clockwise from the oxygen atom.

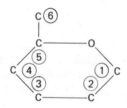

Hexose monosaccharides differ from each other in the arrangement of the hydroxyl (OH) and other groups relative to the carbon ring. Molecules such as these that have the same molecular formula but a different structural arrangement are said to be isomers.

Glucose

Galactose

Note that the carbon atoms by convention are omitted from the ring.

You will notice that the only difference between the molecules of glucose and galactose is the position of the hydrogen and hydroxyl group at the C-4 position.

Pentoses Pentose sugars have five carbon atoms in their molecules. Ribose is an example of this type of sugar. It is not of any importance in cooking, but plays many important physiological roles. It is a constituent of riboflavin and occurs in the reproductive material of cells, either as ribose itself or as the related sugar deoxyribose.

Disaccharides Disaccharides are formed by condensation of two simple sugars with the elimination of one molecule of water (see Fig. 5.10).

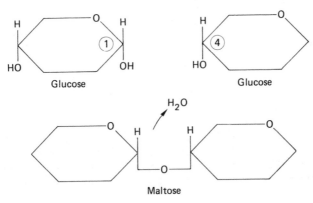

Glucose

Glucose

Maltose

Fig. 5.10 Maltose is formed by linking two glucose units at the 1–4 position

The bond between the two molecules is a glycosidic bond. A similar linkage between glucose and galactose forms lactose.

The process of condensation can be reversed by hydrolysis, when water

161

splits the molecules apart. This can be achieved by chemical action, as happens during the inversion of sugar in jam making, or by biological action, as in the digestion of sugars.

Other sugars Some sugars contain more than two saccharides. Raffinose, which is found in sugar beet, cotton seed, bananas, and soya and other beans, contains three sugar units linked together.

Polysaccharides These are formed by condensation of very large numbers of sugar units.

Starches

Starches are long-chained polymers of glucose. In the natural state the chains are packed closely together to form characteristically-shaped grains. There are two forms of starch chain: straight and branched. The proportion of each type varies from one type of starch to another.

Amylose These are straight chains of glucose varying from 50 to 1500 units long. The linkage is C 1–4, as in maltose.

Amylopectin This type of starch chain has short side-branches attached to the main chain by C 1–6 linkages (see Fig. 5.11). These tree-like branched chains may contain between 2000 and 220000 units (see gel formation, Chapter 4).

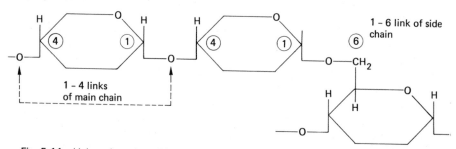

Fig. 5.11 Linkage in main and branch chains of amylopectin

Glycogen Glycogen, or animal starch, is chemically very similar to the amylopectin in plant starches. It differs only in the branches being shorter and more numerous. It is a short-term storage product, found mainly in the liver and muscles of animals.

Cellulose

Cellulose is the main structural carbohydrate in plant cell walls, and forms the bulk of the fibre in our diet. The glucose units in cellulose are linked 1–4, but the units are twisted relative to each other so one is in the 'up' position and the next the 'down'. This gives a ribbon-like arrangement to the chain (see Fig. 5.12).

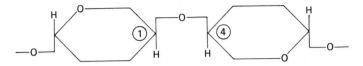

Fig. 5.12 The glucose units are twisted relative to each other in cellulose

In the plant cell wall, bundles of these flat chains lie closely together, forming microfibrils. They give the characteristic strength and insolubility to structural cellulose. The twist of the glucose molecules relative to each other prevents human enzymes, which digest starch, from hydrolysing cellulose. Hence, cellulose passes unchanged through our digestive systems. On the other hand, ruminant animals harbour symbiotic bacteria in their stomachs, and these organisms produce enzymes which can break down cellulose.

Self assessment questions

The chemistry of carbohydrates
1 Write the formula for a hexose sugar.
2 Name three hexose sugars commonly found in foods. Give an example of a pentose sugar.
3 How do these hexose sugars differ from each other?
4 Explain how (a) monosaccharides can be condensed to form disaccharides and (b) how this process can be reversed.
5 Name three food polysaccharides.
6 How do the two forms of starch chain, amylose and amylopectin, differ from each other?
7 In what way is the arrangement of glucose units different in starch and cellulose?
8 Account for the ability of cellulose to form strong plant cell walls.
9 Why are human amylases (starch enzymes) incapable of digesting cellulose?

Lipids
We saw in Chapter 4 that dietary fats and oils consist of triglycerides in which three long-chained fatty acids are attached to a molecule of glycerol. As the glycerol is the same in each case, it is the nature of the fatty acids which determine the properties of the lipids.

Arrangement of fatty acids within triglycerides
The fatty acids in any one triglyceride may be all similar (as in tristearin), two similar or all different. If different, the fatty acids can be arranged in different orders. So the numbers of combinations, even for the most commonly occurring fatty acids, are very large.

Three stearic acid molecules

163

The length of the fatty acid chain

The fatty acids in lipids vary considerably in chain length. Butyric acid is found in butter, and has only four carbon atoms in the chain while stearic, on the other hand, a common fatty acid occurring in animal fats, has a 'backbone' of 16 carbon atoms.

The 'backbone' of stearic acid
$CH_3(CH_2)_{16}COOH$

Degree of saturation

We saw previously (p. 74) that fatty acids can be saturated or unsaturated. In the saturated fatty acids each carbon atom apart from the terminal ones combines with two hydrogen atoms, as in butyric acid. The common saturated fatty acids in the diet are stearic, lauric, myristic and palmitic acids (see Table 5.14).

Table 5.14   The common saturated fatty acids

Name	Formula	Occurrence
Lauric acid	$CH_3(CH_2)_{10}COOH$	Coconut
Myristic acid	$CH_3(CH_2)_{12}COOH$	Animal fats and coconut
Palmitic acid	$CH_3(CH_2)_{14}COOH$	Animal and vegetable lipids
Stearic acid	$CH_3(CH_2)_{16}COOH$	Animal fat, but also present in vegetable oils in smaller amounts

In unsaturated fatty acids two adjacent carbon atoms each have a hydrogen atom missing, and a double bond forms. A fatty acid with a single double bond is monounsaturated. For example, oleic acid, found in olive oil but also in many animal and vegetable oils, is monounsaturated.

Oleic acid
$CH_3(CH_2)_7CH=CH(CH_2)_7COOH$

Polyunsaturated fatty acids contain two or more double bonds, and are often represented by their initials P.U.F.A.s. Polyunsaturated fatty acids predominate in vegetable oils. The common fatty acids of this kind are given in Table 5.15.

164

Table 5.15 Common polyunsaturated fatty acids

Name	No. of double bonds	Occurrence
Linoleic acid	2	Sunflower, soya bean oil, corn oil, but also in smaller amounts in animal fats
Linolenic acid	3	Linseed oil
Arachidonic acid	4	Animal fats and egg yolk

All of these factors, fatty acid composition, chain length, and degree of saturation, influence the cooking properties of lipids.

Influence on melting points of lipids
 1 The longer the chain of a saturated fatty acid, the higher the melting point. Butter contains many short-chained fatty acids, and has a low melting point compared with other animal fats.
 2 When fatty acids of similar chain lengths are considered, the greater the number of double bonds (the lower the saturation), the lower the melting point. This accounts for the fact that oils melt at well below room temperature and fats have higher melting points. Coconut oil is an exception as it is highly saturated, which accounts for its high melting point despite the predominance of short-chain fatty acids in the oil.

Margarine
Margarine, like the butter it is made to resemble, is a stabilised water-in-fat emulsion (see Chapter 4, Eggs). The watery phase is composed of skimmed

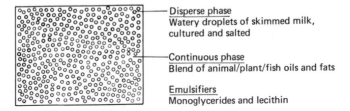

Disperse phase
Watery droplets of skimmed milk, cultured and salted

Continuous phase
Blend of animal/plant/fish oils and fats

Emulsifiers
Monoglycerides and lecithin

milk which has been cultured with lactic bacteria to give the required buttery flavour.
The lipid content consists of a blend of animal fats, plant and fish oils, according to availability and the intended properties of the final product. The manufacturer can change the properties of the available lipids in a number of ways so that the final product has the precise properties required.

 1 Hydrogenation is one method by which plant oils can be hardened into solid fats. The process introduces hydrogen, in the presence of a nickel catalyst, into sufficient double bonds to bring the melting point of the plant or fish oil to the value required.
 2 Heating lipids in the presence of a different catalyst (sodium ethoxide or sodium methoxide) allows modification of the fatty acid composi-

tion of the triglycerides. The order of the fatty acids within a triglyceride may be changed, or an exchange can take place between triglycerides.

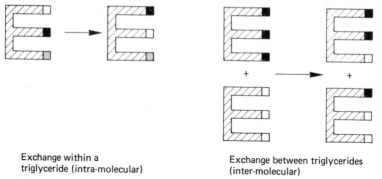

Exchange within a
triglyceride (intra-molecular)

Exchange between triglycerides
(inter-molecular)

3 All lipids consist of a mixture of liquid and solid triglycerides. By heating and cooling under controlled conditions the more liquid fraction can be separated from the more solid one.

This control over the composition of fatty acids by blending the lipids and by the modifications described above also affects the amount of crystalisation in the final product. In lipids which contain relatively few types of triglycerides there is a tendency for them to pack together and form large crystals. Where the fatty acids have been exchanged between the triglycerides a more random arrangement occurs, leading to smaller crystals and better creaming properties in the fat (see Fig. 5.13).

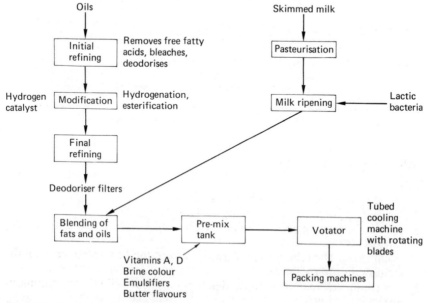

Fig. 5.13   Margarine manufacture

Margarines have three main uses: pastry making, cake production and spreading. Each requires distinct properties in the product. Table 5.16 gives a summary of these properties and an indication of the differences in composition which make them possible.

Table 5.16   Types of margarine and low fat spreads

Type	Desirable properties	Composition
Hard cooking or pastry margarine	A relatively high melting range. Crystalline structure able to withstand rolling	Includes stearic acid. High content of saturated and monounsaturated fatty acids
Soft cooking or cake margarine	Lower melting range. Plasticity and good creaming properties	Greater content of oleic acid (monounsaturated). Lower saturated fatty acid content
Soft spreading margarine	Ease of spreading straight from the refrigerator. Pleasant flavour, ability to melt rapidly without tasting oily	Generally contain more polyunsaturated fatty acids such as linoleic than types above
Polyunsaturated margarines	Advertised as less likely to be associated with high blood cholesterol levels and therefore less likely to be a factor in heart disease	Contain about 40% polyunsaturated fatty acids. Largely or wholly based on plant oils: corn, sunflower, and safflower oils
Low fat spreads	Intended for slimmers to reduce the total fat in the diet	Contain more than 10% water
Dairy spreads	Low energy content. Easier to spread than margarine. Buttery flavour	Contains butter oil and soya bean oil emulsified in butter milk. High in polyunsaturates

Self assessment questions

Lipids
1 What is meant by an unsaturated fatty acid?
2 Name two polyunsaturated fatty acids (P.U.F.A.s).
3 How is the melting point of a lipid affected by the length of the constituent fatty acids?
4 What effect does the degree of saturation of the fatty acids have on the melting point of a lipid?
5 Which ingredients make up (a) the disperse phase and (b) the continuous phase of a margarine?
6 Explain the methods manufacturers use to adapt the properties of the

lipids used to produce margarines to the different requirements for pastry, cake making and for spreading.

7 Which properties are required in (a) a pastry margarine, (b) a cake margarine and (c) a spreading margarine?
8 Which of the above types of margarine is likely to contain the greatest amount of animal fat? Which will contain a high proportion of polyunsaturates?
9 What is meant by (a) a low fat spread and (b) a dairy spread?

Calculation of calorific values

A useful introduction to calorific values is to group foods into high, low and intermediate groups according to their energy values. Table 5.17 shows some foods grouped in this way.

Table 5.17   Energy values (kcal/100 g) of groups of foods

°Under 20	*20–50	**50–100	***100–250
Vegetables and fruit	Vegetables and fruit	Low fat milk products and vegetables	Lean meat and fish
Cauliflowers	Apples	Milk	Bread
Cabbages	Carrots	Yoghurt	White fish
Mushrooms	Grapefruit	Cottage cheese	Eggs
Tomatoes	Melons	Tripe	Stewing beef
Lemon juice		Potatoes	
Cucumbers		Baked beans	

****250–500		*****500–750	****** More than 750
Fatty meats, cereals and dairy products		Nuts and products containing cereals and fat	
Bacon	Spaghetti	Potato crisps	Butter
Roast lamb	Cornflakes	Milk chocolate	Cooking oil
Pork sausage	Oatmeal	Flaky pastry	Lard
Cheese	Rice	Peanuts, Almonds	Margarine
Double cream	Sugar		

Find the star rating for liver, low fat spread, red wine, roast chicken and boiled frozen peas from the tables in the Appendix. These star ratings are a rough guide as to whether a particular food is a major energy component in a dish. A useful exercise is to pick out a few examples from each group of foods and weigh out a 100 kcal sample. Table 5.18 shows 100 kcal amounts for a selection of foods.

In finding the calorific value that a food contributes to a meal, the portion size must also be taken into account. We do not eat equal weights of each type of food. A table of average portions is given as a guide in the Appendix. Caterers should get practical experience by weighing portions of food in the kitchen whenever the opportunity arises. An alternative way to become

Table 5.18 100 kcal amounts of some foods

Star rating	Food	Quantity (g)	Approx. quantity (oz.)
6* (more than 750 kcal/100 g)	Butter	14	$\frac{1}{2}$
	Cooking oil	11	$\frac{1}{3}$
5* (500–750 kcal/100 g)	Peanuts, roasted	17.5	$\frac{2}{3}$
	Milk chocolate	19	$\frac{2}{3}$
4* (250–500 kcal/100 g)	Bacon	23	$\frac{3}{4}$
	Double cream	22.4	$\frac{3}{4}$
3* (100–250 kcal/100 g)	White fish	130	$4\frac{1}{2}$
	Bread	43	$1\frac{1}{2}$
2* (50–100 kcal/100 g)	Milk	154	5
	Potatoes, boiled	127	$4\frac{1}{2}$
1* (20–50 kcal/100 g)	Apples	214	$7\frac{1}{2}$
	Carrots	429	15
o (Less than 20 kcal/100 g)	Cucumber	770	27
	Cauliflower	1111	29

familiar with portion sizes is to examine standard recipes and divide the amounts by the number of people the dish is expected to serve.

To find the energy value of a main course

100 g of fried cod contains 200 kcal

150 g of fried cod contains x kcal

$$x = \frac{150^*}{100} \times 200 = 300 \text{ kcal}$$

* is the 'factor' referred to in the following tables — the most convenient way to enter the calculation into a calculator.

Food	Energy (kcal/100 g)	Portion size	Factor	Energy in portion (kcal)
Fried cod	200	150 g (6 oz.)	$\frac{150}{100} = 1.5$	300
Chips	225	150 g (6 oz.)	$\frac{150}{100} = 1.5$	338
Peas	40	50 g (2 oz.)	$\frac{50}{100} = 0.5$	20
			Total energy	658

Complete the calculation for the main course in the table below.

Food	Energy (kcal/100 g)	Portion size (g)	Factor	Energy in portion (kcal)
Pork chop, grilled	350	150	$\frac{150}{100} = 1.5$	526
Cauliflower		50		
Potatoes, boiled		150		
			Total energy =	———

Example of the energy value of a standard recipe
The following recipe for chicken pie yields four portions (Martland and Welsby, p. 184.)

Food	Energy (kcal/100 g)	Quantity required	Factor	Energy in quantity required (kcal)
Cooked chicken	150	500 g	5	750
Chicken velouté	see below	300 ml		315
Cream, single	190	100 g	1	190
Onion	22	50 g	0.5	11
Butter	700	25 g	0.25	175
Puff pastry	590	200 g	2	1180
			Total energy	2621

Chicken velouté amounts for 300 ml:

Food	Energy (kcal/100 g)	Quantity required (g)	Factor	Energy in quantity required (kcal)
Butter	700	30	0.3	210
Flour	350	30	0.3	105
			Total energy	315

300 ml white stock, Bouquet garni, mushroom trimmings are also required, but the energy content of these items is small, and can be ignored.
The total calorific value for the chicken pie is 2621 kcal, so one portion has an energy value of 2621/4 = 655 kcal.

Calculate the energy per portion for the cheese souffle dish opposite.

Can you account for the large difference in energy value of the two dishes? Similar methods of calculation can be applied to whole meals, a day's meals or the week's menu in an institution. Then these figures can be compared with the R.D.A.s for energy for the group of people concerned.

Cheese soufflé (Martland and Welsby, p. 181). Recipe for four portions.

Food	Energy (kcal/100 g)	Quantity required (g)	Factor	Energy in quantity required (kcal)
Milk, liquid		200		
Egg		200		
Cheddar cheese		100		
Butter		50		
Flour		25		
(salt and pepper)				
		Total energy =		
		Energy in one portion =		

Understanding food analysis tables

There are a number of points which must be taken into consideration when using analysis tables.

1 The tables give an average figure for each type of food. For some foods (such as sugar, bread and milk) there will be little difference in composition from one sample to another. Other foods (such as meat) will show much greater variation between samples. One sample of stewing steak may contain more fat or gristle than another.

2 Wastage occurs at all stages of preparation of foods. Unless the entry in the table indicates to the contrary, the values are for the edible part of the food. In a chop, for instance, the bone is not included in the sample analysed.

Again, people do not always eat all the food on their plates. It is pointless doing elaborate calculations on school dinner menus if the wastage is ignored.

3 Nutrients can be changed or lost in cooking. When calculating cooked meals use the values for cooked ingredients where they are available in the tables.

Understanding the Recommended Daily Allowance figures

1 All nutrients can be stored in the body for short periods, so it is not essential to consume the recommended amounts of nutrients each day. The amounts can average themselves out over several days.

2 The R.D.A. figures are for healthy people. People who are sick may be unable to benefit fully from the diet provided.

3 The R.D.A.s provide sufficient or more than sufficient of the nutrient concerned for the particular group. Taking greater quantities is of no benefit, and may be harmful (for example, energy content or fat-soluble vitamins).

4 The R.D.A.s for particular nutrients are calculated on the assumption that the needs for the remaining nutrients are being satisfied. If this is not so, the full value of the R.D.A. may not be available to the consumer. For instance, the energy value of a food will not be released if sufficient B group vitamins are not available to metabolise it.

171

Meal analyses in relation to energy needs

The energy analysis for two whole meals is given below. We will examine them in relation to the energy requirements of two groups:

(a) women aged 18–54 years in an average occupation and
(b) men aged 18–34 years doing strenuous work.

Meal A

Food	Energy (kcal/100 g)	Portion (g)	Factor	Energy in portion (kcal)
Main course A				
Portion, cheese soufflé				319.4
Lettuce	8	50	0.5	4
Tomato	12	50	0.5	6
Cucumber	9	50	0.5	4.5
Salad cream	387	25	0.25	96.8
		Total energy in main course		430.7
Sweet A				
Apple pie	280	100	1	280
Custard sauce	90	25	0.25	22.5
		Total energy in sweet course		302.5
		Total energy in meal		733

Meal B

Food	Energy (kcal/100 g)	Portion (g)	Factor	Energy in portion (kcal)
Main course B				
Portion, chicken pie				655
Boiled potatoes	80	50	0.5	40
Peas	40	50	0.5	20
Cauliflower	13	50	0.5	6.5
		Total energy in main course		721.5
Sweet B				
Trifle	160	100	1	160
		Total energy in meal		881.5

Meal A gives a total calorific value of 733 kcal. For our first group this will provide $(733 \times 100)/2150 = 34\%$ of the R.D.A. If we assume this is the main meal of the day, this is a reasonable figure. On this basis, a rough distribution of the calorific value of the diet might be:

Breakfast	400 kcal
Lunch	650 kcal
Dinner	750 kcal
	1800 kcal

This would leave a generous allowance of 350 kcal for drinks and between-

172

meal snacks. If, on the other hand, trifle was eaten instead of the apple pie with the same main course, the total would be only 430.7 + 160 = 590.7, which would give only 27% of the R.D.A. If the other meals were proportionally light the distribution would be:

Breakfast	320 kcal
Lunch	520 kcal
Dinner	600 kcal
	1440 kcal

This would be 710 kcal short of the R.D.A.; a mildly reducing diet for most people in this group.

If, on the other hand, our first group had the second meal it would provide 882/2150 = 41% of the R.D.A. This would balance out only if the remaining meals were light. If in proportion, the main meals would be above the R.D.A. and would leave no allowance for drinks or the occasional snack:

Breakfast	480 kcal
Lunch	780 kcal
Dinner	900 kcal
	2160 kcal

If we contrast the position for men doing strenuous work where the R.D.A. is 3350 kcal the result is quite different.

Meal A would supply only 22% of the energy needed, obviously insufficient.

Meal B would be somewhat better, providing 26% of the R.D.A.

As regards energy content, this group would be satisfied best by Main Course B and Sweet A, which together would provide 1022 kcal, or 30.5% of the R.D.A. In practice, one would not combine the two, as both courses contain pastry, but sweet of equivalent calorific value would be appropriate.

Slimmers' diets
The theory behind slimming is simple. Pay less into the energy bank than is taken out so the current account is overdrawn, and the deposits must be depleted. In practice it is not easy, as it involves retraining of lifelong habits.

Theoretically, four different approaches to weight reduction are possible:

1 use of appetite suppressants,
2 use of special slimming foods,
3 extra exercise and
4 low calorie diets.

1 Drugs are available which reduce the desire for food. These can only be temporary measures, and should be used only under medical guidance.
2 Many special slimmers' foods are advertised. Most of them aim to provide bulk with a low calorific value. They tend to be expensive and evade the underlying need to retrain the appetite.
3 Most people would benefit from taking more daily exercise. However,

exercise on its own does not remove a significant amount of weight, permanently. Jockeys and boxers lower their weight by taking vigorous exercise, but the loss is of water not fat, and is quickly replaced. The example below illustrates the difficulty of removing weight by exercise alone.

Mr Jones usually sits reading his paper after breakfast and then catches the bus to work. While sitting down he uses 1.4 kcal per minute or 42 kcal in the 30 minutes. If he decides to go out earlier and walk to work his journey takes 30 minutes. By walking briskly he expends 4.76 kcal per minute or 142 kcal for the journey. So by walking to work he has used an extra 100 kcals. The same effect would have been achieved by eating one less round of toast for breakfast. So a low calorie diet is the only effective way of slimming.

General rules for planning slimmers' meals

1 Plan menus for a week. Nutrients required in small amounts need only to be supplied on a few days of the week (vitamins A and D).
2 Use a wide variety of foods and cooking methods. Boredom drives slimmers back to their former diets. Watch the cooking methods. Grill, poach, pot-roast, bake or dry fry as far as possible.
3 Plan around the protein foods which make meals satisfying. Examine the calorific values of portions of these foods. Remove obvious fat from meat.
4 Take special care to check the levels of nutrients which are limited to particular classes of foods, especially if their normal sources are to be cut because of high energy values (for example, oils, fats and cereals).

If we analyse the Weight Watchers' menu planner given in Table 5.19 we can illustrate the general rules and show that a low calorie diet can be both interesting and nutritious.

Table 5.19   Weight Watchers' Menu Planner No. 1

Morning	Midday	Evening
Monday		
4 fl. oz. orange juice	Savory scramble*	6 oz. lamb chop*
1 oz. hard cheese*	Green beans	Grilled tomatoes
1 slice bread	Sliced tomatoes	2 oz. onion
1 level teaspoon	2 level teaspoons	2 oz. peas
special margarine	special margarine	Cauliflower
	Raspberry soufflé	1 fruit
Tuesday		
1 orange	4 oz. cottage cheese*	4 fl. oz. tomato juice
1 oz. cereal with	Sliced cucumber	6 oz. smoked haddock*
skimmed milk	Sliced tomato	3 oz. cooked rice
	2 teaspoons oil and	1 level teaspoon
	2 teaspoons vinegar	special margarine
	1 slice bread	4 oz. peas*
	1 fruit	Cabbage
		1 fruit

174

Table 5.19 — *continued*

Morning	Midday	Evening
Wednesday		
$\frac{1}{2}$ grapefruit	4 oz. salmon	Liver kebabs*
1 egg (poached)*	2 teaspoons	3 oz. peas
1 slice toast	mayonnaise	Jasmine fruit salad
1 level teaspoon	1 slice bread	
special margarine	1 fruit	
Thursday		
8 fl. oz. tomato juice	2 oz. hard cheese*	4 fl. oz. tomato juice
1 oz. cereal with	Celery	6 oz. white fish*
skimmed milk	Pickled cucumber	4 oz. butter beans*
	1 slice bread	4 oz. No. 4 vegetables
	1 level teaspoon	Asparagus
	special margarine	2 level teaspoons
	1 fruit	special margarine
		2 fruits
Friday		
4 fl. oz. orange juice	4 oz. chicken*	Spinach soup
2 oz. cottage cheese*	Green beans	6 oz. rabbit*
1 tomato	Grilled tomatoes	2 oz. peas
1 slice bread	1 slice bread	2 oz. carrots
1 level teaspoon	2 level teaspoons	Cabbage
special margarine	special margarine	1 fruit
Saturday		
1 orange	4 oz. white fish*	4 fl. oz. tomato juice
1 egg (boiled)*	Braised celery	6 oz. grilled steak*
1 slice toast	Cauliflower	4 oz. No. 4 vegetables
1 level teaspoon	2 level teaspoons	Cabbage
special margarine	special margarine	1 fruit
Sunday		
4 fl. oz. grapefruit juice	Sweet and sour pork*	6 oz. fish*
1 oz. cereal with	fillet with bean sprouts	mixed salad
skimmed milk	3 oz. jacket potatoes	3 oz. beetroot
	or cooked rice	2 teaspoons oil
	1 level teaspoon	and 2 teaspoons vinegar
	special margarine	1 slice bread
	Weight Watchers' icecream	2 fruits

Protein The foods marked * provide the R.D.A. of protein. A wide variety of meats, offal, eggs and cheese have been used.

Calcium Calcium is mainly confined to milk and cheese in normal diets. The pint of skimmed milk allowed in the diet and the hard and soft cheese provide sufficient calcium.

Iron Since liver is included in the week's menu in addition to the other meats, enough iron is present.

Retinol The liver also provides ample retinol. The green vegetables also contribute to the supply of this nutrient.

Thiamine Thiamine is found in a wide variety of foods. It is needed in proportion to the total energy content of the diet, so less will be required in slimmers' menus. Ample thiamine is provided in the wide selection of animal and plant foods included in the meals.

Riboflavin Riboflavin is also widespread in the diet. The milk, cheese, eggs and meat provide sufficient of this nutrient.

Other B vitamins
Nicotinic acid. Found in meat, whole-grain cereals, liver and yeast extract. The variety of foods in the menus provides the 18 mg recommended daily.

Pyridoxine. Widespread in fish, meat and vegetables.

Cyanocobalamin (vitamin B_{12}). Only found in animal foods. The liver, meats and eggs provide sufficient of this nutrient.

Folic acid. Found in raw green vegetables, bananas and oranges, so well-supplied in these meals.

Ascorbic acid The amount needed daily is supplied by the fruit or juice at breakfast. Additional vitamin C comes from the fruit and vegetables at other meals.

Cholecalciferol (vitamin D) The meals are intended for healthy adults, who do not need dietary sources of the vitamin as they produce sufficient by the action of the sun on the skin.

Energy Obviously the energy content of the diet is the most important aspect. This will be not more than two-thirds of the normal intake. The exact amount cannot be calculated from the meals alone, as slimmers are permitted additional amounts of foods in our 1* and 0 categories to provide interest and variety in their meals.

Exercises in calculating calorific values
1 Estimate the calorific value of the main meal you had yesterday. Write down all the ingredients, estimating their weight in grams with the help of the portion table in the Appendix. Look up the calorific values in the tables and multiply by the factors for the portion sizes. Find the total calorific value. Look up the R.D.A. for energy for your age and sex. Find what percentage of the R.D.A. the total calorific value of your meal is. For a main meal it should be about one-third of the R.D.A.
2 Design a weight-watcher's menu for lunch. Choose foods which will supply sufficient protein, minerals and vitamins. Check the calorific value. Remember for slimmers you should subtract 1000 kcal from the R.D.A. for the group for which it is designed, and lunch should be about one-third of this.

Proteins
Proteins are polymers of amino acids (see Chapter 4, Eggs). All amino acids have at least one amino group (H_2N) and a carboxyl (COOH) in their molecules. They differ in the side-chains (see Fig. 5.14). The simplest amino acid is glycine, where the side-chain consists of one hydrogen atom.

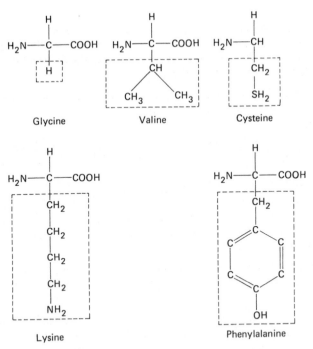

Fig. 5.14 Some amino acids

Amino acids link together by forming peptide bonds between the amino group of one amino acid and the carboxyl group of another, eliminating one molecule of water in the process. Linking many amino acids in this way forms polypeptide chains. The order of the amino acids in the polypeptide chains of a protein is determined by instructions from the DNA in the chromosomes of the cell in which it is formed. The order of amino acids and the precise manner in which the polypeptides fold to form a stabilised three-dimensional shape decides the functions of a particular protein in the body.

The main functions of proteins are:

1 maintenance, repair and growth of soft tissue,
2 synthesis of enzymes and polypeptide hormones,
3 formation of the structure of skin, bones, hair and nails and
4 production of milk proteins.

Sources of protein
In normal diets, protein comes from both animal and plant sources.

Dairy foods	25%	From percentage contribution made by
Meat	28%	groups of food to the nutrient content of
Fish	4%	the average household diet (*Manual of*
Eggs	5%	*Nutrition*, H.M.S.O.).
Vegetables	9%	
Cereals	26%	

The role of proteins in the body

Calculating the R.D.A. for protein is more complicated than that for energy, since protein, in addition to the functions listed above, has a secondary role in providing energy. Proteins also vary widely in their amino acid content, so their biological value has to be taken into consideration when assessing their value for tissue replacement.

Biological value

The biological value of a protein is determined experimentally by feeding a young animal a diet containing a limited amount of protein. Under these conditions all the protein is used for growth, provided the amino acid content is suitable. The nitrogen content of the protein in the diet and in the urine of the animal is found by chemical analysis. In this way the amount of protein retained in the body can be compared with the amount absorbed from the diet:

$$\text{biological value} = \frac{\text{amount of protein retained in the body}}{\text{amount of protein absorbed from the diet}}.$$

On this scale, the perfect (or reference) protein has a biological value of 1.0. This protein — if it existed — would be used with 100% efficiency in tissue production, as it would contain all the amino acids required for human proteins in the correct proportions. The proteins which almost match the reference protein are egg and human milk protein (see Table 5.20).

Table 5.20   Biological value of proteins

Protein	Biological value
Human milk Egg	0.9–1.0
Meat Fish Cows' milk	0.75–0.8
Soya	0.7
Wheat bread	0.5
Peanuts	0.4–0.45

Protein quality is also expressed in terms of Net Protein Utilisation (N.P.U.). In this measurement, the digestibility of the protein is taken into account:

$$\text{N.P.U.} = \frac{\text{protein retained in the body}}{\text{protein supplied in the diet}}.$$

So for proteins we have to consider quality (biological value) as well as quantity. In the U.K. the average adult eats about 80 g of protein daily, which is more than sufficient for tissue replacement and energy production. The position is quite different in the Third World, where young children often receive little milk, fish or meat, but a diet consisting mainly of cereals or roots. The biological value of the proteins concerned is often very inadequate for the rapid growth of children, and protein deficiency diseases such as kwashiorkor frequently occur as a result.

Complementation

We have seen that the biological value of a protein food depends on its ability to supply the essential amino acids in the proportions needed to build human tissue. Proteins of animal origin have a higher biological value than plant proteins. For this reason animal proteins have, in the past, been designated as 'first class' proteins and plant proteins as 'second class'. This classification is misleading as the individual amino acids are the same whatever their origin.

Because animals mature slowly, their proteins tend to be expensive compared with those from plant sources. This is of no consequence to the Head Chef of a high class restaurant. He or she orders the best ingredients for the dishes, and adjusts the costs accordingly. However, in other establishments the cost of protein may be of more consequence. There is no need for meals to be of low protein value just because costs must be kept down. A high biological value can be maintained by choosing protein foods which complement each other.

Proteins complement each other if:

1 Together they provide the essential amino acids in the reference pattern. One protein provides the amino acid which is missing in another.
2 The proteins are consumed at the same meal so that the total amino acids supplied are available at the same time to build human proteins.

The amino acid which is in least amount in a protein compared with the reference pattern is said to be *limiting*. Cereals tend to be limited by lysine, while animal proteins are most often limited by methionine.

If you compare the amino acid content of cheese with the pattern in the reference protein in Table 5.21 you can see that the sulphur amino acids are limiting, while there is an excess of lysine. The reverse is the case in bread. So a Welsh rarebit is an economical snack where the animal and plant proteins complement each other.

Table 5.21   Amino acid content (in mg/gN) of cheese and bread

Amino acid	Reference protein	Cheese	Bread
Leucine	300	630	460
Isoleucine	270	400	230
Lysine	270	490	120
S. amino*	270	180	260
Valine	270	440	260
Phenylalanine	180	310	310
Threonine	180	290	180
Tryptophan	90	90	80

* Methionine + cysteine.

Comparison with the reference protein also confirms that lacto-vegetarian meals are not inferior to mixed diets in protein value (see Table 5.22). Eggs have a higher biological value than meat, while cheese — when complemented by cereals — also gives a very satisfactory biological value.

Amino acid content (in mg/gN) of selected foods

Amino acid	Reference protein	Egg	Meat	Corn	Soya
Leucine	300	560	49	750	480
Isoleucine	270	360	320	250	330
Lysine	270	420	510	190	390
Methionine	140	190	150	130	80
Valine	270	450	330	350	320
Phenylalanine	180	330	260	300	300
Threonine	180	330	280	260	240
Tryptophan	90	110	80	50	80

From *Plant Protein Foods*. A Unilever Educational Booklet.

Vegetarian diets

It is in the preparation of vegetarian diets that a knowledge of complementation is most valuable. It can perhaps be best illustrated by the work of the Institute of Nutrition of Central America and Panama (I.N.C.A.P.). This institute has been able to make inexpensive milky drinks to supplement the protein-poor diets of young children in Central America and Panama. The supplements consist of a complementary mix of cereal foods which contain 27.5% protein of high biological value. One version of the diet supplement contains 58% corn (maize) and 38% soya. It can be seen from Table 5.22 that these two vegetable proteins complement each other.

Soya is playing an increasing role in the diet of Western countries also. It is processed to provide textured vegetable protein (T.V.P.) granules or chunks, which are used as meat extenders in commercial and institutional catering. If used as not more than 25% of a dish such as shepherd's pie an inexpensive product can be produced without loss of flavour or nutritional value.

Vegan diets

Complementation is essential in such diets. The wider the variety of plant proteins used — nuts, pulses and cereals — the greater the likelihood that a satisfactory biological value will be attained.

Soya, with its high biological value (0.7) has an important part to play in vegan meals, providing the deficiencies are appreciated. These are the following:

1 It has a pronounced beany flavour, which needs disguising.
2 Soya is limited by methionine. This can be provided by cereals, some vegetables (spinach, broccoli) and certain nuts (brazil, walnuts).
3 Soya is low in iron. Inorganic iron can be added to T.V.P., otherwise it can best be added in a curry sauce.
4 Vitamin C is also low, and is needed to absorb the iron. Tomato purée could be used in a T.V.P. version of spaghetti bolognese.
5 Extra calcium will be required. A fortified flour would supply this deficiency.
6 Vitamins of the B group, particularly B_{12}, are lacking. Yeast extract supplies flavour and this group of vitamins.

7 Vitamin A is also low, but can be provided by carrots or green vegetables.
8 Soya contains two unusual sugars (raffinose and stachyose) which cannot be digested and cause flatulence. For this reason the quantity of soya used in the diet should be limited.

Estimating protein values

Protein values of dishes and meals
Protein values of dishes can be analysed in the same way as for calorific values.

Food	Protein (g/100 g)	Portion size (g)	Factor	Protein in portion (g)
Fried cod	20	150	1.5	30
Chips	4	150	1.5	6
Peas	5	50	0.5	2.5
			Total protein in portion	38.5

How well would the fish, chips and peas course above provide for the protein needs of a boy aged 15–17 years?

The R.D.A. for protein for a boy aged 17 years is 72 g, so the meal is providing $(38.5/72) \times 100 = 53\%$ of the R.D.A., which is more than sufficient. It would also be very adequate for a man aged 18–34 years doing very active work (45% of R.D.A.). How would the lacto-vegetarian dish (below) compare with the above main course?

Macaroni cheese: Quantities for three persons for a main dish

Food	Protein (g/100 g)	Quantity (g)	Factor	Protein in quantity (g)
Macaroni	11	100	1	11
Cheese	25	100	1	25
Margarine	0.2	50	0.5	0.1
Flour	10	50	0.5	5
Milk	3.5	600	6	21.0
			Total protein in dish	62.1

One portion contains 20.7 g of protein, so this would provide 28.9% of the R.D.A. for protein for a boy aged 15–17 years, or 24.6% for the active man aged 18–34 years, (33% for a woman) so the lacto-vegetarian dish also gives satisfactory protein values.

Would the vegan dish on the next page supply the necessary protein?

As the recipe stands, the portion would only yield 11% of the R.D.A. for protein for a boy aged 15–17 years (15% for a girl) or 9.5% for an active man (12.9% for an active woman). Only the beans provide a significant amount of protein. Even doubling the amount of beans in the recipe would only bring the protein value up to 18% of the R.D.A. This illustrates the difficulty of finding sufficient protein from plant foods alone if the diet is not to be exces-

Winter casserole (quantities for four persons)

Food	Quantities (g/100 g)	Quantity (g)	Factor	Protein in quantity (g)
Potatoes	1.4	225	2.25	3.15
Celery	0.9	100	1	0.9
Onions	0.9	100	1	0.9
Carrots	0.7	50	0.5	0.35
Tomatoes	0.8	200	2	1.6
Rice (or barley)	6.5	50	0.5	3.25 (3.85)
Margarine	0.2	25	0.25	0.05
Haricot beans, dry	21.4	100	1	21.4
		Total protein in dish		31.6 (or 32.2)
		Protein in portion		8

From *The Complete Vegetarian Recipe Book, I* by Baker and Bell.

sively bulky. Since the protein value is low, it is important that the biological value is as high as possible. From the values given in Table 5.23, decide which of the alternative rice or barley would complement the beans best.

Table 5.23 Amino acid composition (in mg/g) of selected plant proteins

Amino acid	Reference protein	Rice	Barley	Haricot beans
Leucine	300	530	430	510
Isoleucine	270	290	240	380
Lysine	270	190	210	440
Methionine	140	130	90	80
Valine	270	410	310	410
Phenylalanine	180	300	310	390
Threonine	180	240	230	290
Tryptophan	90	90	220	80

From *The Composition of Foods*, by McCance & Widdowson, H.M.S.O.

Protein values of foods

The contribution different foods make to the protein content of the diet can best be visualised by weighing out quantities which provide one-third of the R.D.A. If the quantity of food yielding 1 g of protein is calculated first, this amount can be adjusted to the needs of different groups by multiplying by one-third of their R.D.A.

These figures give a general idea of the relative amounts of protein in particular foods. However, it does not take into account the waste involved in preparation, or the amount of food which is inedible. The tables in the *Manual of Nutrition* give the percentage waste of foods.

To find the amount of food needed to give 1 g of protein in the prepared food
Example Old potatoes contain 27% waste, so only 73% is edible. The edible portion contains 2.2 g protein/100 g. Were there no waste, 100/2.2 = 45.4 g of potato would provide 1 g of protein. As there is waste we must prepare

Food	Protein (g/100 g)	Weight of food containing 1 g protein	Weight of food supplying $\frac{1}{3}$ of R.D.A.			
			Boys, 5–6 years (14.3 g)	Girls, 15–17 years (17.6 g)	Men, 18–34 years (24 g)	Women, 18–54 years (18 g)
Bread	8	$\frac{100}{8} = 12.5$	179	220	300	225
Cheese	25	$\frac{100}{25} = 4$	57	70	96	72
Spaghetti	10	$\frac{100}{10} = 10$	143	176	240	180
Raw beef	20					

more food to obtain 1 g of protein. The amount needed is $(45.4 \times 100)/73 = 62.2$ g.

So to provide one-third of the R.D.A. of protein for a woman aged 18–54 years (18 g) $62.2 \times 18 = 1119$ g of potato are needed.

From Table 5.24 you can see the big difference between the protein contribution of the meats and the vegetables and also the effect the waste has on the amount of food that has to be bought and prepared compared with that actually consumed.

Table 5.24 Protein contribution of meats and vegetables

Food	Protein (g/100 g)	Percentage edible	Weight of raw food containing 1 g protein	Weight of of food needed to yield 1 g of protein	Weight of food supplying $\frac{1}{3}$ of R.D.A.		
					Boys, 5–6 years (14 g)	Men, 18–34 years (24 g)	Women, 18–54 years (18 g)
Potatoes	2.2	73	45.4	62.2	871	1493	1119
Raw beef	20	83	5.0	6.0	84	144	108
Bacon, raw	14	89					
Broad beans	7	25	14.2	57	798	1368	1026

Fill in the value for bacon.

Cost of protein from different sources

Since protein is the most expensive nutrient in the diet, it is worth comparing the cost of protein from different sources by the amount which can be bought for 1 p. For these calculations you require an up-to-date list of the trade prices of the foods concerned. At present some foods are still costed in imperial amounts, while other are metricated. Examples of both calculations are given below.

Example 1. Cost per gram
106 g of sardines cost 48 p
100 g of sardines contain 25 g/100 g protein
106 g of sardines contain $\frac{106}{100} \times 25$ g protein $= 26.5$ g

26.5 g protein cost 48 p, $\frac{26.5}{48}$ g cost 1 p, <u>0.55 g protein/p.</u>

Example 2. Cost per ounce
Stewing steak costs 114 p per lb
1 oz. contains 5.6 g protein
5.6×16 g protein cost 114 p
$\dfrac{5.6 \times 16 \text{ g}}{114}$ protein for 1 p, $\underline{0.78 \text{ g protein/p.}}$

Table 5.25 gives some calculations based on 1985 prices. You will note the big difference in cost between animal and plant protein. Find the present prices of the following items and calculate the amount of protein obtained for 1 p:

Sirloin of beef,   Baked beans,
Beef sausages,   Potatoes.
Cheddar cheese,

Table 5.25 Cost of protein from different sources

Food	Price	g Protein per 100 g food	g Protein per oz food	g Protein per penny
Milk, dried skimmed	438 p/2 kg	36.4	10.3	1.66
Milk, liquid	22 p/pint	3.3	0.9	0.8
Canned peas	136 p/3 kg	6.2	1.8	1.3
Lentils (dry)	36 p/lb	23.8	6.8	3.02
Frying steak	346 p/lb	19.3	5.4	0.24

Self assessment questions

Proteins
1 Which type of chemical bond links the amino acids in a protein?
2 Explain what is meant by the biological value of a protein food.
3 How do vegetable proteins compare with animal proteins in biological value?
4 Give an example of a vegetable protein with a high biological value.
5 The Net Protein Utilisation is sometimes used instead of the biological value. How do they differ?
6 Why is it misleading to term animal proteins 'first class' and vegetable proteins 'second class'?
7 Which amino acid is generally limiting in (a) cereals and (b) most animal foods?
8 List the advantages of T.V.P. to the welfare caterer.
9 Under what conditions do two foods complement each other in protein value?
10 Why is complementation of particular importance in vegan diets?
11 When using soya to replace meat in vegetarian diets, what limitations do you have to bear in mind?

Exercise
Check the meal you examined for the calorific value for its content of protein using the method employed on p. 181.

6
Food preservation

Part A

Summary of food preservation methods. Advantages of food preservation.

Preservation methods aim to destroy cell enzymes which change the *organoleptic* qualities of food (taste, colour, texture and odour). They are also designed to kill spoilage organisms or to deny them the factors needed for growth (see Table 6.1 and Chapter 3).

Foods can be preserved by:

1	applying high temperatures	canning, bottling, sterilising and pasteurising;
2	using low temperatures	chilling and freezing;
3	removal of water	drying and dehydrating;
4	increasing the osmotic pressure	salting, jamming, crystallising and candying;
5	addition of preservatives	smoking
6	lowering the pH	pickling.

Advantages of food preservation

Modern methods of food preservation have improved catering in many ways by:

1 making normally seasonal foods available all the year round,
2 stabilising the cost of commodities by reducing waste in times of scarcity or glut,
3 enabling the import of exotic foods to increase the variety in the diet and
4 reducing labour costs, since preserved foods need little preparation.

Part B

Advantages of preserved foods. Methods of preservation. High temperature—canning, pasteurisation; low temperature—quick and slow freezing, cook–chill, cook–freeze systems; drying–sun, roller and spray drying; high sugar and salt preservation, smoking; pickling. Multiple-choice questions.

186

Table 6.1 Methods of food preservation

Preservation methods	Favourable conditions for microbial growth	Preservation methods
SO₂ / Organic acids — chemical inhibitors added →	Suitable food	→ modify pH add acid or develop acid in the food
−30°C — lower → Freezing ——— 10°C — Chilling →	Moderate temperature	→ 63°C Pasteurisation — raise → 115°C Sterilisation
Turn to ice ←	← Sufficient moisture → Remove water →	freeze / tunnel / spray / roller } drying
	added salt or sugar	
	jams, salted foods	

Food preservation methods

High temperature preservation
The main methods are sterilisation, pasteurisation and ultra-high temperature (U.H.T.) methods.

Canning
Canning was the first major breakthrough in commercial food preservation. Two inventions made the canning industry possible:

1 the retort — which allowed rapid heat treatment with accurate temperature and time control and
2 the invention of the can, an inexpensive container, effectively sealing the preserved food from contaminating air or fluids.

Stages in canning
1 The food is inspected, washed and prepared.
2 It is blanched. This is necessary to:
  kill the mould spores on the surface of the food,
  deactivate the enzymes which would autolyse the cells,
  expel the gases from the spaces in the food,
  make it soft and reduce bulk, and
  fix the colour and taste.
3 The food is placed in cans with brine or sugar syrup leaving a 'head space' for expansion.
4 The cans are heated, driving out the air so that steam fills the head space. Then the lids are crimped on to the can bodies.
5 The cans are heated to the 'sterilising' temperature and held for the appropriate time. Low-acid and medium-acid foods are generally processed at 115°C. Acid and high-acid foods can be processed at 100°C.

   Commercial sterilisation aims at a 'botulinum cook', i.e. a time and temperature sufficient to destroy C. botulinum spores. The treatment may not kill all the spores of thermophilic organisms (see Chapter 3), but these are only likely to cause spoilage in cans stored at a high temperature.

Aseptic canning (High temperature, short time; H.T.S.T.) In this method the food is heat-treated before canning and then transferred aseptically to sterile containers which are then sealed. Unlike the standard method it can be used to process any size of can.

Pasteurisation
Pasteurisation reduces the number of spoilage organisms, and so increases the shelf life of a product. It kills vegetative pathogens, but not bacterial spores. In addition to its use in safeguarding liquid milk supplies it is applied to bulk liquid and powdered eggs, ice cream mixes and in the production of vinegars.

Milk pasteurisation A number of methods are employed.

1 L.T.H. (low temperature holding method). The milk is held at 62.8°C for 30 minutes.
2 H.T.S.T. (high temperature, short time). A temperature of 71.7°C is held for 15 seconds.

Milk is also sterilised by the ultra-high temperature (U.H.T.) process. It is held at 135°C for 1–3 seconds and then packed aseptically into cartons. This 'long life' milk can be stored at room temperature for long periods, and will retain its fresh condition.

Low temperature preservation

Freezing does not destroy enzymes or microorganisms. The activity of both is merely arrested. When the food is thawed and the food held at a warm temperature for any length of time, activity is resumed.

Freezing
Vegetables go through a number of stages prior to freezing. These are:
1 preparation (grading, washing, slicing, etc.),
2 blanching to destroy enzymes,
3 cooking (if necessary) and
4 draining.
Vegetables are then frozen as rapidly as possible. Fruits are often lightly sugared before being frozen.

Methods of freezing can be divided into two types (see Figs 6.1 and 6.2).

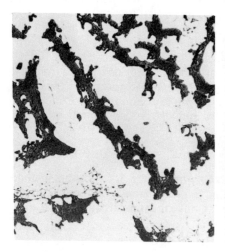

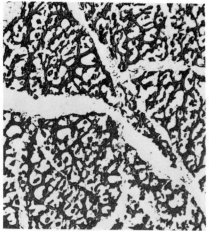

Fig. 6.1 Meat flesh frozen slowly   Fig. 6.2 Meat flesh frozen quickly

Slow (or sharp) freezing The foods are frozen by contact with cold air at –15°C to –29°C. Air circulation by natural ventilation or electric fans may be used, but in both cases the freezing may take 3–72 hours to complete.

Quick freezing Foods are frozen within 30 minutes, using refrigerants or a blast of very cold air. Quick freezing produces a better product in most, but not all, categories of food. It seems to have little advantage over the slow methods in the case of fish.

In slow freezing there is time for fluids to be drawn out of the cells and to form large, sharp crystals in the intercellular spaces. The texture may suffer and nutrients be lost in the drip when the food is thawed. In fast freezing smaller ice crystals form throughout the food, so less damage is likely to be caused. The rapid rate of freezing deactivates cell enzymes and kills or induces dormancy in microorganisms, thus preserving the quality of the food.

Methods of quick freezing

Blast freezing This method of freezing is suitable for most foods, whether raw or cooked. Complete meals can also be frozen, provided their maximum thickness is no greater than about 4 cm. Air is circulated around a freezing compartment by a fan. The blast of cold air reduces the temperature of the food very quickly. The food must be kept in storage units at a temperature of –20°C to –30°C after freezing.

Plate freezing In this method, the food is held between hollow plates through which a refrigerant circulates. Meat and fish are commonly frozen in this way, also vegetables such as spinach, broccoli spears and asparagus. The food is usually first wrapped and then placed between the plates, which are compressed to give good contact during refrigeration.

Tunnel freezing Small whole or sliced vegetables are frozen by this method. The food passes through the tunnel on a slatted belt. Freezing air is forced up through the food particles to keep them in constant motion and prevent them from sticking together.

Cryogenic freezing This method is used to freeze certain delicate fruits such as strawberries. The prepared fruit is immersed in liquid nitrogen, which has a boiling point of –196°C. Freezing is extremely rapid, so the texture of the soft tissues is unchanged. It is not a widely used method, however, because it is a costly process.

Cook–freeze This is a recent development in which complete meals are blast frozen and stored at –20°C until required.

The dishes must be prepared with strict attention to hygiene. Some starch and egg-thickened dishes have to be specially formulated to prevent separation on regeneration.

Many large catering operators find it convenient to use cook–freeze systems today. The meals are prepared by specialist staff, frozen rapidly to –20°C and held at this temperature. The food can be distributed to branch outlets in the frozen state and regenerated by microwave or micro-air ovens when required for service.

Accelerated freeze drying (A.F.D.) The food is first frozen and placed in a vacuum chamber. Gentle heat is applied to cause the ice to sublime (vaporise without turning to water). The product is brittle, light and porous. It needs careful packing to prevent reabsorption of water. When rehydrated the texture and taste is very similar to the fresh product. A.F.D. is an expensive process mainly used for vegetables, shrimps and the better quality dried coffees.

Chilling
Chilling is a term describing foods held between 1°C and 4°C. It is suitable for meats, fish, vegetables and some fruits. The foods do not freeze, but become very firm. Small ice particles may form on the moist surfaces, but no depth of ice is produced to affect the structure of the food. Fish and seafoods deteriorate more quickly than poultry. The time for which fish can be held at chilling temperatures varies with the type of fish, but is rarely more than 5 days.

Cook–chill
This is a similar system to that of cook–freeze, but the dishes are held between 0°C and 3°C instead of being frozen.

A cook–chill system operates as follows:

1 The food is cooked in the normal way, care being taken to ensure that a temperature of at least 70°C is achieved in the centre of the food.
2 Portioning is carried out under very hygienic conditions.
3 Chilling must commence within 30 minutes of cooking. Rapid chilling devices are used to bring the temperature of the food down to 3°C. The maximum allowable time for the chilling process is $1\frac{1}{2}$ hours.
4 Food can be stored for up to 5 days, providing the temperature can be maintained reliably between 0°C and 3°C.
5 Regeneration must take place immediately the food is removed from the chiller. As with cook–freeze, it is best carried out by infra red, microwave or forced circulation hot-air ovens. On heating, foods must reach a minimum internal temperature of 70°C.

Drying
Drying is the oldest method of food preservation. It depends on removing sufficient water to prevent deterioration by cell enzymes and microbial growth. Sun-dried foods are dried by exposure to sun and wind, dehydrated foods by artificial heat under controlled conditions.

Sun-dried fruits
Currants, sultanas, raisins and dates are sun-dried. They are treated with lye (an alkaline solution) and covered with olive oil, then spread on racks. Drying increases the sugar content to around 75%.

Evaporated fruits
Apples, pears, figs, peaches and prunes can also be sun-dried, but are more often air-dried in heated chambers. The fruit is halved, pithed and exposed to

sulphur dioxide, which kills the surface organisms and maintains the colour of the fruit. Unlike the dried fruit mentioned above, evaporated fruits need soaking before cooking.

Spray drying
This method is suitable for liquids such as milk, eggs and instant coffee. The liquid is sprayed into a heated chamber at an internal temperature of up to 150°C, according to the nature of the liquid being dried. Moisture is evaporated from the minute droplets, leaving the food solids in the form of a fine powder. This is cooled and packed in airtight containers. Milk and eggs are pasteurised before being dried.

Roller drying
Roller drying is mainly used for milk and semi-liquids such as soups and instant breakfast cereals. The product is played onto heated rollers at a temperature high enough to evaporate the moisture from the food but not to impart a cooked flavour. The dried food is scraped off the rollers, cooled and packed into airtight containers. It should be stored in cool dry conditions.

Increase in osmotic pressure
High concentrations of salt or sugar bind the water in a food, and make it unavailable for the growth of microorganisms.

Salting
Salt may be used to preserve foods in a dry state, or to assist in the curing of meats such as bacon, hams and certain dried continental sausages and fish. The curing medium is a brine; either a cover pickle, containing 15% salt, in which the meat is immersed or a more concentrated solution which is injected into the meat. Salt is also added to cheese and butter as a preservative and to add flavour.

Sugar
Sugar is mainly used to preserve fruit in various forms as jams, marmalades, glacé fruits and crystallised fruits, and in the form of a syrup for canned fruits.

Jams Jams are generally made with 1 kg of sugar to each kilogram of fruit, and this results in a product containing about 70% sugar, which prevents it from deteriorating.

Glacé fruits Cherries are the most commonly used fruit for glacé. They are bleached, coloured and cooked in a syrup. A final application of melted sugar gives them a sticky coating.

Candied fruits Usually the peel of citrus fruits is preserved by candying. The fruit is halved and the pulp removed. Then the caps are placed in a light sugar syrup until saturated. The process is repeated with syrups of increasing concentration. Finally the caps are drained, and the sugar hardens as the water evaporates.

Crystallised fruits Cut pieces of pears, pineapples, greengages or apricots are processed in a similar way to whole cherries. They are cooked in sugar syrup, then dried so that a crystallised sugar coating remains on the surface.

Smoking

Smoking has a dual purpose. It preserves, and adds desirable flavours to foods. The preservative action is partly due to the absorption of chemical substances from the smoke and partly due to the drying effect on the surface of the food.

Foods are soaked in brine, then smoked in a kiln. Cold smoking is carried out at temperatures between 32°C and 49°C. The wood smoke impregnates the food with a number of bacteriostatic and bacteriocidal substances. Amongst the most effective of these products are formaldehyde and the cresols.

In hot smoking, temperatures of 100–120°C are used. This partially cooks the food and produces a much drier surface to the product. Many continental sausages are hot smoked. The fish that are smoked are the oily varieties: herrings, mackerel and salmon. Smoking has the advantage of retarding the rancidity which soon develops on storage.

Modern smoking methods inhibit, rather than kill, microorganisms, so smoked foods should be refrigerated. They should be stored away from other foods, as they may taint them.

Pickling

In pickling, an acid — usually vinegar (acetic acid) — is used to lower the pH of a food. The method is applied to vegetables such as onions, cabbages, cauliflowers, gherkins, capers and cucumbers, and also to young walnuts. Pickled foods have a limited use in the catering industry because of their strong vinegary taste.

Multiple-choice questions

Food preservation

1 Which initials represent pasteurisation of milk at 71.7°C for 15 seconds?
   (a) U.H.T.
   (b) T.T.
   (c) L.T.H.
   (d) H.T.S.T.
2 A.F.D. is:
   (a) a vacuum-drying process in which ice sublimes off as water vapour
   (b) an air-drying process to produce dried fruits
   (c) 'Additives in Foods' Directive
   (d) anti-fungal disinfectants used on kitchen walls
3 Dishes prepared for the cook–chill system must be held between:
   (a) –20°C and –30°C
   (b) 0°C and 10°C
   (c) 0°C and 3°C
   (d) 10°C and 15°C

4 Cook–chill dishes can be stored for up to:
  (a) 2 days
  (b) 3 days
  (c) 5 days
  (d) 7 days
5 In the initial cooking and reheating, the food for the cook–chill system must reach a minimum temperature of:
  (a) 60°C
  (b) 63°C
  (c) 65°C
  (d) 70°C
6 Control of microbial growth depends on creating a high osmotic pressure in the food fluids in:
  (a) sauerkraut and pickled beetroot
  (b) chilling and freezing
  (c) pasteurised and U.H.T. milk
  (d) jams and salted meats
7 Commercial sterilisation means:
  (a) removal of all microorganisms from the food
  (b) heat treatment to kill *C. botulinum* spores
  (c) killing all vegetative bacteria and spores in the food
  (d) killing all vegetative pathogens in the food
8 Quick freezing turns the water in foods to ice within:
  (a) 30 minutes
  (b) 40 minutes
  (c) 60 minutes
  (d) 3 hours
9 Match the appropriate storage conditions with the products.
  (a) smoked fish
  (b) dried milk powder
  (c) cook–freeze foods
  (d) U.H.T. milk

  (i) in airtight containers in a dry store
  (ii) under refrigeration, away from other foods
  (iii) in freezers at – 20°C
  (iv) on the larder shelves

7
Using microorganisms to produce food and drink

Part A

Introduction to food fermentations

Microorganisms have been used since the early days of human civilisation to change the nature of foods to make them less perishable and to impart new flavours. Broadly, food fermentations can be divided into two groups.

Acidic fermentations

The bacteria added produce lactic or other organic acids which impart a tangy flavour to the food. As the acidity of the food rises, other less desirable organisms are inhibited, so the food keeps well and is unlikely to harbour pathogenic organisms.

Alcoholic fermentations

Yeasts ferment sugars to alcohol and carbon dioxide. The gas lightens doughs while the alcohol, when it is allowed to accumulate, prevents the growth of less desirable organisms.

Part B

Acid fermentations—cheese, yoghurt, koumiss, butters, sauerkraut. Alcoholic fermentations—bread, wine, beers, vinegars. Questions.

Acid fermentations

Cheese
Cheese-making converts milk into a solid, less perishable form. There are hundreds of varieties of cheeses. They can be classified by their texture into:
    hard (2–16 months of ripening),
    semi-hard (1–8 months of ripening) and
    soft (unripened);

and by their method of ripening:
by the natural flora,
by external mould and
by internal mould.

The milk most commonly employed is cows' milk, but milk from goats, ewes and water buffalo is used in different parts of the world. Cream, whole milk, skimmed milk, buttermilk or any combination of these products can be used. The basic method of cheese-making can be illustrated by the production of Cheddar cheese.

Production of Cheddar cheese

1 The milk is pasteurised.
2 A starter of lactic streptococci is added to the milk, which ferments the lactose and lowers the pH to 6.6. The temperature is held at 29°C.
3 Rennet is added. The enzyme coagulates the milk protein (casein) forming the curd.
4 The curd is cut into pieces with knives to allow the whey to escape.
5 The curd is 'scalded'. It is stirred at a temperature of 43°C for 1 hour to expel more of the whey.
6 The whey is drained off, so the curd settles to form a dense mat.
7 The settled curd is 'cheddared'. It is cut into blocks which are piled on top of each other. The blocks are re-piled every 10 minutes. The whey runs away leaving the curd rubbery in texture.
8 The curd is milled and salted, then pressed into cloth-lined hoops. It is steamed while being held in a powerful press.
9 After removal from the hoops the cheese is left to ripen for several months. The flavour matures during the ripening period.

Natural ripening

Cheeses such as Cheddar, Cheshire and Wensleydale are ripened by the natural flora of the milk. The salt in the cheese inhibits the growth of unwanted bacteria and favours the growth of lactic bacteria whose enzymes partially break down the fat and proteins, releasing lactic acid, fatty acids, amino acids and other substances which contribute to the flavour and aroma of the cheese.

Ripening assisted by Propionibacteria

The holes in Gruyère and Emmental cheeses are the result of gas production. A culture of *Propionibacteria shermanii* is used in addition to the lactic starter. The bacteria produce carbon dioxide, and propionic and other acids, giving the cheese its characteristic texture and flavour.

Ripening by external moulds

Soft cheeses such as Camembert and Brie are ripened by *Penicillium camemberti*. The mould forms a dense mat of white mycelium over the surface of the cheese. As the mould hyphae penetrate, the cheese ripens from the outside towards the centre.

Ripening by internal moulds

The blue veining in cheeses such as Roquefort, Gorgonzola, Stilton and Danish blue is due to inoculation with *Penicillium roqueforti*. The mould can tolerate the high concentrations of salt and carbon dioxide and the low oxygen content in the centre of the cheese.

Yoghurt

Yoghurt originated in the Balkans, Bulgaria and parts of Turkey, and is now very popular in Britain. The first stage in making yoghurt is to scald the milk. It is then cooled to 45°C. A mixed starter of *Lactobacillus bulgaricus* and *Streptococcus thermophilus* is used to sour the milk. The lactose in the milk is converted into lactic acid. The acid coagulates the casein to give a smooth thick product. This is usually flavoured by the addition of various fruits.

Koumiss

A number of fermented milk drinks are produced in different parts of the world. Koumiss is one which was originally made from mares' milk. Now skimmed cows' milk is more often used. The milk is fermented with a mixed starter of lactic bacteria and yeasts so that both acid and alcohol are formed. The product is creamy with a sour taste, and may contain up to 2% alcohol.

Butter

Butter is made from pasteurised cream which has been churned to a solid mass. Churning inverts the emulsion of the milk so that it becomes a water-in-fat dispersion. Butters can be fresh, salted or ripened. Each has its own distinctive flavour.

Fresh butters

These are made from unripened pasteurised cream and do not have any salt added to them. Their flavour is mild, so they are suitable for serving with cheeses, making butter creams, and baking shortbread and other confectionery. Fresh butters do not have good keeping qualities.

Salted butters

Fine dairy salt is added to these butters, which gives them better keeping qualities than the fresh varieties. They may be made from pasteurised or ripened cream.

Ripened butters

These butters are made from cream ripened with four different strains of streptococci. *Streptococcus lactis* and *S. cremoris* grow rapidly in the cream, producing the acid flavours, while *S. dextranicus* and *S. citrovorus* grow more slowly, producing the aroma compounds such as diacetyl.

Ripened butters do not have good keeping qualities. Salted and ripened butters are used for sandwiches, soups and sauces where a full flavour is required.

Lactic fermentation in vegetable preservation

Lactic bacteria can be used to preserve vegetables such as cucumbers and

196

cabbage, and are involved in the processing of green olives.

Sauerkraut

The cabbage is wilted and then shredded and salted. The salt draws out the sugary juices and encourages the growth of lactic bacteria. It also inhibits unwanted organisms. When finished the product has a total acidity of about 1.7%. The pH is between 3.1 and 3.7, low enough to inhibit all but acidiphilic organisms.

Alcoholic fermentations

Yeasts are used to raise doughs and to produce a wide variety of alcoholic beverages.

Baker's yeast

Baker's yeast, *Saccharomyces cerevisae*, can be purchased as fresh yeast in compressed blocks or in the form of dried granules. Fermentation commences when sugar, moisture and warmth are supplied. The temperature must be carefully controlled, as too low a temperature will retard the growth of the cells and too high a value will kill the yeast.

Bread-making

Successful bread-making involves two processes which have to be managed to take place at the same rate:

1. conditioning of the dough to make the flour proteins sufficiently elastic to hold the gas and
2. fermentation of sugars by yeast to produce the carbon dioxide to raise the gluten layers in the dough.

Conditioning

The two insoluble proteins gliadin and glutenin form the basis of the eventual structure of the loaf. When the flour mixture is moistened and kneaded the two proteins bind water to themselves, forming a complex (known as gluten) which is strong and elastic, and therefore capable of capturing the gas as it is produced. In hand-raised doughs, the conditioning occurs as a result of kneading and the action of proteolytic enzymes on the flour proteins. The enzymes are supplied by the flour itself, by the yeast and by malt if it is added.

Commercial bakers use a variety of methods to hasten the conditioning of dough. In the Chorleywood process, ascorbic acid and fat are added to the dough which is then subjected to intense mechanical mixing and stretching. The Activated Dough Development method involves the addition of cysteine and ascorbic acid, but the dough is less vigourously mixed.

Gas production

Doughs are raised as a result of fermentation of sugars to carbon dioxide and alcohol:

$$\text{Glucose} \xrightarrow[\text{yeast enzymes}]{} \text{Carbon dioxide} + \text{Alcohol}$$
$$C_6H_{12}O_6 \qquad\qquad 2CO_2 \qquad\qquad 2C_2H_5OH$$

The sugar for fermentation comes from a variety of sources. Some is provided by the flour itself. Flours contain small amounts of sugars, but the main carbohydrate is starch. This has to be converted to maltose by the amylases in the flour before it is available to the yeast. This is known as the diastatic activity of the flour:

$$\text{Starch} \xrightarrow[\text{flour amylases}]{} \text{Maltose}$$

The sugars provided by the flour are frequently supplemented by the addition of extra sugar or malt.

In traditional bread-making, the fermentation temperature is moderate — around 27°C. Normal strains of yeast (Saccharomyces) are used and raising may take 2–4 hours. In the fast commercial methods rapid gas production is required to match the fast maturation of the gluten. Special fast-fermenting strains of yeast are used and the temperature employed is higher, around 35°C.

Baking
When the raised dough is baked there is a sudden increase in volume during the first 10 minutes in hot oven conditions. This is called 'oven spring' and is due to a sudden release of gas as the fermentation rate increases. By the time the dough reaches 50°C the yeast has ceased to be active. When 70°C is reached the structure of the loaf has formed, as the gas has escaped and chemical changes in the dough have taken place. The starch has gelatinised and the gluten coagulated, forming the solid structure of the loaf. Finally the crust colours as the starch dextrinises in the intense heat and a browning reaction occurs between the amino acids of the flour and the sugars present.

Wine-making
Wines are produced by alcoholic fermentation of grapes or other fruits. In the past, the wild yeasts in the 'bloom' on the grape skins were used to ferment the fruit sugars. Today a special strain of *Saccharomyces cereviseae* is used (called '*ellipsoideus*') to ensure consistent quality in the final product. Wine yeasts differ from bread yeasts in that they can withstand a concentration of 10% or more alcohol, grow well in a pH of 3–4 and can survive the sulphur dioxide added to combat spoilage.

White wines
The grapes are crushed to extract the juice. The fermentation temperature is controlled at 10–15°C. If a dry wine is required the fermentation is allowed to continue until all the sugar has been converted into alcohol, for a sweet wine the fermentation is stopped before this stage. This can be done by adding alcohol — since concentrations of alcohol above 17% inhibit the growth of yeasts — or the yeasts can be filtered off. Sparkling wines are bottled before fermentation ceases to retain the carbon dioxide bubbles.

Red wines

The grapes are crushed and fermented with the skins. As the alcohol content rises the red pigment in the skin is dissolved and colours the wine. The fermentation is maintained at a higher temperature than that for white wines. It is held at 24–27°C for 3–7 days. This favours the wine yeasts and discourages the growth of wild yeasts and spoilage bacteria from the grape skins. The gas produced during fermentation causes the pulp to rise to the surface. This crust has to be broken up to prevent spoilage of the wine by contaminating organisms.

Storing and ageing of wines

After fermentation, the young wine is aged by storage for periods ranging from months to many years. This induces desirable changes in the wine, giving it a distinctive flavour and aroma.

Some wines are flash-pasteurised before storage to precipitate the proteins. Most are cooled and filtered, and kept in wooden casks or in plastic-lined concrete tanks. All of the containers must be full and airtight to prevent spoilage by acidophilic bacteria such as *Acetobacter* and *Lactobacillus*. After a suitable ageing period the wine is drawn off from the bottom of the container and bottled.

Beers

Beers are produced by fermentation of malted barley and are flavoured with the female flower of the hop plant.

The yeast used for brewing the traditional British beers is a brewer's strain of *Saccharomyces cereviseae*. This is a 'top' yeast in that it floats on the surface of the brew on a raft of bubbles. Lager-type beers are brewed with *Saccharomyces carlsbergensis*, which settles to the bottom of the wort.

The first stage of beer production is malting. The barley is soaked and kept at a temperature of 15.6–21.1°C to allow the grain to germinate. During germination the enzymes of the grain, the amylases and proteoses, begin the hydrolysis of the proteins and starch. When the grain sprouts have grown sufficiently they are removed and the 'malt' is dried and ground to produce grist. Additional sources of energy are added at this stage in the form of 'malt adjuncts', which can be any fermentable material such as corn, rice or potatoes.

The next stage is mashing, in which the grist is mixed with water and maintained at 70°C. In the warm conditions the starches in the malt and malt adjuncts are completely hydrolysed to sugars. The mash is then boiled to destroy the enzymes. The proteins coagulate and settle to the bottom of the vat. The clear liquid wort is filtered off and the hops are added. The liquid is boiled for about 2 hours and then filtered through the waste hops. The hops add flavour to the brew and act as an antiseptic, as well as removing any remaining protein from the wort. At this stage the yeast is added to begin the fermentation. It is often 'pitched' from one brew to another, though this may lead to contamination with wild yeasts or acidophilic bacteria.

After an initial 'lag phase' the yeast absorbs the nutrients in the aerated wort and reproduces at a rapid rate. The oxygen in the medium is soon exhausted and fermentation begins. The pH drops to 5.2 and the temperature rises. Cooling coils are used to reduce the temperature so that favourable conditions for fermentation are maintained until the desired concentration of alcohol (specific gravity) is attained. At this stage the yeast is separated off and the beer transferred to casks or bottles, where further fermentation may take place.

Lagers

Lagers are brewed on the Continent and are popular in the U.S.A. Lager beers are lighter in colour and density than British beers.

The fermentation with *Saccharomyces carlsbergensis* is slower than with the top yeast used by the British brewer, and takes place at a lower temperature.

The young beer has to be stored or 'lagered' in vats at $0°C$ for several months to allow proteins, resins and the yeast to precipitate, to clear and mellow the beer. It is then carbonated with the carbon dioxide which was collected during fermentation. After cooling, filtering and pasteurising it is bottled or canned.

Vinegar production

Vinegars are produced from a variety of fermentable materials such as fruit juices, starchy vegetables or cereals, or waste alcoholic drinks. The initial process is to produce alcohol by fermentation using the natural yeasts in the product or added wine yeasts:

$$C_6H_{12}O_6 \longrightarrow 2C_2H_5OH + 2CO_2$$

The second stage involves oxidation in the presence of a mixed culture of acetic acid bacteria:

$$C_2H_5OH + O_2 \longrightarrow CH_3COOH + H_2O$$

Alcohol + Oxygen   Acetic acid + Water
(ethanol)   (ethanoic acid)

The oxidation of the alcohol can be accomplished in a number of ways.

Slow method (Orleans method)

In this method casks are half-filled with wine which is left to sour under a surface mat of acetic bacteria. The plug in the cover of the barrel allows free passage of air, but keeps other organisms out.

When all the alcohol has been converted to acetic acid, half of the liquid is drawn off and replaced with another batch of wine. This process is slow, but produces a better-flavoured vinegar than the quicker method.

Quick methods

Trickling filter The trickling filter employs beech shavings to support the film of acetic bacteria. The wine or beer wort is trickled down the filter, while air is forced upwards through the mass. This ensures rapid oxidation of the alcohol. The heat produced by the reaction creates a constant updraught through the chimney of the reactor.

Submerged process Vinegars are also made by the submerged process, where the bacteria are suspended in an alcoholic medium and aerated from below. Cooling coils regulate the temperature, and a spinning disc at the top of the vessel prevents excessive foaming.

Malt vinegar Brewed malt vinegar is made from malt to which yeast is added to produce alcohol, and this is converted to acetic acid as in the Orleans method. This product is matured before bottling.

Some vinegars are synthetically-produced solutions of acetic acid. These have a sharp flavour and a strong smell.

Vinegars generally contain 4–6% of acetic acid, and are suitable for table condiments, salad dressings and as tenderisers for fish and meat. Vinegars for pickling must have a much higher acid content to allow for the water in the pickled food. Some vinegars are distilled. This removes the colour and increases their acid content.

Self assessment questions

Using microorganisms in production
1. Which type of yeast is used for bread-making?
2. What is meant by the 'diastatic activity' of a flour?
3. Write a word equation or chemical equation to represent the fermentation of glucose.
4. What is the purpose of conditioning gluten?
5. How is the gluten conditioned in hand-raised bread?
6. Give three differences between the hand-raising of doughs and the fast commercial methods.
7. What happens during 'malting'?
8. What is the purpose of mashing?
9. Give two reasons why hops are added to beer worts.
10. Which yeast is used for lager production?
11. What is meant by lagering?
12. What special characteristics are possessed by the yeasts used for wine production?
13. State two ways in which the production of red wines differs from that of white wines.
14. Wine is matured in full sealed casks. Why is it important to keep the air out of the maturing wine?
15. Name three different types of substance which can be used for vinegar production.
16. Write a word equation or chemical equation to represent the conversion of alcohol to acetic acid.
17. Why are stronger vinegars used for pickling meats than for salad dressings?

8
Hygiene

Part A

Personal hygiene. Methods of food service. Food hygiene—food preparation, cooking, cooling, reheating, holding and serving. Hygiene of equipment and premises—working surfaces, machines, hand equipment, refrigerators and cold rooms, ovens. Summary of food hygiene regulations. Questions.

Hygiene is a word derived from the Greek which means the science of establishing and preserving health. In an industry as diverse as catering it is necessary to practise a very high standard of hygiene. Hygiene in the catering industry can be divided into three main areas.

Personal hygiene	dealing with individuals, their habits and personal cleanliness.
Food hygiene	food offered for sale must be of a standard acceptable so as not to cause any discomfort to the consumer. Raw and cooked foods, if not handled properly, can cause food poisoning.
Hygiene of premises and equipment	to produce food which is wholesome, the food rooms must be in good repair and the equipment must be clean and in good condition, whether it is cooking equipment, serving equipment, cutlery or crockery.

All departmental managers and supervisory staff must ensure that all employees understand their duty in maintaining the standards of hygiene required. To achieve this all employees must be fully instructed in food hygiene and be made aware of the serious consequences that may arise from failure to observe the hygiene regulations.

Personal hygiene

All food handlers must have self-respect and pride in their personal appearance. Kitchens are warm steamy areas which are the ideal breeding conditions for germs, that can be transferred to food. A bath or shower after going off duty and a change of clothing is ideal, leaving the kitchen clothes to air. Outdoor clothes should not be worn in the kitchen when handling food; similarly, kitchen clothes should not be worn outside the kitchen.

202

The kitchen uniform must be designed and made from suitable material to withstand hard wear, to absorb perspiration, and to be protective, comfortable and washable. The food handler must always be clean in appearance, and when the uniform or apron becomes soiled it must be changed. The head must always be covered when handling food, and footwear must be comfortable, strong and give adequate protection to the feet.

Male chefs and commis wear the traditional uniform of double-breasted jackets to give protection to the chest from heat and splashes. The long sleeves should not be rolled up, as this leaves the arms unprotected. Aprons must be worn so that they reach below the knees to give protection to the legs from spilt liquids. The blue-and-white check trousers should be loosely fitted, so that they can be removed easily and lessen the severity of any burns or scalds to the legs. Industrial boots or shoes are ideal to wear in the kitchen because they give adequate protection from dropped equipment, knives, meat cleavers, heavy pots or spilt liquids. The boots or shoes must be in good repair. Neckerchiefs are worn to absorb perspiration; when working over the stove they should be loosened, and when leaving the stove to go to a cooler part of the kitchen they should be tightened close to the neck to prevent a rush of cold air getting to the chest. Neckerchiefs need frequent changing, because they soon become wet and grubby. Hats must cover the head to keep the hair clean and prevent loose hair falling into foods. The most suitable material for chefs' uniforms is cotton, as this is absorbent, hard-wearing and able to withstand high temperatures during laundering.

Female chefs should wear long white coats or overalls of suitable design to give the required protection. Hats should cover the head and contain the hair. The apron should be of a suitable pattern, preferably with a bib, to give added protection to the chest. Stout shoes with a comfortable heel and protection to the feet are required. Today female chefs often wear the male uniform, as this gives better protection than the traditional female dress.

It is essential that food handlers wash their hands thoroughly before preparing food, particularly after smoking or using the toilet. Finger-nails must be kept short and clean. Dirty finger-nails can be a good breeding ground for bacteria, which can be transferred to foods (see Fig. 8.1). Germs can be transferred from the nose, ears or mouth; therefore, when handling food, hands should be kept away from these areas. All cuts and areas of open skin must be covered by regulation blue waterproof plasters when food is being handled. These should be changed for flesh-coloured plasters at the end of the working session. If any wound is festering, then food must not be handled even if the area is covered. In the event of food handlers having been on sick leave with gastro-enteritis, diarrhoea or any similar illness, then they must have a medical certificate of clearance from their doctors before handling food.

Food service staff must practise a high standard of food and personal hygiene when handling food at the table. Personal freshness is essential and hands must be clean with clean well trimmed fingernails. Uniforms must be clean and well pressed and jewellery kept to a minimum. Hair must be similarly styled to give a neat appearance. Perfume and body sprays should not be overpowering.

Fig. 8.1   Plastic gloves used by food handlers

They must not:
  Sneeze or cough near food or customers.
  Lick their fingers to turn the pages of the order pad.
  Stuff their waiters cloth in a pocket.
  Scratch their heads with a pencil when taking orders.
  Breath on glasswear to polish it.
  When handling glasses they must be carried by bowl, stem or base and never with the fingers inside the bowl. Plates must be handled by the rim and cups by the handles. Any items of cutlery accidentally dropped on the floor should be returned to the plateroom and not replaced on the sideboard. Cutlery must always be held by the handles and polished with a dry cloth. Glasses should be held over boiling water and then polished with a clean, dry cloth.

Methods of food service
Foods may be served by various methods at the table and these are:

Silver service
The food is dished on the appropriate silver serving dish and presented to the customer at the table and then served by the waiter using spoon and fork.

Plate service
The course or meal is served on a plate and is complete in itself.

Family service
The host serves or carves the main course and the family or guests help themselves to the vegetables which have been placed on the table.

The following methods are used in other catering establishments:

Counter or cafeteria
The customers pass along the servery collecting the dishes they require, the main course and vegetables being served by counter staff. This type of service should be fitted with glass protection screens to prevent customers breathing over the food.

Self-service
The customers help themselves from the selection of food available, including beverages.

Fast food/take-away establishments
The order is taken over the counter and is then cooked or served immediately from foods ready prepared and kept hot.

With all the variations in food service today, a high standard of food and personal hygiene is essential and all the points applicable to hygiene generally must be enforced at all times.

Food hygiene

Even if all the points of personal hygiene are observed, food can still be contaminated and made unfit for consumption by bad handling, storage and insufficient care in production and cooking.

Food preparation
Raw meat and fish must be prepared on very clean tables or preparation surfaces. Poultry and game must not be cleaned in the same area as meat is prepared. Meat entering the kitchen must be checked for cleanliness and must not be contaminated with dirt of any kind. Fish must be very fresh, with no signs of contamination or decomposition.

Under no circumstances must cooked meat be prepared on the same surface as raw meat, nor cooked meat handled unless the hands have been thoroughly washed. Any knives used for cutting raw meat must have been sterilised. Bacteria transferred from the raw meat will multiply rapidly on the cooked meat, and this will be heavily contaminated by the time it is consumed.

Shellfish such as cooked prawns, crab, lobster and shrimps must be handled as little as possible and kept refrigerated until required for service. If there is in any doubt about the freshness of shellfish, then it is best to dispose of it immediately. Oysters and mussels must be purchased from reputable suppliers to ensure that they have been thoroughly cleansed. Oysters must be opened to order and served immediately. They must not be used if the shells are open, as this indicates that they are dead.

Frozen meat, poultry, game, fish and shellfish must be allowed to defrost slowly in a refrigerator or cold room. Foods of this nature need thorough defrosting, otherwise they do not reach temperatures above 62.7°C — the minimum necessary to kill food-poisoning bacteria.

Synthetic and fresh cream, milk and frozen eggs must be handled as little as possible and kept refrigerated until required. Equipment must be sterilised before whipping cream. Frozen eggs, once defrosted, must be kept in a cold room or refrigerator and used within 24 hours. The eggs of ducks, geese and gulls must always be well-cooked and never eaten as omelettes, soft-boiled, poached, fried or scrambled, because of the great risk of Salmonella poisoning. Eggshells are porous and these birds lay their eggs in the most unhygienic places.

The cold buffet

Food for cold buffets is prepared in the larder because the food must be kept as cold as possible during the preparation, storage and finishing of the dishes prior to service. A high standard of hygiene and cleanliness is essential. Cold meats and fish must be handled as little as possible after cooking and kept in the cold room until required. All salad items must be very fresh, well washed and kept cool. The buffet table should be dressed with the cold food as late as possible to prevent the growth of any micro-organisms.

Sandwiches and cold savouries must be kept protected with plastic covers or a film wrapping to protect them from dust and flies. All cold foods should be served with food tongs, appropriate serving spoons or carved and served with a fork. Under no circumstances must be food be handled with the fingers or hands.

Cooking

The stock pot is essential for making stocks for soups and sauces, but if sufficient care is not taken it can become a breeding ground for bacteria. Stock is made by simmering bones and sometimes meat, to extract the flavour and nutrients, over a period of 8 hours. The stock should then be strained off and cooled as quickly as possible to below 10°C before being refrigerated. The bones should be removed and placed in the swill area, not left in the kitchen overnight. The stock must be brought to the boil before it is allowed to simmer to ensure that any bacteria will be killed.

Sauce such as espagnole which requires a long cooking time should be cooled down as quickly as possible and placed in a cool area or cold room overnight. It should not be left in the kitchen on the side of the stove, where it would cool down slowly. The following day it must be boiled as quickly as possible before being allowed to simmer. All soups and sauces must be brought to the boil before being placed in the bain-marie, which must keep the sauces and soups above a temperature of 62.7°C.

Pork must always be thoroughly cooked because it may be affected by trichinosis. This is a disease caused by a nematode worm. Meats and meat dishes such as stews, which are to be frozen, should be cut into thin slices or small pieces so that they will heat through as quickly as possible: if they are boiled for too long the meat will become tough. Sausages must be well-cooked and any large joints of poultry (e.g. turkey) must be cooked in one operation, and not started one day, cooled, and the cooking finished off the following day. Poultry and game birds, if stuffed, must be stuffed lightly and only at the neck end, to ensure that the birds and stuffing are thoroughly cooked.

Generally speaking, vegetables are not a cause of food poisoning, but cooked rice can be dangerous if it is cooked and reheated many times. When sweated onions are added to raw or cold cooked meat dishes, the onions must be cold before being added, otherwise the heat is retained in the mixture and the temperature of the meat rises, promoting growth of bacteria.

Cooling
Cooked foods to be refrigerated must be cooled as quickly as possible to below 10°C before being placed in the refrigerator or cold room. The ideal area for this is a cool room or chiller with slatted shelves on which the food is placed. This ensures a circulation of cold air, which will help the food to cool. Soups, sauces, stews and stocks may be cooled in various ways according to the quantity.

1 Placing the food in shallow containers with a larger surface area, so that the heat can be removed quickly. When cooled the food can be placed into suitable containers.
2 If small quantities, they can be placed in a sink of cold water and stirred.
3 Placing the food into shallow trays and using a blast freezer to remove the heat.

Joints of meat and poultry are best cooled in a current of cold air. Remember that, because of their density, meat and poultry retain heat for long periods, therefore they require a long time for the internal temperature to be reduced to below 10°C.

All foods being cooled should be placed in clean containers. Any splash marks should be wiped off. Cooled meats should be placed on clean trays for cold storage. The foods should be covered with clean muslin to allow the heat to escape and prevent flies, dust or dirt from coming into contact with the meat. Foods must not be left to cool in containers with the lids on or be left in a warm kitchen.

Reheating
Foods which have been cooked and are surplus to requirements can be used to produce various hot dishes. These dishes are known as rechauffé dishes. The best known of these dishes is shepherd's pie. When making rechauffé dishes there are certain rules which must be observed at all times.

1   All meats must be well-cooked.
2   The foods must be kept refrigerated and used as soon as possible.
3   Food should be handled as little as possible.
4   The meats must either be minced or finely chopped to allow reheating to take place quickly.
5   The cooked meats must not be prepared on the same surface as raw meat or mixed with raw meat.
6   Soups and sauces must be brought to boiling point.
7   The meat must be boiled in the binding sauce for cottage pie, shepherd's pie or ham cutlets.
8   Fish cakes and meat cutlets must not be too thick when moulded, otherwise the food will not heat through thoroughly.
9   The ingredients for made-up dishes must all be of the same temperature, unless the mixture is going to be boiled.

Any surplus food which has been used for rechauffé dishes should be disposed of. Foods must not be reheated more than once, since continued heating and cooling will spoil the dish and may be a cause of food poisoning.

Holding and serving food
Food being kept for service using the hotplate/servery, hot trolleys or carving trolleys, must be held at a temperature of not less than 63°C, as required by the Food Hygiene Regulations.

The hotplate/servery counters may have infra-red heat lamps under which hot food can be placed to keep hot prior to service.

Green vegetables will deteriorate rapidly if kept in a hotplate for any length of time. It is better to cook them, refresh and reheat in small quantities as required. In this way it is possible to retain the colour, texture and some of the nutrients and vitamins. Other vegetables benefit from being cooked and served in this way.

Care must be taken when serving meat, fish and poultry dishes from the servery, so as not to break them up and spoil the presentation or dry them out.

The hotplate must always be kept spotlessly clean and the hot cupboards and bain-maries must be checked at regular intervals to ensure that the thermostats are maintaining the correct temperature of 63°C. Any spillage must be wiped up immediately with dish cloths of the disposable type, or cotton cloths kept in a sterilizing agent. Small particles of food must not be allowed to collect on the counter. All service and portion control equipment, ladles, spoons, scoops and fish slices must be kept clean at all times and food must not be allowed to congeal on them.

Any food dropped on the floor by the restaurant or kitchen staff must be cleared up immediately to prevent accidents.

Equipment and premises

Vehicles used for carrying unprotected foods such as meat, poultry, fish, bakery goods, cooked meats and dairy products must be kept clean and hygienic at all times. Frozen foods must be delivered in vehicles which have deep-freezes to maintain the necessary temperature of –20°C. All unprotected foods must be placed on clean trolleys and taken to the correct storage area immediately on delivery. They should not remain at the delivery point, where they can be contaminated by dirt, dust, flies or animals. If the trolleys have been used for raw meat and fish they must be thoroughly cleaned immediately.

Working surfaces

Foods must always be prepared on very clean surfaces. No food scraps must be allowed to accumulate between the joins of tables or corners where the tables are close to walls.

Table tops must be thoroughly scrubbed with hot water and a detergent, rinsed and dried. The chopping surface of butchers' blocks must not be washed, but scraped with a metal scraper to remove all particles of meat, sprinkled with salt and scrubbed with a wire brush. The block becomes impregnated with salt, which prevents growth of bacteria. Chopping boards must be thoroughly washed after use, rinsed and dried. If wooden boards are used they must be checked regularly, and any boards which have splits or cracks must not be used, neither must those which have rough surfaces and tiny splinters.

Food mincing machines

Food mincing machines are mainly used for mincing raw meat and fat, therefore they must be sterilised after use. The mincer components must be dismantled and all scraps of food removed and the attachments sterilised using a sterilising agent or boiling water with detergent. There are certain areas on the attachments where food becomes trapped, and particular attention must be paid to ensure that all traces of food have been removed from them. These areas are the holes in the mincer plates, the crevice between the mincer plate and the main shaft and the right angle of the food hole, as indicated in Fig. 8.2.

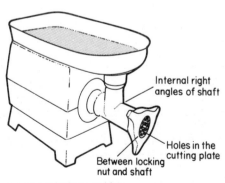

Internal right angles of shaft

Holes in the cutting plate

Between locking nut and shaft

Fig. 8.2 Food trap areas on a mincing machine

Food slicing machines

Food slicing machines are mainly used for slicing bacon and cooked meats, ham, beef and a variety of continental sausages. The machine must be dismantled, thoroughly cleaned and sterilised if it has been used for slicing raw meat (bacon) and is to be used for slicing cooked meats. If underdone beef has been sliced, then the machine must be cleaned before it is used for ham or other well-cooked meats. To dismantle a slicing machine requires great care. Each component must be sterilised, including the blade. The food traps are the meat grips on the carriage and the crevices in the guards of the blade and the blade itself (see Fig. 8.3).

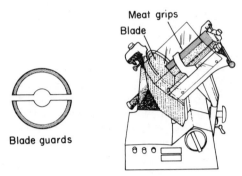

Fig. 8.3 Food trap areas on a slicing machine

Hand equipment
All kitchen knives, meat cleavers and meat saws must be sterilised at the end of each day. Most kitchen knives produced today have special plastic handles which can be sterilised. Wooden handles may harbour bacteria, and should not be used. Meat hooks must be sterilised after use, and knives which have been used for preparing raw meat must not be used for cutting cooked meat until they have been sterilised. Particular attention must be paid to whisks, as food can congeal on the wires and become trapped where the wires join the handle. With wire sieves, food can be trapped in the mesh and between the mesh and frames of the sieves.

Piping bags or savoy bags must be kept scrupulously clean, and must be washed and boiled after use, using a suitable detergent, then dried.

Refrigerators and cold rooms
Because refrigerators and cold rooms are used for storing perishable foods, they must be kept clean and maintained at the correct temperature. Scraps of food must not be allowed to accumulate in corners or on shelves, and food must not be stored so long that it turns mouldy. Regular cleaning and defrosting is essential, and this includes washing all internal surfaces and racks with a solution of water and bicarbonate of soda or an approved cleansing agent. All foods must be placed on clean trays and should be moved to another refrigerator at the same temperature during the cleaning and defrosting period. Walk-in cold rooms require extra attention as the floor gets dirty very quickly. This must be cleaned whenever necessary.

More recent models of cold rooms and refrigerators are fitted with temperature controls and dials which register the internal temperatures.

Food mixers, bowl choppers and vertical cutter mixers

Food mixers, bowl choppers and vertical mixers require special attention since they can be used for processing a variety of foods, both raw and cooked. Food mixers are frequently used for whipping cream and meringue and for making mayonnaise, so these items can soon be contaminated from dirty whisks or bowls and great care must be exercised to ensure that these are thoroughly cleaned and sterilised before and after use. Bowl choppers and V.C.M.s must be sterilised after use when used for fish or meat. This entails carefully removing the cutting knives and all moveable parts and checking the knives for particles of food, which must be removed. All parts must be sterilised before being reassembled.

Ovens, stoves and boiling tables

Ovens require regular cleaning to remove burnt particles of food and carbonised fat from roasting meat. An appropriate oven cleaner is recommended: these generally have a caustic base, and must be used with care. Stove tops must be cleaned daily and any spillage should be wiped up, otherwise it burns and is more difficult to remove. Grease accumulates around gas taps and oven doors, and on the bars and racks of open stoves, so these areas must be cleaned regularly.

At the end of each day the kitchen must be thoroughly cleaned, including the floors. All foods must be stored in the refrigerator, cold room or cooling room. No scraps of food must be left in the kitchen, because this would attract vermin, flies and other pests.

Premises

All premises where food is prepared or stored must be clean and in good repair, and should be suitable for the purpose. The areas must be well-ventilated, and the walls and floors must have suitable coverings. All toilets must be kept clean and have the necessary notices displayed in prominent positions. There must be sufficient sinks or washing machines for washing food and equipment. Sterilising sinks must be available and in working order. The water supply must be wholesome and from the mains, particularly the water for drinking. An ample supply of hot water must be readily available. A suitable area for storing waste food awaiting collection, with hygienic covered bins, must be provided.

Summary of legal regulations concerning hygiene

The provisions of the Food Hygiene (General) Regulation, 1970 as they relate to the day-to-day running of food premises can be summarised as follows (the regulations concerning individuals are listed first, then those about premises).

7.1. Articles or equipment cleanable and kept clean.
  2. Containers kept clean.
9. Food handlers protect food from contamination:
   (a) not place food so as to become contaminated,
   (b) keep food unfit for consumption apart,
   (c) keep food for sale covered or screened,

211

(d) not keep open animal food in a food room.
10. Food handlers:
   (a) keep clean,
   (b) keep clothes clean,
   (c) keep cuts covered with waterproof dressing,
   (d) not spit,
   (e) not smoke or take snuff.
11. Food handlers wear clean and washable overclothing.
12(b) Food handlers wrap food with clean paper and not with printed paper which is not specially designed for food wrapping.
13. Food handlers notify employer if suffering from or a carrier of an infection which may cause food poisoning or a food-borne infection in others; and employer notifies CEHO.
16. 1(a) Sanitary conveniences kept clean and working.
   2. Sanitary convenience room kept clean.
   3. No sanitary convenience room used as a food room.
18. 3. Soap, nail brushes and drying facilities provided at wash hand basins.
   4. Wash hand basins kept clean and working.
   5. Wash hand basins used only for food handlers' washing.
19. First aid materials provided.
21.3. Food and equipment sinks kept clean and working.
24.1 and 2. Do not sleep in a food room or in an adjacent room.
25. Structure of food rooms cleanable and kept clean.
26.2. Waste food not allowed to accumulate in a food room.
27.1. Certain foods at certain times must not be kept between 10°C and 63°C.
6. Premises not insanitary.
14.1 and 2. No direct air connection between a soil drainage system and a food room.
15. Water in a cistern serving a food room must be protected from contamination from a sanitary convenience also supplied by the cistern.
16. 1(a) Sanitary convenience placed so that no offensive odours reach a food room.
   2. Room with a sanitary convenience well lighted and ventilated.
   4. No open food in a room next to a sanitary convenience room.
   5. 'Now wash your hands' notice provided.
18. 1. Enough suitably placed wash hand basins.
   2. Hot and cold water supplied.
20.1. Provision made for outdoor clothing.
21.1. Facilities for washing food and equipment provided.
   2. Hot and cold water provided for washing food and equipment, but (a) and (b) cold water only in some cases.
22. Adequate lighting provided.
23. Adequate ventilation provided.
26.1. Provision made for temporary storage of waste in food room.

Food hygiene
1 List the points of personal hygiene which are essential to the food handler.
2 Write brief notes on the handling of foods, stating the precautions necessary to prevent cross-contamination and deterioration of food.
3 Why is it necessary to cool cooked hot foods as quickly as possible if they are to be refrigerated? How may the heat be removed from foods?
4 What precautions must be borne in mind when reheating food or preparing rechauffé dishes?
5 Make a list of the areas of premises and plant and small equipment which are most likely to cause food contamination.

Part B

The main food poisoning organisms—sources, characteristics, methods of transfer, prevention. Multiple-choice questions.

Microorganisms causing food illness

Food and drink can transmit a number of food illnesses which affect the gastro-intestinal tract (stomach and intestines). These illnesses can be divided into broad groups as follows.

Food infections
These illnesses require the presence of live organisms in the infecting medium.
   A further sub-division can be made.

1 Infections where the food or drink merely provides the vehicle, but does not sustain the multiplication of the organism. As growth does not take place before ingestion, the incubation period is generally long. Examples of such infections are typhoid, paratyphoid, brucellosis and cholera.
2 A group in which the food supports the growth of the organism. The incubation period is therefore shorter but, even so, illness is not produced unless a considerable number of organisms are present. The most important members of this group belong to the genus *Salmonella*.

Food poisoning
These illnesses are due to toxins (poisons) produced by the bacteria concerned. Examples are botulism and staphylococcal poisoning. This group cause true food poisoning, though the term is often applied to food infections as well.
   When considering the details of food-poisoning organisms and the diseases they cause, it is important to remember that illness occurs as a consequence of a chain of events not of one single lapse of hygiene.

For food illness to occur:

1 the organism must gain access to food or drink,
2 the food must be consumed and
3 the bacteria must be able to multiply to sufficient numbers to cause disease. This requires time and suitable conditions as regards nutrition, temperature, pH and atmospheric conditions (see Chapter 3).

The main food-poisoning organisms are described below, with their origins and methods of prevention. The bacteria are grouped according to their microscopic appearance.

Salmonellae

Organisms of this genus are responsible for two types of disease: the enteric fevers (typhoid and paratyphoid a and b) and food poisoning, more correctly called food infection.

Salmonellae are small rod-shaped bacteria. They do not produce spores, but possess flagella and so are motile.

Their main habitat is in the intestines of man, animals and insects. Persons suffering from Salmonella infection excrete large numbers of organisms in their faeces. Some individuals are carriers and excrete organisms in their faeces for long periods without showing any symptoms of disease. Poultry are frequently infected with Salmonellae. Rodents and insects can contaminate stored food with these organisms.

Salmonellae are more resistant to prolonged periods of drying or cold conditions than are most vegetative organisms. Their growth range is from 5°C to 55°C, with the optimum around 37°C. Although growth ceases at 5°C they are not killed even at much lower temperatures.

Most species of Salmonella are easily killed by heat. Holding food at 66°C for at least 12 minutes is sufficient to kill all but the most heat-resistant Salmonellae. An exception is *Salmonella senftenburg*, which can survive this treatment but is killed in a few seconds at 71.2°C.

The disease

The incubation time, the interval between ingestion of the infected food and the onset of symptoms, is generally between 12 and 24 hours, though it can be as little as 6 hours or as much as 48 hours.

Diarrhoea is the main symptom of the disease. There may be some abdominal pain, but this is never severe. Vomiting may occur if the food is heavily infected. Symptoms usually persist for 2–3 days.

Sometimes Salmonellae get into the patient's bloodstream and cause a more severe illness. This is more likely to occur when *S. virchow* or *S. choleraesuis* are the infecting strains.

Preventive measures

Prevention of infection

1 Employers should ensure that the food handlers they engage are healthy (are not carriers) and are aware of their obligations under the Food Hygiene Regulations to report illness to them.

2 Food handlers should observe careful personal hygiene, especially in washing hands after using the toilet.

3 Kitchens and storerooms should be kept clear of vermin and insects.

Infected food

1 Caterers should realise that poultry, meat and eggs are commonly contaminated with Salmonellae. They should keep raw food away from any cooked food or salad vegetables which will be eaten raw.

2 Poultry must be prepared and cooked so as to kill Salmonellae in all parts of the bird. To ensure this is so poultry must be:
thawed until the bird is above 0°C inside as well as out,
washed inside,
stuffed only in the neck and
cooked until all parts of the bird including the stuffing reaches 75°C.

Treatment of cooked food

Cooked food should be consumed immediately or held *hot* (above 63°C) or cold (10°C or below). If required later, it should be cooled *quickly* and then refrigerated or frozen.

Escherichia coli

Escherichia coli is normally a harmless commensal in the colon. However, a limited number of strains have been shown to produce enterotoxins and been incriminated in outbreaks of diarrhoea and vomiting. One such outbreak occurred in the U.S.A. in people eating contaminated soft cheeses. The fact that *E. coli* can sometimes cause such illness underlines the importance of scrupulous hygiene on the part of food handlers.

Staphylococcus aureus

Staphylococcus aureus appears under the microscope as round cells in grape-like clusters. It is non-motile and non-sporing.

Staphylococcus aureus is a very common commensal of the skin of human beings. Over 50% of people carry staphylococci in their noses and throats, and half of them on their hands as well. The organism is responsible for skin infections such as boils, styes and barber's rash. Cows excrete the bacteria in their milk if they suffer from mastitis. Human contamination is the most common cause of the disease. Outbreaks tend to occur from the consumption of cold meats, sweets and bakery goods which are likely to be handled.

The growth range is from 10°C to 45°C, the optimum being about 35°C. They grow best in the presence of oxygen, but are facultative anaerobes. Staphylococci are salt-tolerant and can withstand drying and freezing.

Only a limited number of strains are capable of causing food poisoning. These produce an extracellular toxin, called an enterotoxin since it irritates the gut (enteron). A large number of cells are needed to initiate toxin production; at least one million per gram of food. The poison diffuses into the surrounding food, which remains poisonous even if the bacteria themselves are subsequently killed.

The optimum temperature for toxin production is between 20°C to 36°C.

At these temperatures appreciable amounts are formed within 5 hours. The toxin is very stable towards heat. It will withstand boiling for up to an hour, or even pressure-cooking.

The disease
The incubation period is very short, 1–6 hours. A restauranteur could therefore have the embarrassment of having clients ill on the premises, knowing the origin of their distress! The enterotoxin causes vomiting, which may be very severe, abdominal cramps and diarrhoea. The illness usually lasts only 24 hours.

Preventive measures
1 Cover minor cuts and spots on the hands and face with waterproof dressings.
2 Keep hands away from the nose. As far as possible avoid preparing cold sweets or other susceptible foods when suffering from a cold, sinus infection or sore throat.
3 Keep foods covered and the kitchen as dust-free as possible. Use disposable towels, or boil cloth towels frequently. A hot air drier is ideal for hands.
4 Use clean implements to lift slices of cold meats.
5 Take great care in decorating trifles and other cold sweets. Use disposable piping bags. Remember not to cough near food. Wash hands thoroughly before doing this kind of work; preferably use plastic gloves.
6 Store cold sweets covered and under refrigeration.

Food poisoning due to sporing bacteria

Clostridium perfringens (welchii)

Food poisoning due to *Clostridium perfringens* (welchii) is widespread in the U.K. The cells are shaped like long cylinders.

The normal habitat is in the intestines of animals, birds and man. Over 5% of normal people carry the spores in their intestines in the faeces. The spores can survive for long periods in the soil in water and in dust. Spores can enter the kitchen in meat and in the soil on root vegetables.

Clostridium perfringens is an anaerobic organism. It grows most readily in the centre of large joints of meat, where anaerobic conditions prevail, and is encouraged by low-temperature moist methods of cooking which drive off oxygen. The growth range of the vegetative organism is 20–50°C, the optimum being about 43–47°C. *Clostridium perfringens* is easily killed by heat, disinfectants and penicillin when in the vegetative form, but the spores are very resistant to heat and other lethal agencies. Some strains of spores can survive for 1–4 hours at 100°C, so many types of cooking fail to kill them.

Food poisoning by *C. perfringens* is due to an enterotoxin which is produced as the vegetative cells are forming spores. It is released along with the spores as the cells disintegrate. The toxin is heat-sensitive, being destroyed by heating to 60°C for 10 minutes.

The disease This type of food poisoning generally occurs when meat dishes are prepared one day and eaten the next. When the meat is cooked, some of the heat-resistant spores survive. If the food is eaten immediately no harm occurs. If, however, the food is inadequately cooled and then reheated, the spores germinate and the vegetative cells multiply and produce toxin. Symptoms usually appear between 8 and 12 hours after consumption of the contaminated food. Abdominal pain and diarrhoea are the main characteristics of this type of poisoning. Vomiting rarely occurs.

Preventive measures
1 Whenever possible prepare meat dishes on the day of consumption. Serve immediately or maintain the food at a hot temperature (above 63°C) for not more than one hour before service.
2 If meat dishes must be prepared in advance, cool thoroughly and quickly after cooking, and refrigerate or freeze. Reheat just before service, making sure all the food reaches a temperature of at least 65°C.

Bacillus cereus

Bacillus cereus is an aerobic spore forming bacteria. It is a common soil organism which is found in cereal foods such as rice, but has also been implicated in outbreaks of illness due to consumption of meat dishes.

The growth range is from 10°C to 50°C. It grows rapidly in foods held between 30°C and 40°C. The spores are as heat-resistant as those of *C. perfringens*.

Spores probably enter foods from the dust in the air. A number of outbreaks occurred in this country in Chinese restaurants, due to the habit of keeping cooked rice at room temperature overnight before frying the following day.

The disease There are two forms. The most common is similar to that produced by *C. perfringens*. The more severe form has often been associated with the consumption of fried rice. It has a short incubation period, and the symptoms resemble those of staphylococcal poisoning.

Preventive measures
1 The same points apply as for *C. perfringens*.
2 While cereal foods are 'safe' during dry storage, they are just as vulnerable as protein foods after moist cooking. Rice should be prepared in batches which can be used up quickly. Any left at the end of the day should be discarded.

Clostridium botulinum

Clostridium botulinum is an anaerobic spore-bearing bacillus which causes a rare, but often fatal, form of food poisoning. Six types of *C. botulinum* are distinguished—known alphabetically, A to F. Most outbreaks of the disease in man are due to types A, B and E.

The normal habitat of *C. botulinum* is the soil. Type E is unusual in that it occurs in fish and marine mammals in certain parts of the world: in the U.S.S.R., Japan and the Great Lakes area of the U.S.A. and Canada. The foods most implicated in botulism cases have in the past been home-canned or home-bottled vegetables and preserved meats and fish.

Clostridium botulinum is an obligate anaerobe, so spore germination and growth are assisted by inadequate heat treatment, which drives off atmospheric oxygen without killing the bacterium. Vacuum-packing also makes favourable conditions for the growth of this organism. The optimal growth temperature for the bacillus is around 37°C. The minimum varies with the strain: A and B cease to grow near 12°C, but type E continues to do so down to 3°C. The maximum for growth is between 45°C and 50°C. Concentrations of salt in the food in excess of 10% inhibit growth of *C. botulinum*.

The pH of a food has a marked effect on growth and toxin production. The organism grows best around neutrality, which is why vegetables and meats are likely vehicles of this type of food poisoning. Growth and toxin production cease below pH 4.5. For this reason, highly acidic fruits can be processed safely at home and given the mildest treatment commercially.

Types A and B spores will resist boiling for hours, but are killed within 5 minutes at 121°C. Other types are somewhat less heat-resistant. Commercial canning times and temperatures are based on the conditions needed to kill *C. botulinum* spores, leaving a good margin for safety.

Spores can persist in frozen foods for long periods. If frozen foods are thawed and left at room temperature for some time, growth and toxin production can occur.

Botulinum toxins are the most toxic substances known. Minute quantities are sufficient to cause death. The toxins are absorbed in the small intestine and become irreversibly attached to nerves, causing gradual paralysis of the involuntary muscles. Heating food to a full boil for 15 minutes destroys the toxin.

The disease The incubation period of botulism is generally longer than that for other food poisoning, 12–36 hours. The disease is difficult to diagnose, since the early symptoms of nausea, dizziness and headache mimic those of other conditions. Later, difficulty in swallowing, double vision and respiratory distress make the cause clear. By this time it may already be too late to save life. Antisera to the toxins are available, and if administered early in the course of the disease improve the chances of recovery.

Preventive measures
1 Freeze any surplus vegetables rather than attempting home-bottling or canning.
2 Examine all commercial cans carefully before opening, and discard or return to the manufacturer any which show the following defects:
  any signs of pressure (flipper, springer, soft or hard swell),
  any serious rusting,

any serious denting or
any signs that seams are defective.
3 Cook frozen vegetables directly after thawing.
4 Keep smoked fish frozen during storage.
5 Keep vacuum-packed meat, fish and vegetables refrigerated before use.
6 If the appearance or smell of a food suggests it may be 'off' do not taste
   it to make sure!

Worm infestation

Apart from bacterial illnesses, foods can also transmit large organisms, such
as worms. A generation ago beef and pork tapeworms were common
amongst children in the U.K. Now the incidence of worm infestation is much
lower as a result of better sanitation and meat inspection.

Another type of worm is still found in pork in Britain and, more
commonly, in the U.S.A. It is a nematode worm, *Trichinella spiralis*. The
infestation arises from the consumption of undercooked pork, either as meat
or as manufactured pork products. The worm larvae encyst in the meat. They
are freed from the cysts during digestion of the food. Release of the larvae
causes symptoms similar to food poisoning, but accompanied by profuse
sweating. The incubation period is very variable, from a few days to several
weeks.

The larvae mature and reproduce in the intestine of the host. The second
generation of larvae make their way through the blood circulation to the
voluntary muscles. As a result pain and swelling are experienced as the larvae
encyst in the muscles.

Preventive measures
1 Pork and pork products should be cooked to an internal temperature of
   at least 60°C to kill any larvae which may be present.
2 The larvae are destroyed if pork is held at or below –15°C for 20 days.
3 Alternatively, the meat can be treated with ionising radiation.

Multiple-choice questions

Microorganisms causing illnesses
1 Toxin in the food is the cause of illness due to:
   (a) *Salmonella*
   (b) *Brucella*
   (c) *Clostridium botulinum*
   (d) *Escherichia*
2 The type of food poisoning most likely to occur as a result of consuming
   reheated food, incorrectly prepared is:
   (a) *Clostridium botulinum*
   (b) *Clostridium perfringens* (welchii)
   (c) *Staphlycoccus aureus*
   (d) *Salmonella*

3 Growth and toxin production of *Clostridium botulinum* cease when the pH of the food is at:
  (a) 4.0
  (b) 6.0
  (c) 7.0
  (d) 8.0

4 The incubation period of staphylococcal poisoning is:
  (a) 12–24 hours
  (b) 1–6 hours
  (c) 8–12 hours
  (d) 12–48 hours

5 The type of food poisoning most likely to be caused by an uncovered septic spot is due to:
  (a) *Bacillus cereus*
  (b) *Salmonella*
  (c) *Clostridium perfringens* (welchii)
  (d) *Staphylococcus aureus*

6 Food-poisoning organisms are most likely to grow in foods held between:
  (a) 0°C and 10°C
  (b) 10°C and 15°C
  (c) 10° and 63°C
  (d) 65°C and 70°C

7 Frozen poultry should be carefully thawed and cooked to an internal temperature of 75°C to prevent food poisoning due to:
  (a) *Escherichia*
  (b) *Salmonella*
  (c) *Clostridium botulinum*
  (d) *Bacillus cereus*

8 The main symptom of staphylococcal poisoning is:
  (a) fever
  (b) diarrhoea
  (c) paralysis
  (d) vomiting

9 Trichinosis is most likely to occur as a result of eating:
  (a) home-canned vegetables
  (b) undercooked ducks' eggs
  (c) undercooked pork
  (d) reheated beef stew

10 A hot food required for service next day should:
  (a) be placed in the refrigerator immediately after cooking
  (b) left in the kitchen to cool for 6 hours
  (c) cooled rapidly then refrigerated and later reheated to 65°C
  (d) cooled rapidly, refrigerated, added to hot gravy next day

9
Cleaning operations and the HASAWA

Part A

Kitchen planning. Materials for work surfaces, walls, floors and ceilings. Cleaning methods and schedules. Questions. The Health and Safety at Work Act. Questions.

Kitchen planning

In planning the layout of a commercial kitchen it is essential that the work flow and the distribution of goods is efficient. The goods should be handled as little as possible, so that the minimum amount of dirt is conveyed to the cooking and food storage areas. The removal of refuse and swill is very important and there should be easy access to the refuse area. There are no hard-and-fast rules for kitchen layout because every kitchen is different. Kitchens may be purpose-built units or part of an existing building being converted to a catering unit. There are many points which must be borne in mind when planning the layout of a kitchen. These are:

work flow,
siting of equipment in relation to services,
food storage areas,
delivery of goods and supplies and
removal of refuse and swill.

The vegetable store should be situated near the goods entrance, as should the refrigeration store and the dry store. This ensures the minimum amount of dirt being brought into the cooking area. The vegetables should be prepared in a vegetable preparation area.

The kitchen
Many items of kitchen equipment are supplied as modules having standard dimensions and fitting together to give complete units. When siting equipment ample space should be left between and behind the items to allow access for cleaning. When stoves and cooking equipment are centrally placed, sufficient space should be left between the items for cleaning.

All work tables placed against the walls must be movable to enable cleaning to be carried out. All stoves, deep fat fryers, salamanders and roasting ovens should have canopies and a ventilation system to remove fumes. Fire dampers must be fitted. Steamers and boiling pans should be sited near an external wall to avoid long drainage channels in the kitchen. These channels must be covered with suitable covers which can be removed easily for cleaning. Sinks with hot and cold running water should be sited against the walls to avoid unnecessary pipe work and drainage. The sinks should be of stainless steel and sufficient to cope with the volume of work. Potato peeling machines should be sited near a sink suitable for the purpose.

A scullery is essential and should be equipped with at least two deep stainless steel sinks — one for washing and one for rinsing — and a sterilising sink. Ample pot racks should also be available to take all pots and pans.

The plateroom for washing crockery, cutlery and, maybe, glass is usually equipped with a dishwasher, and sinks must be available for glassware and dishwashing in the event of the dishwasher breaking down. Sinks used for dishwashing must not be used for washing any type of food or washing hands, and vice versa. Wash hand basins must be situated in all food preparation areas.

Cleaned and sterilised crockery should be stored in clean dry cupboards. Cups should only be held by the handles or base, never by the rim or the inside. Plates must be handled by the rim and never by the centre. Sterilised cutlery should be stored in partitioned drawers or boxes and must never be handled by the blades, prongs, or bowls.

Work flow

It can be seen from Fig. 9.1 that the storage areas are close to the delivery point. The vegetable preparation area is ajacent to the vegetable store and has easy access to the main kitchen. The dining room is situated next to the kitchen.

The dirty pots are taken to the pot wash, while the dirty tableware is deposited in the plateroom. The stores for tableware are situated near the plateroom.

Swill and refuse are removed from the appropriate areas.

Kitchen layout

The requirements mentioned above can be clearly seen on Fig.9.2. The refrigeration area is equipped with deep-freezes, refrigerators and a cold room. There is easy access from the vegetable store to the vegetable preparation area. The sinks here are on an outside wall for easy drainage, a potato peeler is placed over a sink.

The main cooking area shows sinks and tables sited close to the walls. The stoves are centrally placed, while steamers and boilers are close to the water supply for the pot wash. Here ample pot racks are shown, together with the various sinks.

In the plateroom the dishwasher is centrally sited for easy access and the sinks for hand washing are close to the point for the dirty tableware. These sinks are placed on an outside wall.

The refuse area is accessible, but without causing obstruction to the delivery point or exit. Wash hand basins are situated where necessary.

222

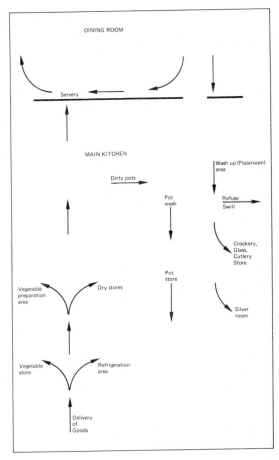

DINING ROOM

Servery

MAIN KITCHEN

Wash up (Plateroom)
area

Dirty pots

Pot
wash

Refuse
Swill

Crockery,
Glass,
Cutlery
Store

Pot
store

Vegetable
preparation
area

Dry stores

Silver
room

Vegetable
store

Refrigeration
area

Delivery
of
Goods

Fig. 9.1   Work flow

The servery

The servery is the point in the kitchen where hot or cold food is served or collected by the restaurant staff. This area is generally referred to as the hot plate. The design of the hot plate/servery varies according to the type of food service and the establishment. Most hot plates have the standard equipment, which consists of:

1 Bain maries for holding containers of soups, sauces or stews.
2 Fitted bain-marie containers for vegetables and other foods. These fitted containers vary in size and shape from deep square ones, to shallow oblong ones.
3 Beneath the bain-marie are hot cupboards for heating plates and silver service dishes. These cupboards are also used for keeping food hot, just prior to service.
4 A heated rack above the bain-marie is used to keep the lids to the silver dishes warm.

223

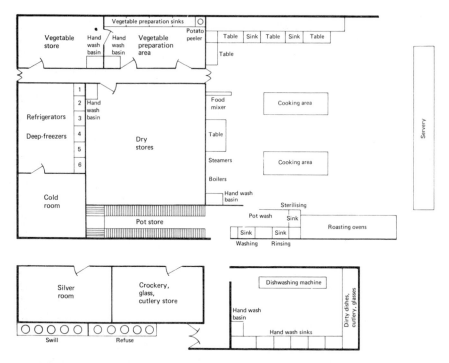

Fig. 9.2 Kitchen layout based on work flow diagram

5 A refrigerated cold counter may be included to keep salad items, cold sweets and cold drinks.

6 A still for the service of tea and coffee.

A still and cold counter would not be included in the hot plate of a large hotel because the salads would be collected direct from the larder and all beverages from the still room.

Materials suitable for floors

Kitchen floors have to be able to withstand foot traffic and trolleys, and to support the weight of heavy equipment. The surface must be impervious, so as not to absorb water or grease, and evenly laid, to prevent accidents. There should be no cracks or open joints which could harbour bacteria. The surface should be smooth without being slippery and, above all, easy to clean. Kitchen floors should have a gradual slope towards a trapped gulley to allow water to be easily removed. All floors must be kept in a good state of repair. The most suitable surfaces for kitchen floors are kiln-fired quarry tiles, granolithic chips or terrazo. Quarry tiles are set in cement, and it is essential that the joints are level with the tiles. The floor must be well laid, otherwise water may seep beneath the tiles and loosen them, which would be a safety and health hazard. Terrazo and granolithic chips are very hard-wearing and give a good surface providing they have been laid correctly.

Walls

The requirements for kitchen walls are that they should be light-coloured, smooth, durable and impervious to grease. Where the walls meet the ceiling and the floors they should be rounded to prevent dust and grease from accumulating and to facilitate easy cleaning. White glazed tiles are the ideal wall surface in the kitchen, but emulsion paint is an adequate alternative providing a smooth finish is achieved. The walls around sinks and wash hand basins should be glazed tiles and the joins between sinks and walls should be filled with a suitable water-resistant mastic.

Thermoplastic wall coverings have recently been produced which give a tough, smooth, durable surface, suitable for new and existing walls. These plastics are available in various finishes and colours, although white is usually used for food preparation areas. Professional advice must be sought, as certain materials of this nature are not suitable for some areas because of the possibility of a fire hazard. The walls must be covered to a height of at least $3\frac{1}{2}$ metres from the floor, and the corners should be rounded to prevent accumulation of dirt and grease.

Ceilings

Ceilings must be kept clean and in a good state of repair, with no cracks or flaking surfaces. They should be made of an absorbent material, to prevent condensation or moisture dropping onto foods. The surface should be smooth, so as not to harbour grease or dirt, and easily cleaned. Canopies placed over cooking equipment prevent the drift of steam to outer areas.

Thermoplastic coverings can be used for ceilings. The coving between ceilings and walls should be round for easy cleaning.

Food preparation surfaces

The surface materials must be free from cracks or joins, impervious to liquids and easily cleaned. Suitable surfaces are stainless steel, Formica or a hard wood. A butcher's block is essential for any large-scale butchery. When working on a stainless steel or Formica surface, a chopping board must always be used. Chopping boards are made from plastic, compressed rubber, nylon or wood, but wooden boards are best, providing they are made without joins. Wooden boards which are split or splintered must be discarded because they are a danger to health. Marble is the best surface for pastry-making because it keeps the pastry cool and the surface is easily cleaned.

Cleaning methods and schedules

Pot wash or scullery

The kitchen porter responsible for washing the pots and pans is called a scullery person or plongeur. The duties also include keeping the copper clean and bright.

The procedure for cleaning pots and pans is as follows:

1 Remove all food particles before washing.
2 Any burnt saucepans should be left to soak with cold water and common salt or an appropriate bio-soak.
3 Wash in hot detergent water and rinse in clean water.
4 Sterilise at a temperature of 77°C and place on galvanised pot racks to air-dry.

To keep copper clean a pickle made of silver sand, vinegar and salt is mixed to a paste, applied with lemon skins and worked over the copper. The pans must be rinsed thoroughly and then sterilised.

Equipment should be stored hygienically (see Fig. 9.3). The sculleryperson should wear industrial rubber gloves and an apron of a suitable material.

There are pan-washing machines (see Fig. 9.4), but the range of sizes and shapes of the pots they can handle is limited.

Fig. 9.3 Hygienic storage of equipment

Fig. 9.4   A pot and pan washer

Hot plates, hot cupboards and hot food trolleys
These should be cleaned as follows after each service:
1 All unused food must be returned to the appropriate storage place or disposed of.
2 All food particles should be removed and the surfaces and shelves washed with detergent and hot water, and rinsed and dried if necessary.
3 Scraps of food must not be allowed to accumulate.

Cooking stoves and ovens
Stove tops must be cleaned daily, preferably after each service, and any spillage should be wiped up before it becomes burnt. Solid top stoves should be rubbed with a pumice block to remove all burnt food. When properly cleaned the surface should be lightly oiled to prevent rusting.

Open stoves should have the bars removed, and be cleaned at least once a week or when necessary using an appropriate stove cleaner. The under trays should be cleaned after each service or when necessary.

Tables and butchers blocks

Tables should be thoroughly washed or scrubbed with hot detergent water, rinsed and dried during the working day. Chopping boards must be thoroughly cleaned and allowed to dry. Stainless steel and Formica surfaces should be hand-washed with hot water and a detergent, rinsed and dried. Table legs and under shelves should be washed daily.

Butcher's blocks should be cleaned with salt as described in Chapter 4. They must not be washed because water would spoil the chopping surface, creating a safety hazard.

Tea and coffee urns

Tea and coffee urns should be cleaned after each service as follows:

1 Empty and fill with hot water, scrub with a long-handled urn brush.
2 Repeat the above operation.
3 Refill and add an urn-cleaning powder, and leave with the heat on for 30 minutes, brush thoroughly and empty.
4 Rinse thoroughly and clean all pipes and taps, using the appropriate brushes.

The restaurant

It is important that the restaurant or dining room is properly cleaned and dust must not be allowed to accumulate at any point. The cleaning of the restaurant may be divided into schedules so that all areas are cleaned regularly.

The day-to-day cleaning should be carried out by the housekeeping staff and any heavy work such as washing down paintwork, walls and ceilings will be carried out by the maintenance staff or specialist contract cleaners. Contractors would also be hired to clean heavy carpets.

Cleaning schedule

Twice daily: Dust all window sills, tables, sideboards, wine racks, chairs. Vacuum or hoover all carpets. Polish chairs, table and sideboards and mirrors.
Weekly: Move all sideboards and tables and dust behind. This work may need to be done more frequently.
Monthly: Wash down paintwork, walls, ceilings and clean curtains by vacuum.

Cleaning silverware

Silver becomes tarnished and must be kept clean by using a plate powder, a burnishing machine, or a silver dip. The plate powder is mixed to a smooth paste with methylated spirit. The spirit evaporates very quickly leaving the powder which is removed using a soft, dry cloth. This is followed by thoroughly rinsing in hot water and polishing with a dry cloth.

The burnishing machine is a revolving drum half-filled with ball bearings. The silver items are placed in the drum with a measured amount of soap powder and a constant flow of water. The drum revolves and the action of the water, soap powder and ball bearings removes the tarnish from the items. After burnishing they should be rinsed in hot water and polished.

The silver dip is placed in a plastic container and the dirty silver is dipped for a very short time, polished, rinsed in hot water and thoroughly dried.

Table linen

Tablecloths and napkins must always be clean and fresh. Starching improves the appearance and finish and any stains are more easily removed. Table linen is sterilised when it is ironed and must be stored in a clean cupboard to retain this condition until required for use on the table. When tablecloths are soiled on the table, they should be covered with a slip cloth until they are able to be changed completely.

Glass washing in bar service

Special machines are recommended for glass washing behind the bar. All bars must be provided with adequate sinks supplied with hot and cold water and this would normally require a double sink. One section is used for a hot water wash with a detergent or sterilant. The other section for a hot water rinse. The glasses should be left to air dry where possible, but if wiped, the cloths should be of the disposable type. Re-using wet, dirty cloths is prohibited. Where a washing sink for glasses is provided with cold water only, a suitable bacteriacidal agent must be used.

The 'dip and dry' method must not be used, as it is most unhygienic because lipstick smears and streaks cannot be removed. Specialist suppliers or manufacturers of bactericidal agents and sterilants are always available to assist with products best suited to the bar staffs' requirements.

Staff concerned with drinks, whether serving or dispensing, must practise a high standard of cleanliness and hygiene. Dust must not be allowed to accumulate on shelves, bottles or glasses. Any spillage must be wiped up immediately. The backing to the bar should be fitted with glass mirrors, and these must be thoroughly cleaned daily. Bar counters must be wiped down when necessary and all dirty glasses removed promptly. Any boards used for cutting orange or lemon must be kept clean. The floors must be swept and washed if necessary after each session. Any cloths used for wiping or washing down surfaces must be boiled in hot soapy water, rinsed and dried.

Self assessment questions

Cleaning operations
1 What important points are essential to good commercial kitchen planning?
2 Make a list of suitable materials for the following surfaces in a commercial kitchen (state briefly the reason for your choice):
   (a) floors,
   (b) walls,
   (c) food preparation surfaces,
   (d) ceilings.
3 Why is it necessary to have cleaning schedules, and how may these best be carried out?

4 Plan the layout of a kitchen using the principles of work flow and siting of equipment in relation to the services. Take into account the hygiene and cleaning required for the equipment.
5 What precautions must be observed when washing glasses behind the bar or in bar service?
6 What are the three methods of cleaning silver? Write short notes on each method.

The Health and Safety at Work Act 1974

The philosophy of the HASAWA, introduced in 1979, was that all employers and proprietors should within reason, provide for their employees a safe, healthy and pleasant working environment. The Act also covers contractors, delivery staff and the general public.

As the hotel and catering industry is a service industry it relies on the public for its income and therefore their safety must be high on the employers list of priorities. This section has been included to reinforce the importance of safety, hygiene and the Food Hygiene Regulations of 1970 as applied to the catering industry.

The Act imposes duties on everyone concerned with work: employers, employees, the general public and those in charge of premises. The duties are expressed in general terms so that they apply to all types of situations and work activity. They are comprehensive and designed to encourage employers and employees to take a wide view of their roles and responsibilities. Failure to comply with the requirements under the Act may lead to legal proceedings. Magistrates have the power to impose fines of up to £2000 under the Act.

Duties of the employer
These duties apply to all employers, even those who have certain duties under other legislation, such as the Factories Act or Offices and Shops Act.

The following duties are preceded by the clause 'The employer must so far as is practicable'
1 Provide machinery, equipment and other plant that is safe and without risk to health, and must maintain them in a safe working condition.
2 Ensure that working systems are safe and without risk to health by
   systematic organisation of work.
   correct layout of workplace.
   laying down safe work schedules.
   specifying precautions required before carrying out certain tasks, e.g. machinery correctly assembled, correct operating procedure.
3 That the health and safety of employees are not at risk when handling dangerous materials or in storage or transportation.
4 Provide for all employees the information, training and supervision necessary to ensure their health and safety at work. Information must include

   hazards of workplace and how to avoid them, e.g. slippery stairs during certain weather conditions;

spillage of liquids or grease on floors;

notices for machinery and operating instructions.

This information may include statutory notices, copies of the Act, Regulations and Codes of Practice.

Training may include safety instructions and emergency procedures, e.g.

regular servicing of machinery.

fire drill.

first aid.

special training for tasks involving a high degree of risk.

re-training when new machinery requires the introduction of safety procedures.

Managers and supervisors must be made fully aware of their responsibilities, and have sufficient knowledge and skills to carry them out. Training is necessary for managers and supervisors to

5 Ensure that any place under their control where their employees work is kept in a safe condition. This includes buildings, open-air sites, tents and temporary structures. These are widely used by private caterers.

All entrances and exits are safe and without risk to health. Floor surfaces and coverings are in good repair, stairs and passages are well lit.

6 Ensure the health and safety of employees' working environment, e.g. lighting, heating, ventilation and noise, washing facilities, toilets, changing areas and lockers.

The employers must, under the Act, prepare a written statement of their safety policy. Employers with less than five employees are exempt from this duty. The policy statement must set out the aims and objectives of the employer for improving the health and safety of his or her employees. It will list those responsible for specific areas, e.g. restaurant manager, chef de cuisine and housekeeper.

The written policy statement increases the awareness of safety arrangements. Therefore it must be brought to the attention of all staff.

It should be noted that persons in control of hotels, restaurants and clubs are duty bound to provide adequate fire protection and precautions, including escape routes (The Fire Precautions Act 1971).

Duties of employees

All employees must take reasonable care for the health and safety of themselves, their colleagues or anyone else who may be affected by what they do, or fail to do, at work. This implies not only avoiding silly or careless behaviour, but also taking positive steps to understand the hazards of the workplace. They must ensure that:

their actions do not put others at risk, e.g. wiping up spillage on floors immediately.

all floors and gangways are kept free of obstruction.

machinery is reassembled and tested before leaving it.

they do not run in areas where machinery or equipment is in use.

231

knives are carried correctly.
colleagues are aware of temporary hazards, e.g. flour indicating that saucepan handles are hot.

The employee must co-operate with the employer to enable the duties to be carried out. All defects which may affect the safety of others must be reported to the person responsible. Examples of defects are:

broken power socket.
frayed flex on a vacuum cleaner.
loose floor tiles.
broken window catch.
broken light bulbs in dark areas.

Duties of all people
A duty imposed on all people by the Act is not to intentionally interfere with or misuse anything that has been provided in the interests of health and safety, or welfare of others. Provisions include:

fire-fighting equipment.
escape route and warning notices.
protective clothing.
guards for machinery.
special containers for dangerous substances, e.g. cleaning chemicals.

The various points outlined in the Act have been covered in detail elsewhere in the book—please refer to the sections on storeroom management (pp. 60–69); food hygiene (pp. 202–213) and kitchen planning and cleaning operations (pp. 221–230).

Self Assessment Questions
1   Why is the Health and Safety at Work Act important? List some of the duties of the employer. How can the employee help the employer carry out these duties?

Part B

Cleaning materials—soaps, detergents (neutral, anionic, non-ionic, cationic, acid and alkaline). Abrasive cleaners. Sanitisers. Washing-up — hand and machine-washing methods. Pest control—rodents, flies. Multiple-choice questions.

Cleaning materials

The largest maintenance task in hotels is floor cleaning, since most of the dirt which enters any building comes in on the users' footwear. Loose dirt is easily removed by vacuum cleaning and washing. Kitchen cleaning is more difficult since it involves the removal of baked-on grease. Removal of greasy deposits requires the assistance of detergents.

Detergents
The term can be applied to any substance which will remove grease. Detergents can be soapy or non-soapy (synthetic detergents).

Soaps
Soaps are produced by boiling animal fats or plant oils with strongly alkaline substances such as caustic soda or potash. They play only a minor role in modern cleaning operations as they are uneconomical and inefficient cleansers when used in hard-water districts. Soaps react with calcium and magnesium salts in hard water to form a scum which dulls fibres and makes floors slippery. Their chief use is in personal washing, though they are still the basis of some laundry powders.

The non-soapy detergents can be divided into classes, mainly by their pH.

'Neutral detergents'
These are neutral only in the sense of being neither highly alkaline nor highly acid. They form the basis of washing-up liquids and some specialised detergents. They have two valuable qualities:

1 they lower the surface tension of water and
2 they emulsify greases.

Water on its own is a poor cleansing agent as it makes little contact with the surface to be cleaned. If water is dropped onto a greasy surface it forms spherical drops. If a little detergent is added the drops flatten and make good contact with the surface to be cleaned (see Fig. 9.5). The surface tension has been lowered. The ability of a neutral detergent to lower surface tension is due to the molecules having two different ends. The head end is attracted to water (hydrophilic) and the tail is repelled by water (hydrophobic).

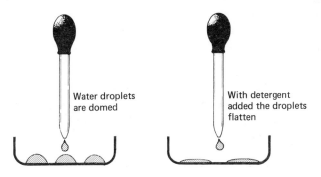

Fig. 9.5   Adding detergent to water drops

The high surface tension of water is due to the attraction of water molecules to each other. In the centre of a drop of water the forces of attrac-

233

tion are in all directions, while in the surface layer all the force is directed inwards. This leads the droplets to take up a spherical shape. When a detergent is added to water the head ends of the molecules insert themselves into the surface layer and break the surface tension. Neutral detergents are often called surfactants because they have this property of lowering surface tension. When oil and water are shaken together a milky suspension is produced temporarily, but this very quickly separates as more and more drops coalesce. If a little detergent is added the oil and water do not separate, but form an emulsion (see Chapter 4, Salad creams). The oil is suspended in the form of minute droplets, each surrounded by a monolayer of detergent molecules which prevents the emulsion from breaking up (see Fig. 9.6).

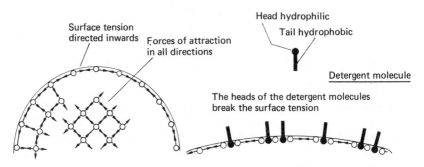

Fig. 9.6 Surface tension

Neutral detergents therefore have two essential properties which assist cleaning: emulsification of grease and the reduction of surface tension.

Neutral detergents can be divided into four groups according to the charge carried in the head end of the detergent particles.

Anionic detergents

Anionic detergents carry a negative charge when in solution. Their pH is between 7 and 9. Their main use is in washing-up liquids and as part of the surfactant system in washing powders. They have good wetting properties, but tend to produce a lot of foam.

Their low price, mild pH and negative charge makes them suitable for hand-washing of glass, crockery and steel surfaces. They can be used on floors for removal of emulsion waxes, but their foam makes rinsing laborious.

Non-ionic detergents

Non-ionic detergents do not ionise, so do not carry a charge on their molecules. They are neutral in pH. Non-ionics have good emulsifying power, yet produce little foam. They can be mixed with other detergents to form part of the surfactant system in washing powders.

They are more expensive than anionic detergents, but their low foaming property makes them suitable for use in floor-cleaning machines.

234

Cationic detergents

Cationic detergents carry a positive charge. Their pH is acidic. They possess both detergent and disinfectant properties (see under 'Disinfectants', below). Cationics are particularly useful for washing plastic tumblers, which cloud when washed in anionic detergents. They have antistatic properties, so are used in fabric conditioners.

Note: Cationic and anionic preparations should not be mixed, as they form a scum and deactivate each other.

Amphoteric detergents

Amphoteric detergents are speciality detergents, which behave differently according to the pH of their surroundings:

Acid ——————— Neutral ——————— Alkaline

Cationic   Non-ionic   Anionic

Amphoterics are used in some oven cleaners and medicated liquid 'soaps'.

Acid detergents

The main use for strongly acid detergents is to remove the limescale which encrusts lavatory basins in hard-water districts. The powders used for this purpose contain the acid salts sodium persulphate and sodium bisulphate. They should be handled with care and kept away from the skin or eyes.

Note: Other products which are used to bleach and disinfect lavatories contain sodium hypochlorite. These bleaches must not be mixed with acid preparations, as the two together form chlorine, a highly toxic gas.

Alkaline detergents

Alkaline detergents are highly alkaline substances (pH 9–12.5) which function by converting fats into soluble soaps.

Sodium hydroxide (NaOH, caustic soda) Sodium hydroxide is used to remove burnt-on grease from ovens. It is also employed in mechanical bottle-washing machines in dairies, as it is an effective disinfectant as well as a grease dispersant.

It should be handled with caution, as it is damaging to eyes and skin. Use goggles and heavy-duty gloves when oven-cleaning. Avoid using sodium hydroxide on aluminium or galvanised surfaces containing zinc, as it is highly corrosive to these metals.

Drain-cleaners contain sodium hydroxide, together with aluminium filings. When water is added the reaction between the ingredients produces heat melting the blocking fat which is then saponified and washed away.

Sodium carbonate ($Na_2CO_3.10H_2O$, washing soda) Washing soda is used to soften hard water and to remove grease, floor wax and carbon heel marks. The floor should be neutralised afterwards by adding a little vinegar to the rinsing water. Do not use on linoleum, as it removes the linseed oil and changes the colour in some cases.

Abrasive cleaners
Abrasive cleaners may be in the form of powders, pastes or liquids. They contain the following ingredients.

1 An abrasive to rub off the dirt. The substance used varies according to the purpose of the preparation, from very gritty (such as powdered pumice) to smooth (such as china clay).
2 A detergent to emulsify grease. This is usually an anionic surfactant, either soap or synthetic detergent.
3 A water softener and dirt dispersant. Sodium carbonate or sodium phosphate are commonly used.
4 Some liquid products contain ammonium hydroxide, supposedly added to assist grease removal. The strong smell encourages users to think the product is 'powerful'.
5 A hypochlorite bleach is often included, with a dye to demonstrate the efficiency of action. The purpose is to remove stains and to disinfect.

Note: Abrasive cleaners never contain both bleach and ammonium hydroxide because the mixture could produce chloramines, which are irritant gases.

Sanitizers, sterilants and disinfectants
The aim of cleaning operations in the kitchen is to sanitize. This American word means to reduce the number of microorganisms to an acceptable level. Heat is the best sanitizer in kitchens. If hot water containing detergents is applied vigorously in generous quantities to food-contact surfaces there is rarely any need for chemical disinfectants. Heat, particularly moist heat, is effective and leaves no dangerous residues.

A number of terms are used in connection with disinfection, many in common use are employed inaccurately. Some of these terms are defined below:

Sterilisation. This should mean the removal or destruction of all living organisms on the surface or in the food. This rarely occurs in the kitchen: food surfaces are sanitized not sterilised. The only cooking processes capable of sterilising are high temperature methods such as pressure cooking or roasting, and even these may not be taken to that point if the quality of the food would be affected thereby.

Sterilant. This term is applied to liquids which are powerful disinfectants and will sterilise if used precisely as instructed. An example is the use of sodium hypochlorite solution on clean milk bottles.

Disinfectant. A substance which, if used as directed, will kill vegetative pathogenic organisms (not guaranteed to kill spores).

Germicide. A term meaning the same as disinfectant.

Bacteriocide. A substance which kills bacteria.

Bacteriostat. A substance which prevents the multiplication of bacteria but does not necessarily kill them.

Antiseptic. A substance which kills pathogenic microbes when diluted as directed and is safe to use on living tissue.

236

If disinfectants are used in the kitchen they must be selected with care. Many disinfectants which are satisfactory in hospital wards are unsuitable for use on food-contact surfaces.

No disinfectant is ideal, but the following properties are appropriate in a food-contact disinfectant.

1 It should have a wide range of activity. Caterers do not know which bacteria, viruses or fungi may be present, so a disinfectant which is active against most microbes is needed.

2 It must be efficient in the presence of organic material. Many disinfectants are seriously inactivated by blood, egg or other organic substances.

3 It must be soluble in all proportions. Disinfectants must be used at the prescribed dilution to be effective. Too great a concentration is wasteful, and may be injurious to surfaces or the user's hands. Too low a concentration would be ineffective.

4 It must be stable over a range of temperatures. If used in the kitchen it will need to be applied hot; if diluted and used as an antiseptic it must work at a lower temperature.

5 It must not be toxic to the operator. Since human tissue is very similar to microbial tissue, many disinfectants are damaging to the skin, at least in the concentrated form.

6 It should be non-caustic and non-corrosive. Many disinfectants are unsuitable for certain surfaces since they may damage them.

7 It should not inactivated by hard water. Many waters in this country are hard. The presence of calcium or magnesium ions, or the alkaline pH of these waters, may make some disinfectants inactive.

8 Disinfectants to be used near food must not affect the colour, odour or flavour of the commodity. Many excellent disinfectants are ruled out by this requirement because they leave a strong taste or smell on surfaces or containers.

9 A disinfectant which is in daily use must be inexpensive.

Obviously, no one sanitizer will possess all of these properties. Some of those most commonly used in the food industry are described below:

Sodium hypochlorite solutions
(Examples: 'bleach', Milton, Domestos.)

Sodium hypochlorite solutions are suitable for sanitizing food preparation surfaces.

Advantages. These are powerful oxidising agents, killing viruses as well as bacteria. They are cheaper than other agents of equal activity. Their odour disappears quickly, so does not taint food.

Disadvantages. They are poor wetting agents, so should be used after application of an anionic detergent. Organic matter inactivates hypochlorites, so surfaces must be clean when they are used. Bleaches need careful use: wear rubber gloves and use goggles to protect the eyes. Keep away from metals, as they cause corrosion.

237

Quaternary ammonium compounds
(Examples: Task, Cetavlon, Savlon.)

Q.A.C.s — as they are often called — are produced by reacting fatty substances with ammonia. They are cationic detergents which also possess disinfectant properties.

Advantages. These are odourless and colourless. Q.A.C.s are stable to heat. They are non-toxic to the user. They are suitable for use on plastic and steel surfaces.

Disadvantages. They are not effective in killing bacterial spores. Their activity is reduced by organic matter. They are expensive compared with hypochlorites.

Iodophors
(Examples: Betadine, Pevadine.)

Iodophors are soluble complexes between iodine and detergents.

Advantages. These are a rapid-acting group of disinfectants with a wide range of activity.

Disadvantages. They are expensive, and can corrode metals.

From the above examples you can see there are no ideal disinfectants, though several disinfectants have sufficient number of the required qualities to be useful in the food industry.

Washing up

Washing up is an unpopular and poorly paid job. It is often given to the least trained personnel, on the assumption that anyone can wash up. Yet it is essential to the smooth running of the kitchen and restaurant. Shining china, glassware and cutlery are indications of the general standard of care and hygiene in the parts of the establishment that the diner cannot see.

The aims of washing up are:

1 to remove food particles and grease,
2 to sanitize and
3 to leave items spotless and dry.

These aims can be achieved by hand-washing or washing by machine. The choice of method will depend on the turnover and labour costs of the establishment.

Hand-washing methods

Two-sink method
The first sink is used to prepare and then wash the dishes. The second is the hot rinsing sink.

1 The dishes are scraped or wiped with paper to remove food debris.
2 The dishes are washed in hot water and detergent.
3 The crockery and cutlery is placed in racks and lowered into hot water

for at least 1 minute to sanitize. This sink should have water at 77–82°C. A thermometer should be available for checking the temperature.

4 The washed and rinsed articles are lifted out and left in racks. They should dry very quickly without needing further treatment.

Three-sink method
In this method the first sink is used to prepare the articles, the second to wash and the third to rinse and sanitize.

A modification of the two-sink method is used in some establishments. The hot water runs continuously through the rinsing sink to the washing sink, and then away. This prevents food scraps from collecting in the water.

Dishwashing machines
These vary in size, complexity of operations and degree of automation.

For all machines, food debris should be removed by scraping or foot-operated spray before stacking the articles to wash. Where simpler machines without a pre-wash rinse are used this should be done before stacking.

The dishes are carried through the machines in racks on movable belts. They are sprayed with water at 50–60°C containing specially formulated detergents. These may be hand- or automatically dispensed.

The rinse water comes straight from the mains and is maintained between 66°C and 82°C. It is recirculated to the wash tub, the overflow running away to the drains.

Machine-washing detergents
The special detergents for dishwashing machines should be handled with care, as they are highly poisonous in the concentrated form. They depend largely on alkaline detergents to emulsify grease, and usually contain a chlorine-releasing salt to remove tea stains. The salt will gradually attack plastics and aluminium-ware. Some machines use a rinsing agent containing a low-foaming detergent and an alcohol to effect the final removal of fatty materials.

The hygienic quality of machine-washing depends on good maintenance and the temperature of the final rinsing water. If a high temperature, 80°C or above, is used the articles are delivered hot, and dry quickly to a high hygienic standard.

Handling after washing
Some simple experiments carried out by Thanet Technical College students showed the hygienic standard of crockery immediately after washing by machine and hand-washing to be very similar, providing the articles washed by hand had not been cloth-dried. However, application of carbon powder showed finger marks on the crockery. Some of the prints were on the centre of plates and rims of cups, where contamination of food and drink could occur. This emphasises the need mentioned earlier to take care in handling clean crockery, glassware and cutlery.

Pest control

Food premises provide ideal conditions for a number of animals which compete with man for food. Some are important, as we saw in Chapter 3, from an economic point of view as they damage stored foods. Others are health hazards because they harbour diseases which can be passed on to man. Rodents and flies are the most common carriers of infection in hotels and restaurants.

Rodents

Rats
The Brown rat (*Rattus norvegicus*) is common throughout the British Isles. Black rats (*Rattus rattus*) were once restricted to ports, but they have spread throughout most large towns. Both types of rat are attracted to food premises as a source of food, warmth and sites to nest. They are very agile, climbing, burrowing and even swimming to find entrances into buildings. They breed rapidly, producing up to eight litters of around a dozen young each year. Apart from the danger to health, their gnawing can cause considerable damage to buildings. Their incisor teeth grow throughout life, allowing them to gnaw through woodwork, electric cables and water pipes without damage to themselves. If their presence is not detected in time, their activities may result in fires from exposed cables, or floods from damaged pipes.

The House mouse (Mus musculus)
The House mouse is common wherever there is warmth and shelter. As it is much smaller than the rat, it is even more difficult to exclude from buildings. It can gain entrance through very small cracks, under wooden doors, in the spaces around pipes and through damaged ventilators.

Diseases carried by rodents
Rodents carry food-poisoning bacteria (Salmonellae and *Clostridium welchii*), a jaundice known as Weil's disease, and trichinosis (nematode worm infection). These disease organisms may be passed to foods by the rodent's faeces or urine.

Signs of infestation
There a number of signs which should alert caterers to the presence of rodents in their premises:
1 Damaged packets and sacks of food materials.
2 Gnawed holes in woodwork.
3 Spindle-shaped droppings.
4 Footprints in spilled flour or other foods.
5 Hairs and greasy marks from the rodents' coats.
6 Their characteristic smell.

Rodent control
Keeping rodents out of food premises is largely a matter of vigilance and

good housekeeping (see Chapter 3).

Access of rodents to food may be prevented by:

1 Storing foods in containers with tightly fitting lids, and sweeping up spillage immediately.
2 Storing edible rubbish in bins which are emptied regularly, and keeping yards clean.

Access into buildings may be prevented by paying attention to the following points.

Rodents frequently find entry to buildings via the sewers and drains, so:

1 Sewers and drains should be checked regularly for breaks and to see that the water seals are intact and
2 Pipes should be protected inside by wire balloons and externally by metal collars.

Rodents gnaw their way into buildings, so:

1 Protect wooden doors by fitting metal kick-plates and
2 Seal cracks.

Large catering firms will employ specialist firms to make regular checks on their premises to control rodents. As even well-maintained buildings will attract rodents occasionally, these operators will use poisoned baits to eliminate the rats and mice they have detected.

Warfarin is a material which has been extensively used in rodent control. Unfortunately, some populations of rats have become immune to its action. A number of alternative rodenticides have been developed. Rodent control is a matter for constant research and expert knowledge, but all caterers can assist by maintaining good standards of cleanliness and building maintenance.

Housefly (Musca domestica) and Blowfly (Calliophora vomitoria)

Flies are the other major disease carriers in kitchens and storerooms. Adult flies have hairy bodies and sticky legs which can transfer food-poisoning and other pathogenic organisms to foods. They also carry the organisms in their intestines, so their faeces may transfer these organisms onto any surface where they settle. However, it is their method of feeding which makes them so dangerous in food premises.

Flies can only take in liquid food. When feeding, a fly presses its sucking tube (proboscis) against the surface of the food. It then passes saliva onto the meal and pumps the predigested nutrients up into the crop. Often the previous meal is regurgitated with the saliva. This means a fly may feed in a dustbin or on a manure heap and then on a food in the kitchen! This unpleasant thought should make caterers careful to keep flies away from their handiwork.

Prevention
Flies lay their eggs in warm places such as rubbish heaps and compost. This

sort of material should be removed from around food premises. Clean yards and well-maintained swill bins will reduce the breeding areas for flies.

Kitchen and storeroom windows can be fitted with gauze to exclude flies.

Control within premises

There are many insecticides which are effective against flies, but relatively few are safe to use near food. Those based on pyrethrum, an extract from a member of the daisy family, are the safest to use on food premises. The method used most commonly in shops and foodstores is the insecticutor. This is a device which attracts the flies by means of an ultraviolet lamp and then kills them electrically. The lamp should be positioned so that staff are not irradiated, and the dead flies should be removed regularly.

Multiple-choice questions

Cleaning materials and practices

1   The high-foaming detergents used for hand-washing of crockery are:
    (a) cationic
    (b) anionic
    (c) amphoteric
    (d) non-ionic
2   The surfactant system in many washing powders consists of an anionic detergent mixed with:
    (a) a cationic detergent
    (b) a non-ionic detergent
    (c) an alkaline detergent
    (d) an amphoteric detergent
3   A detergent suitable for sanitizing plastic tumblers is:
    (a) non-ionic
    (b) cationic
    (c) alkaline
    (d) amphoteric
4   The most appropriate neutral detergent for floor-washing machines is:
    (a) acidic
    (b) non-ionic
    (c) cationic
    (d) anionic
5   Detergents which change their electric charge and properties according to the pH of their surroundings are:
    (a) non-ionic
    (b) acidic
    (c) amphoteric
    (d) anionic
6   Acid lavatory preparations must not be mixed with:
    (a) water
    (b) blue dyes

(c) hypochlorite bleaches

(d) peroxide bleaches

7 The type of detergent employed in fabric conditioners is:

(a) cationic

(b) non-ionic

(c) amphoteric

(d) anionic

8 The best type of sanitizer in the kitchen is:

(a) an antiseptic solution

(b) a cationic detergent

(c) hot water and an anionic detergent

(d) carbolic solution

9 The most germ-free crockery will be obtained by finishing by:

(a) drying with a clean cloth

(b) drying with a disposable paper towel

(c) air-drying after rinsing at 80°C

(d) air-drying after hand-rinsing

10 A sanitizer which would be suitable for steel surfaces is:

(a) hypochlorite bleach

(b) iodophor

(c) an acid detergent

(d) a Q.A.C.

Appendix

This Appendix consists of the following items.

Tables
   A1. Composition of foods — approximate values.
   A2. Average portions of foods.
   A3. Portions of foods obtained from specific quantities
   A4. Common can sizes
   A5. Recommended daily amounts of nutrients for population groups.
Glossary

Table A1   The composition of foods (approximate values per 100 g). In no case is the deviation from *The Composition of Foods* (H.M.S.O., 1978) greater than 10%.

Table published by courtesy of Robert Knight.

* Abbreviations used in column headings:
   Thi   thiamine (= vitamin B_1),
   Rib   riboflavin (= vitamin B_2),
   Nic   nicotinic acid equivalents,
   Asc   ascorbic acid (= vitamin C),
   Ret   retinol equivalents (= vitamin A),
   Chol cholecalciferol (= vitamin D).

[a] Summer values are given; in winter ret = 35 chol = 0.01.
[b] asc falls in storage.
[c] Feb. asc = 25, May asc = 14, Aug. asc = 20, Nov. asc = 22.
[d] Values are given for fortified products: without fortification thi = 0.04, rib = 0.1 and nic = 0.8.
[4] Between 90% and 100% of rib and nic are extracted into an infusion.

Categories of food in the table

Food	Code numbers	Food	Code numbers
Milk	1–9	Vegetables	53–84
Cheese	10, 11	Fruit	85–108
Meat	12–33	Nuts	109–111
Fish	34–40	Cereals	112–127
Eggs	41	Beverages	129–135
Fats	42–46	Alcoholic beverages	136–138
Preserves, etc.	47–52	Puddings, cakes, etc.	139–150

Table A1 The composition of foods (approximate values per 100 g)

		Protein (g)	Fat (g)	Energy (kcal)	Iron (mg)	Calcium (mg)	Thi* (mg)	Rib* (mg)	Nic* (mg)	Asc* (mg)	Ret* (µg)	Chol* (µg)
1.	Cream, double	1.8	48	450	0	70	0.02	0.08	0.4	0	400	0.3
2.	Cream, single	3	18	190	0.1	100	0.03	0.13	0.8	0	160	0.1
3.	Milk, liquid, whole	3.5	4	70	0.1	120	0.04	0.15	0.9	1	44[a]	0.05[a]
4.	Milk, condensed	8	9	300	0.2	290	0.10	0.4	2	3	110	0.09
5.	Milk, evaporated	9	9	170	0.2	290	0.06	0.4	2	2	110	3
6.	National dried milk	30	25	500	7	900	0.3	1.3	7	60	350	13
7.	Milk, dried, skimmed	35	0.9	350	0.5	1300	0.3	1.7	10	10	4	0
8.	Yoghurt, low-fat, natural	5	1	50	0.1	180	0.05	0.25	1.3	0	10	0.02
9.	Yoghurt, low-fat, fruit	5	1	100	0.2	160	0.05	0.22	1.2	1	10	0.02
10.	Cheese, Cheddar	25	35	400	0.6	800	0.04	0.5	5	0	400	0.35
11.	Cheese, cottage	15	4	110	0.4	80	0.03	0.3	3	0	25	0.02
12.	Bacon, rashers, raw	14	40	400	1.0	7	0.4	0.14	6	0	0	0
13.	Bacon, rashers, cooked	25	40	450	1.4	12	0.4	0.19	9	0	0	0
14.	Beef, average	18	17	225	1.9	7	0.06	0.19	8	0	0	0
15.	Beef, corned	25	12	225	3	14	0.01	0.22	9	0	0	0
16.	Beef, stewing, raw	20	11	180	2.2	8	0.06	0.22	9	0	0	0
17.	Beef, stewing, cooked	30	11	225	3	15	0.03	0.3	10	0	0	0
18.	Black pudding	13	22	300	20	35	0.9	0.07	4	0	0	0
19.	Chicken, raw	20	7	140	1.5	11	0.04	0.17	10	0	0	0
20.	Chicken, roast	25	5	150	0.8	9	0.08	0.19	13	0	0	0
21.	Ham, cooked	25	19	250	1.3	9	0.4	0.15	8	0	0	0
22.	Kidney, average	16	2.5	90	6	9	0.4	1.9	11	12	300	0
23.	Lamb, average, raw	16	30	350	1.3	7	0.09	0.19	7	0	0	0
24.	Lamb, roast	22	22	300	2.2	9	0.10	0.25	9	0	0	0
25.	Liver, average, raw	20	8	160	11	6	0.25	3.1	18	30	6000	0.75
26.	Liver, fried	25	14	250	9	14	0.25	4.5	20	20	6000	0.8
27.	Luncheon meat	13	27	300	1	15	0.07	0.12	4.5	0	0	0
28.	Pork, average	16	30	350	0.8	8	0.6	0.16	7	0	0	0
29.	Pork chop, grilled	30	25	350	1.2	8	0.7	0.2	11	0	0	0
30.	Sausage, pork	11	32	350	1.1	40	0.04	0.12	6	0	0	0
31.	Sausage, beef	10	24	300	1.4	50	0.03	0.13	7	0	0	0

Table A1 *contd.* The composition of foods (approximate values per 100 g)

	Protein (g)	Fat (g)	Energy (kcal)	Iron (mg)	Calcium (mg)	Thi* (mg)	Rib* (mg)	Nic* (mg)	Asc* (mg)	Ret* (µg)	Chol* (µg)
32. Steak and kidney pie, cooked	13	21	300	5	35	0.11	0.45	6	0	130	0.6
33. Tripe	9	2.5	60	0.5	80	0	0.01	2.2	0	10	0
34. Cod, white fish	17	0.7	80	0.3	16	0.08	0.07	5	0	0	0
35. Cod, fried in batter	20	10	200	0.5	80	0.04	0.1	7	0	0	0
36. Fish fingers	13	8	180	0.7	45	0.09	0.06	3	0	0	0
37. Herring	17	19	225	0.8	35	0	0.18	7	0	45	22
38. Kipper	20	12	180	1.2	60	0.02	0.3	7	0	45	22
39. Salmon, canned	20	8	150	1.4	90	0.04	0.18	11	0	90	13
40. Sardines, canned in oil	25	14	225	3.0	600	0.04	0.35	12	0	30	8
41. Eggs, fresh	12	11	150	2.2	50	0.09	0.45	3.5	0	140	1.5
42. Butter	0.5	81	700	0.2	15	0	0	0.1	0	1000	1.3
43. Lard, dripping	0	100	900	0	0	0	0	0	0	0	0
44. Low-fat spread	0	40	350	0	0	0	0	0	0	900	8
45. Margarine	0.2	80	700	0.3	4	0	0	0.1	0	900	8
46. Oils, cooking and salad	0	100	900	0	0	0	0	0	0	0	0
47. Chocolate, milk	9	40	600	1.7	250	0.03	0.35	2.5	0	7	0
48. Honey	0.4	0	300	0.4	5	0	0.05	0.2	0	0	0
49. Jam	0.5	0	250	1.2	18	0	0	0	10	2	0
50. Marmalade	0.1	0	250	0.6	35	0	0	0	10	8	0
51. Sugar, white	0	0	400	0	1	0	0	0	0	0	0
52. Syrup	0.3	0	300	1.4	25	0	0	0	0	0	0
53. Beans, canned in tomato sauce	5	0.4	60	1.4	45	0.07	0.05	1.4	3	50	0
54. Beans, broad	7	0.5	70	1.1	30	0.3	0.05	5	30	22	0
55. Beans, haricot	22	0	250	7	180	0.45	0.13	6	0	0	0
56. Beans, runner	2.2	0	22	0.8	25	0.05	0.10	1.4	20	50	0
57. Beetroot, boiled	1.8	0	45	0.7	30	0.02	0.04	0.4	5	0	0
58. Brussels sprouts, raw	4	0	25	0.7	30	0.1	0.16	1.5	90	70	0
59. Brussels sprouts, boiled	3	0	17	0.5	25	0.06	0.10	1	40	70	0
60. Cabbage, green, raw	3	0	22	0.6	60	0.06	0.05	0.7	50	50	0
61. Cabbage, green, boiled	1.7	0	15	0.4	40	0.03	0.03	0.5	22	50	0
62. Carrots, old	0.7	0	22	0.6	50	0.06	0.05	0.7	6	2000	0

63. Cauliflower	1.9	0	13	0.5	22	0.1	0.1	1	60	5	0
64. Celery	0.9	0	8	0.6	50	0.03	0.03	0.5	7	0	0
65. Crisps, potato	6	35	500	2.2	35	0.19	0.07	6	17	0	0
66. Cucumber	0.6	0	9	0.3	22	0.04	0.04	0.3	8	0	0
67. Lentils, dry	25	0	300	8	40	0.5	0.25	6	0	6	0
68. Lettuce	1	0	8	0.9	22	0.07	0.08	0.4	15	170	0
69. Mushrooms	1.8	0	7	1	3	0.1	0.4	4.5	3	0	0
70. Onions	0.9	0	22	0.3	30	0.03	0.05	0.4	10	0	0
71. Parsnips	1.7	0	50	0.6	60	0.1	0.09	1.3	15	0	0
72. Peas, fresh or frozen, raw	6	0	60	1.9	15	0.3	0.15	3.5	25	50	0
73. Peas, fresh or frozen boiled	5	0	50	1.2	13	0.25	0.11	2.2	15	50	0
74. Peas, canned, processed	6	0	80	1.5	25	0.1	0.04	1.4	0	70	0
75. Peppers, green	0.9	0.2	14	0.4	9	0.08	0.03	0.9	90	40	0
76. Potatoes, raw	2.2	0	80	0.7	8	0.11	0.04	1.8	8–30[b]	0	0
77. Potatoes, boiled	1.4	0	80	0.5	4	0.08	0.03	1.2	4–15[b]	0	0
78. Potato chips, fried	4	9	225	1.4	14	0.1	0.04	2.2	6–20[b]	0	0
79. Potatoes, roast	3	1	110	1	10	0.1	0.04	2	6–23[b]	0	0
80. Spinach	2.5	0	22	3	70	0.12	0.2	1.3	60	1000	0
81. Sweet corn, canned	3	0.8	80	0.1	3	0.05	0.08	0.3	4	35	0
82. Tomatoes, fresh	0.8	0	12	0.4	13	0.06	0.04	0.7	14–27[c]	120	0
83. Turnips	0.8	0	18	0.4	60	0.04	0.05	0.8	25	0	0
84. Watercress	3	0	14	1.6	225	0.1	0.16	2	60	500	0
85. Apples	0.3	0	45	0.3	4	0.04	0.02	0.1	5	5	0
86. Apricots, canned (including syrup)	0.5	0	110	0.7	12	0.02	0.01	0.3	5	170	0
87. Apricots, dried	5	0	180	4	90	0	0.2	3.5	0	600	0
88. Bananas	1.1	0	80	0.4	7	0.04	0.07	0.8	10	35	0
89. Blackcurrants	0.9	0	30	1.3	60	0.03	0.06	0.3	200	35	0
90. Cherries	0.6	0	45	0.4	18	0.05	0.06	0.4	5	20	0
91. Dates, dried	2	0	250	1.6	70	0.07	0.04	2.2	0	10	0
92. Figs, dried	3.5	0	210	4.2	280	0.1	0.13	2.2	8	8	0
93. Gooseberries	0.9	0	25	0.4	22	0.04	0.03	0.4	40	30	0
94. Grapefruit	0.6	0	22	0.3	17	0.05	0.02	0.3	40	0	0
95. Lemons	0.3	0	7	0.1	8	0.02	0	0.1	50	0	0
96. Melon	0.8	0	22	0.4	16	0.05	0.03	0.5	25	160	0
97. Oranges	0.8	0	35	0.3	40	0.1	0.03	0.3	50	8	0
98. Orange juice, canned, unconcentrated	0.8	0	50	0.4	10	0.07	0.02	0.2	40	8	0

Table A1 *contd.* The composition of foods (approximate values per 100 g)

	Protein (g)	Fat (g)	Energy (kcal)	Iron (mg)	Calcium (mg)	Thi* (mg)	Rib* (mg)	Nic* (mg)	Asc* (mg)	Ret* (µg)	Chol* (µg)
99. Peaches, fresh	0.6	0	35	0.4	5	0.02	0.05	1.1	8	80	0
100. Peaches, canned (including syrup)	0.4	0	90	1.9	4	0.01	0.02	0.6	4	40	0
101. Pears, fresh	0.3	0	40	0.2	8	0.03	0.03	0.3	3	2	0
102. Pineapple, canned (including syrup)	0.3	0	80	1.7	13	0.05	0.02	0.3	8	7	0
103. Plums	0.6	0	30	0.3	12	0.05	0.03	0.6	3	35	0
104. Prunes, dried	2.5	0	160	3	40	0.1	0.2	1.7	0	160	0
105. Raspberries	0.9	0	25	1.2	40	0.02	0.03	0.5	25	13	0
106. Rhubarb	0.6	0	6	0.4	100	0.01	0.07	0.3	10	10	0
107. Strawberries	0.6	0	25	0.7	22	0.02	0.03	0.5	60	5	0
108. Sultanas	1.7	0	250	1.8	50	0.1	0.03	0.6	0	0	0
109. Almonds	20	50	600	4	250	0.3	0.25	5	0	0	0
110. Coconut, desiccated	7	60	600	4	22	0.06	0.04	1.8	0	0	0
111. Peanuts, roasted	30	50	600	2	60	0.22	0.1	20	0	0	0
112. Barley, pearl, dry	8	1.7	350	0.7	10	0.12	0.08	2.2	0	0	0
113. Biscuits, chocolate	7	25	500	1.5	130	0.11	0.04	1.9	0	0	0
114. Biscuits, cream crackers	8	16	450	2.2	150	0.22	0.05	2.3	0	0	0
115. Biscuits, plain, semi-sweet	7	13	450	1.8	130	0.17	0.06	2	0	0	0
116. Biscuits, rich, sweet	6	22	500	1.3	90	0.12	0.04	1.5	0	0	0
117. Bread, brown	9	1.4	225	2.5	90	0.3	0.07	2.5	0	0	0
118. Bread, starch reduced	11	1.5	225	1.3	100	0.18	0.03	2.5	0	0	0
119. Bread, white	8	1.7	250	1.7	100	0.18	0.03	2.5	0	0	0
120. Bread, wholemeal	10	3	250	3	30	0.25	0.09	1.9	0	0	0
121. Cornflakes	7	0.4	350	0.3	5	1.1d	1.4d	11d	0	0	0
122. Custard powder, cornflour	0.5	0.7	350	1.4	15	0	0	0.1	0	0	0
123. Crispbread, Ryvita	10	2.2	300	3	90	0.4	0.25	1.3	0	0	0
124. Flour, white	10	0.9	350	2.2	140	0.3	0.03	2.5	0	0	0
125. Oatmeal	12	9	400	4	60	0.5	0.1	3	0	0	0
126. Rice	6	1	350	0.4	4	0.08	0.03	1.5	0	0	0
127. Spaghetti	10	1	350	1.2	22	0.09	0.06	1.8	0	0	0
129. Chocolate, drinking	6	6	400	3	5	0.03	0.09	1.4	0	2	0
130. Cocoa powder	19	22	450	7	13	0.08	0.3	5	0	7	0

No.	Food											
131.	Coffee, ground	0	0	0	0	0	0	0.2e	10e	0	0	0
132.	Coffee, instant	4	7	160	4	140	0	0.1	45	0	0	0
133.	Cola drink	0	0	50	0	0	0	0	0	0	0	0
134.	Tea, dry	0	0	0	0	0	0	0.9e	6e	1	0	0
135.	Squash, fruit, undiluted	0.1	0.1	120	0.2	16	0	0.01	0	0	0	0
136.	Beer, bitter, draught	0	0	30	0	11	0	0.05	0.7	0	0	0
137.	Spirits, 70° proof	0	0	220	0	0	0	0	0	0	0	0
138.	Wine, red	3	14	70	0.8	6	0.01	0.02	0.2	2	2	0
139.	Apple pie	6	7	280	0.8	42	0.08	0.02	0.9	0	80	0.5
140.	Bread and butter pudding	8	9	150	0.7	110	0.06	0.22	1.6	0	25	0.25
141.	Buns, currant	3	4	330	1.6	90	0.15	0.1	2	0	35	0.03
142.	Custard	5	16	90	0.2	110	0.04	0.14	0.8	0	60	0.8
143.	Fruit cake, rich	3	14	370	1.6	70	0.07	0.07	1.2	0	0	0.8
144.	Jam tarts	6	24	390	1.3	50	0.05	0.01	0.8	0	80	1.2
145.	Plain cake, madeira	4	8	430	1.4	70	0.08	0.11	1.7	1	100	0.08
146.	Rice pudding	0.8	3	140	0.1	120	0.05	0.14	1	6	35	0
147.	Soup, tomato, canned	3	6	60	0.4	17	0.03	0.02	0.2	2	70	0.3
148.	Trifle	1.4	0	160	0.6	80	0.04	0.1	1.1	0	0	0
149.	Yeast extract			6	7	120	3	6	70			
150.	Ice cream, vanilla	4	11	190	0.3	140	0.05	0.2	1.1	1	1	0

Table A2 Average portions of food

Food	Average portion oz.	g*
Apple	4	100
Apple pudding	4	100
Bacon, gammon	2	50
Banana	4	100
Beans, baked	4	100
Beans, butter	2	50
Beans, French	2	50
Beef, lean only	4	100
Beetroot	2	50
Blancmange	2	50
Bread (3 slices)	3	75
Butter	1	25
Cabbage	4	100
Cake, cherry	2	50
Cakes	2	50
Carrots	2	50
Cauliflower	2	50
Cereal, breakfast	1	25
Cheese	1	25
Chicken, boiled or roast	4	100
Cod, fried	6	150
Egg	2	50
Fish cakes	4	100
Ham, boiled	4	100
Jelly	4	100
Kidney	4	100
Lettuce	2	50
Luncheon meat, canned	4	100
Margarine	1	25
Marrow, boiled	2	50
Milk (1 glass)	7	175
Mince-pie	2	50
Nuts, Brazil, Barcelona	2	50
Orange	4	100
Peas, fresh, boiled	2	50
Pineapple, canned in syrup	4	100
Plaice, fried	6	150
Plaice, steamed	6	150
Potatoes, boiled, chipped, roast	6	150
Salmon	4	100
Salmon, canned	6	150
Sardines, canned	1	25
Sausage roll	2	50
Sausages, fried	2	50
Spaghetti, macaroni	4	100
Sprouts	4	100
Stew, Irish	4	100
Suet pudding	4	100
Tomato, raw	2	50
Trifle	4	100

* For convenience 1 oz. is given an approximately equivalent to 25 g. For accuracy 1 oz. should be taken as equal to 28.4 g.

Table A3 Portions of foods obtained from specific quantities

Food	Portions	Quantity
Soups — Thick	5–6	1 litre
Vegetable	5–6	1 litre
Consommé	7	1 litre
Fish — On the bone	3	500 g
Off the bone	3–4	500 g
Trout	1	150 g
Herring	1	150 g
Mackerel	1	150 g
Sole	1	150–250 g
Lobster	1–2	500 g
Meat — On the bone	3	500 g
Off the bone	3–4	500 g
Offal	4–5	500 g
Poultry — Poussin	1	Per bird
Chicken	4	1.5 kg
Game — Grouse	1	Per bird
Quail	1	2 birds
Pheasant	3–4	Per bird
Partridge	1	1–2 birds
Wild duck	3	Per bird
Vegetables — Potatoes		
New	4	500 g
Old	2–3	500 g
Peeled	4	500 g
Peas — in pod	2–3	500 g
Cabbage	3–4	500 g
Spinach	2–3	500 g
Asparagus	4–5	500 g
Runner beans	4–5	500 g
French beans	4–6	500 g
Fruits — Dried	8	500 g
Stewing	4	500 g
Dessert	4–6	500 g
Frozen foods — Vegetables	6–8	500 g
Shellfish	3–4	500 g
Fish	Generally portion control	Cuts by weight
Meat	Generally portion control	Cuts by weight
Cheese	8–10	500 g
Smoked salmon	8–9	500 g
Pâté	8–9	500 g
Caviar	12–14	500 g

When catering for any number of people it is necessary to have an idea of how much food to order to prevent over- or under-purchasing. The quantities and portions may vary according to the requirements of the establishment, and the use, whether table d'hôte or à la carte. The portions quoted are for the average table d'hôte.

Table A4 Common can sizes

Common name	Approximate capacity (oz.)	(g)	Uses
4 oz.	4	100	Fish, shellfish, cream
8 oz. flat	7.5	220	Fruit, vegetables
A 1	12	340	Soups, vegetables
14 oz.	14	400	Vegetables, meats, fruit pie fillings
1 lb flat	16	470	Tongue, ham, meats, sweet puddings
A 2	20	560	Fruits, vegetables
A 2½	29	870	Fruits, vegetables
6 lb	6	2.72 kg	Vegetables, soups
A 10	6.10	3 kg	Vegetables, soups, fruits

It is difficult to estimate the portions obtained from canned foods because the drained weight varies with the canners. Some brands give a count of the number of pieces in the can, e.g. peach caps 8–10, brisling 16–18 fish, asparagus points 12–14. This count or number is a useful indication to the size of the contents.

When purchasing canned foods in quantity it is advisable to open two cans at random and examine the quality and quantity of the drained weight to see if there is a great difference in quantities of the cans.

The weights vary according to whether contents are solid packs, solids and liquids, or all liquids.

Table A5 Recommended daily amounts of nutrients for population groups (D.H.S.S., 1979)

Age ranges (years)	Energy (MJ)	(kcal)	Protein (g)	Calcium (mg)	Iron (mg)	Vitamin A (retinol equivalent) (µg)	Thiamin (mg)	Riboflavin (mg)	Nicotinic acid equivalent (mg)	Vitamin C (mg)	Vitamin D[1] (µg)
Boys											
Under 1	3.25	780	19	600	6	450	0.3	0.4	5	20	7.5
1	5.0	1200	30	600	7	300	0.5	0.6	7	20	10
2	5.75	1400	35	600	7	300	0.6	0.7	8	20	10
3–4	6.5	1560	39	600	8	300	0.6	0.8	9	20	10
5–6	7.25	1740	43	600	10	300	0.7	0.9	10	20	—
7–8	8.25	1980	49	600	10	400	0.8	1.0	11	20	—
9–11	9.5	2280	56	700	12	575	0.9	1.2	14	25	—
12–14	11.0	2640	66	700	12	725	1.1	1.4	16	25	—
15–17	12.0	2880	72	600	12	750	1.2	1.7	19	30	—

Girls											
Under 1	3.0	720	18	600	6	450	0.3	0.4	5	20	7.5
1	4.5	1100	27	600	7	300	0.4	0.6	7	20	10
2	5.5	1300	32	600	7	300	0.5	0.7	8	20	10
3–4	6.25	1500	37	600	8	300	0.6	0.8	9	20	10
5–6	7.0	1680	42	600	10	300	0.7	0.9	10	20	—
7–8	8.0	1900	48	600	10	400	0.8	1.0	11	20	—
9–11	8.5	2050	51	700	12[2]	575	0.8	1.2	14	25	—
12–14	9.0	2150	53	700	12[2]	725	0.9	1.4	16	25	—
15–17	9.0	2150	53	600	12[2]	750	0.9	1.7	19	30	—
Men											
18–34 { Sedentary	10.5	2510	62	500	10	750	1.0	1.6	18	30	—
Moderately active	12.0	2900	72	500	10	750	1.2	1.6	18	30	—
Very active	14.0	3350	84	500	10	750	1.3	1.6	18	30	—
35–64 { Sedentary	10.0	2400	60	500	10	750	1.0	1.6	18	30	—
Moderately active	11.5	2750	69	500	10	750	1.1	1.6	18	30	—
Very active	14.0	3350	84	500	10	750	1.3	1.6	18	30	—
65–74	10.0	2400	60	500	10	750	1.0	1.6	18	30	—
75 and over	9.0	2150	54	500	10	750	0.9	1.6	18	30	—
Women											
18–54 { Most occupations	9.0	2150	54	500	12[2]	750	0.9	1.3	15	30	—
Very active	10.5	2500	62	500	12[2]	750	1.0	1.3	15	30	—
55–74	8.0	1900	47	500	10	750	0.8	1.3	15	30	—
75 and over	7.0	1680	42	500	10	750	0.7	1.3	15	30	—
Pregnant	10.0	2400	60	1200	13	750	1.0	1.6	18	60	10
Lactating	11.5	2750	69	1200	15	1200	1.1	1.8	21	60	10

1 Most people who go out in the sun need no dietary source of vitamin D, but children and adolescents in winter, and housebound adults, are recommended to take 10µg vitamin D daily.

2 These iron recommendations may not cover heavy menstrual losses.

Glossary

Acidophiles — microorganisms which grow well in acid conditions.

Acrolein — (acraldehyde) irritant substance in the smoke from hot cooking oils.

Actomysin — formed from the proteins, actin and myosin, when muscles contract.

Adipose tissue — stores fat, under the skin, around the kidney and between the muscle fibres of older animals.

A.F.D. — accelerated freeze drying. Foods are frozen; then the water sublimes under a partial vacuum.

Albumins — soluble proteins, coagulated by heat. Found in egg white.

Amylopectin — starches composed of branched chains of glucose units.

Amylose — straight chained starches. (Natural starches contain both types of starch chain.)

Anthocyanins — red to blue flavenoid pigments in radishes, beetroot, blackberries and cherries.

Anthoxanthins — pale yellow pigments in onions and potatoes.

Antioxidants — reducing agents which slow down oxidative rancidity in fats.

Aromatic plants — produce volatile oils which have flavour and aroma.

Ascorbic oxidase — an enzyme which accelerates the oxidation of vitamin C to an inactive form.

Aseptic canning — the food is heat treated and then fed into containers under sterile conditions.

Autolysis — breakdown of a cell by its own enzymes.

Autotrophic — the ability of an organism to produce its own energy-rich foods e.g. by photosynthesis in green plants.

A_w — a scale measuring the water activity of foods and solutions. Pure water has an $A_w = 1.0$. Most bacteria cannot grow below A_w 0.9.

Bacteriocide — a substance which kills bacteria.

Bacteriostat — a substance which prevents bacteria from multiplying.

Baumé scale — a table of specific gravity used for salt and sugar solutions named after the French chemist Antoine Baumé.

B.H.A. — butylated hydroxyanisole, an antioxidant used in fats.

B.H.T. — butylated hydroxytoluene is also used for this purpose.

Binary fission — reproduction by division into two parts as in bacteria.

Biological value — a measure of the usefulness of a protein in building human tissue. Proportion of the protein retained in the human body compared with that absorbed from the diet.

Blue mountain — a region of Jamaica known for its arabica coffee beans.

B.M.R. — basal metabolic rate. The energy output of the body when at rest in a moderate temperature (12 hours after a meal).

Botulism — a form of food poisoning due to the toxin of *Clostridium botulinum*.

Botulinum cook — commercial sterilisation. The time and temperature needed to kill *C. botulinum* spores.

Brassicas — a collective name for plants of the cabbage family.

Buffering agents — substances added to foods to stabilise their pH. Limits changes in their acidity or alkalinity.

Calorie — the amount of heat needed to raise 1g of water through 1°C. Calorific value of a food = energy value.

Capsule — the slime layer on the outside of some bacterial cells.

Caramelisation — heating sugar in the absence of water until it forms a brown bitter substance — caramel.

Carbohydrates — compounds of carbon, hydrogen and oxygen with two hydrogen atoms to each oxygen atom e.g. sugars, starches and cellulose.

Carcinogenic — cancer promoting.

Carotenoids — yellow, orange and red pigments in fruits and vegetables. Beta-carotene is converted into vitamin A in the body.

Carriers — people who carry an infection without showing symptoms of the disease.

Catalyst — a substance which changes the rate of a chemical reaction without being used up in the process.

Choux paste — a paste made by boiling butter and water together and beating in flour and eggs. Used for eclairs and cream buns.

Chlorophylls — the green pigments of plants which absorb light in photosynthesis. Contained in organelles known as **chloroplasts** in higher plants.

Chlorophyllase — an enzyme which splits the phytyl group away from chlorophyll causing the green colour to leak into cooking water.

Chylomicrons — droplets of fat surrounded by a protein coating found in the villi or blood stream.

Coagulation — solidification of a liquid protein on heating.

Collagen — protein in bones, skin and connective tissue. Forms gelatin on moist cooking. The **collagen shrink** point is the temperature at which collagen breaks down and shrinkage occurs in meats.

Colloids — proteins, starches and pectins form dispersions in which the large molecules bind water strongly to them.

Commensal — an organism which lives in or on another — neither partner benefits or is harmed by the association.

Complementation — occurs when two or more proteins are served at the same meal and one supplies the essential amino acids which are lacking in the other.

Continuous phase — the liquid surrounding droplets of the **disperse phase** in an emulsion.

Darjeeling — a name given to a grade of tea produced in this region of northern India.

Deamination — removal of the nitrogenous amino groups(s) from surplus amino acids in the liver.

Demersal fish — live at or near the sea bottom.

Detergent — general name for a cleaning agent. **Anionic detergents** are negatively charged on the head end of the molecules, **cationic** are positively charged and **non-ionic** have no electric charge.

Dextrins — breakdown products of starch produced during digestion or cooking of starch e.g. toasting bread.

Diastatic activity — a measure of the ability of the natural amylases in a flour to break down the starch to sugar.

Disinfectant, germicide — substance which kills pathogenic microorganisms but not necessarily bacterial spores.

Disperse phase — small droplets (or particles) of one substance suspended in a liquid (see **continuous phase, emulsion**).

DNA — deoxyribose nucleic acids are present in the chromosomes. Responsible for the transmission of genetic information and for protein synthesis.

E numbers — additives listed in the E.E.C. regulations have an E number and are grouped into a number of categories.

Elastin — fibrinous protein present in the yellow fibres of connective tissues. Not softened by cooking.

Emulsion — a dispersion of fine droplets of liquid within another liquid. Stabilised by an **emulsifying agent**.

Endomysium — membrane surrounding a bundle of muscle fibres.

Endoplasmic reticulum (ER) — the network of double membranes in the cytoplasm of a cell.

Endosperm — the inner part of a cereal grain where the starch is stored.

Epimysium — the sheath of connective tissue which surrounds the whole muscle and connects it via the tendons to the skeleton.

Essential amino acids — amino acids needed in the diet as they cannot be synthesised in the body.

Esters — formed by a reaction between an alcohol and an organic acid. Many are used as artificial flavourings.

Ethoxyquin — additive used to prevent enzyme browning of apples and pears.

Evaporated fruits — dried fruits such as apricots and prunes which require soaking before cooking.

Fatty acids — organic acids with a carbon chain terminating in a carboxyl group. In **saturated fatty acids** every carbon atom has its full complement of hydrogen atoms; while **unsaturated fatty acids** lack some hydrogen atoms and double bonds are formed.

Farinaceous products — have a flour or starch base.

Fibre, dietary — the roughage in the diet. Plant materials which are indigestible or only partly digested.

Flash point — the temperature at which the vapours of a liquid (e.g. cooking oil) are liable to catch fire.

Flavonoids — water soluble pigments in the central vacuole of plant cells.

Flavour enhancers — additives which bring out the flavour of foods e.g. monosodium glutamate.

Food infections — diseases due to the presence of live microorganisms in food or drink as opposed to **food poisoning** due to toxins produced in the food.

Freezer burn — occurs in improperly wrapped frozen food. Results in drying and discolouration.

Freezing, sharp — a slow method of freezing as opposed to **quick freezing** which freezes the food in not more than 30 minutes.

Gastro-intestinal tract — the whole of the digestive tract.

Gel — a colloidal solution which has solidified, as in the set of pectin in jams and cornflour paste in blancmanges.

Gelatinisation of starches — occurs when starches are cooked in water: the starch grains swell and the liquid thickens. Swelling begins at the I.G.T. initial gelatinisation temperature, characteristic of the starch.

Generation time — the time taken for one bacterial cell to split into two daughter cells.

Germ — the embryo of cereals: wheat germ etc.

Gluten — a protein complex in wheat composed of gliadin and glutenin. Holds the gas in a rising dough.

Glycerides — compounds of glycerol and fatty acids named mono-, di- or triglycerides according to the number of fatty acids involved.

Glycogen — animal starch. Glucose is converted into glycogen for temporary storage in the liver and muscles.

Haemichrome — a tan coloured pigment produced when meat is cooked and the iron in the myoglobin becomes oxidised.

Haemoglobin — the red pigment in the blood which picks up oxygen in the lungs becoming **oxyhaemoglobin**.

Halophilic — organisms which grow well in concentrated salt solutions (brines.)

Heterotrophic — organisms with animal-like nutrition which do not photosynthesise and obtain their energy from their food — animals, fungi.

Hexoses — sugars with 6 carbon atoms e.g. glucose, fructose.

H.T.S.T. — high temperature short time method of sterilisation.

Humectants — substances which hold moisture and keep bakery goods in moist condition e.g. honey, glycerol.

Hydrogenation — addition of hydrogen into unsaturated lipids to harden them to produce margarines and shortenings.

Hypertension — high blood pressure.

Hydrophilic — 'water loving'. Used to describe the head end of detergent molecules which are attracted towards water. The tail ends are

Hydrophobic — as they are repelled by water but attracted to grease.

Improvers — chemicals used to oxidise flours to bleach them and improve their baking qualities — chlorine dioxide, ammonium persulphate, potassium bromate.

Inversion — splitting sucrose into its constituent sugars, glucose and fructose, by boiling in an acid medium.

Ionizing radiations — X rays, beta and gamma rays penetrate and disrupt the normal functioning of cells. Can be used to sterilise foods.

Iodophors — complexes of iodine and detergents. Rapid acting disinfectants.

Joule S.I. — unit of energy, 4.2 J raise 1g of water through 1°C.

Kummel — a liqueur flavoured with caraway.

Lacteal, central — the blind ending tube in each villus which receives the products of fat digestion.
Lacto-vegetarians — eat dairy products and plant foods, but no meat.
Legumes — vegetables of the pea family whose seeds are borne in pods.
Lipases — enzymes which split lipids to glycerol and fatty acids. Lipoxidases split fats by oxidation and cause one type of rancidity.
Lipids — fats and oils found in plants and animals.
Lipoproteins — combination of a fatty material with a protein. Found in egg yolk.
L.T.H. — the low temperature holding method of sterilisation.
Lysosomes — vacuoles containing autolytic enzymes which digest dead cells.

Maillard reaction — non enzymic browning due to a reaction between reducing sugars and amino acids during cooking.
Malt adjuncts — additional materials added to the malt to increase the fermentable substances in the production of beer — corn, rice, potatoes etc.
Malting — sprouting barley or other cereal. This is followed by **mashing** to extract the soluble materials from the dried, ground malt to produce wort.
Mèges-Mouriés — a French chemist who won a prize for inventing a substitute for butter — margarine.
Mesophiles — organisms with an optimum growth temperature of 20°C–40°C. **Thermophiles** have a higher optimum 45–55°C and **Psychrophiles** can grow well at 10°C–15°C.
Micelle — small groups of molecules as in emulsified fat droplets in the blood or the groups of detergent molecules formed in the washing action of surfactants.
Molluca islands — a group of islands in the Far East in the Celebes sea where many spices originate — the Spice islands.
Monosaccharides — simple sugars e.g. glucose, fructose.
Disaccharides — double sugars e.g. sucrose, maltose.
Monosodium glutamate — flavour enhancer used in Chinese cookery and many convenience foods.
Mycelium — the mass of fungal threads or **hyphae**.
Myoglobin — an oxygen carrying pigment found in muscles — forms **oxymyoglobin** — a bright red pigment.
Mysore — coffee growing region in India.

N.P.U.–Net protein utilization — a measure of the quality of a protein which takes into account digestibility — biological value x digestibility.

'Neutral detergents' — soaps and synthetic detergents with pH values around neutrality.

Neutrophiles — organisms which grow best at a neutral pH.

Nitrosomyoglobin — produced by the action of pickling salts on the myoglobin of meat — pinkish red. Fades in the light to the yellow-brown colour of **metmyoglobin**.

Non-crystalline sugar products — produced by boiling sugar at a high temperature and cooling rapidly e.g. hard crack, spun sugar.

Oily fish — contain about 15% oil as compared with 1–2% in **white fish**. The oil is present in the flesh as well as in the liver.

Orange Pekoe — the term refers to the copper colour of the bud in the black tea.

Organoleptic — qualities of a food which appeal to the sense of taste, smell etc.

Osmophilic — organisms which can grow in foods with high sugar contents e.g. syrup, honey etc.

Osmosis — movement of water across a semi-permeable membrane from a dilute salt or sugar solution to balance the water pressure on the other side of the membrane.

Osmotic pressure — the ability of a concentrated salt or sugar solution to draw water through a semi-permeable membrane.

Osteomalacia — decalcification of the bone in frequently pregnant women or elderly people.

Osteoporosis — loss of bone tissue, common in elderly people particularly women.

Oven spring — the sudden increase in volume in a dough during the first ten minutes of baking.

Pathogenic organisms — disease producing.

Pekoe — from the Chinese for 'white hair'. Refers to the fine downy hair on the underside of the tea leaf.

Pelagic fish — live near the surface of the water — herrings, mackerel etc.

Pentoses — sugars with 5 carbon atoms e.g. ribose.

Proteoses — breakdown products of proteins. Digestion of proteins yields amino acid chains of shortening length: **proteoses → peptones → polypeptides → amino acids**.

Perimysium — connective tissue binding groups of bundles of muscle fibres.

Peristalsis — the waves of muscular contraction which move food along the alimentary canal.

pH scale — measures the acidity or alkalinity of a solution.

Phaeophytins — are dull greenish pigments produced when the chlorophyll in green vegetables is pickled in acid or over-cooked.

Photosynthesis — the process whereby green plants synthesise energy-rich foods from carbon dioxide and water using the radiant energy of the sun.

Phytic acid & salts — substances occuring in the bran of cereals, in pulses and some nuts which interferes with absorption of calcium and magnesium from the diet.

Phytyl group — ester side chain of chlorophyll.

Plasmolysed cell — a cell whose water content has been depleted by immersion in a concentrated salt or sugar solution.

P.O.E.M.S. — polyoxyethylene monostearate. Emulsifier used in bakery goods — a crumb softener.

Porphyrin ring — a ring system surrounding a central metal atom as in haemoglobin and chlorophyll.

Q.A.C. — Quaternary ammonium compound, substance produced by reacting fatty materials with ammonia — cationic detergents, anti-static agents.

Rancidity, hydrolytic — breakdown of fats and oils involving water. Usually due to contamination of the lipid by microorganisms.

Rancidity, oxidative — deterioration of fats and oils due to oxidation at the double bonds of unsaturated fatty acids.

R.D.A. — Recommended daily allowance. Provides sufficient or more than sufficient of the nutrient or energy for 97% of the healthy people of a particular group of the population.

Rechauffé dishes — are made up of cooked foods which require reheating.

Reference protein — the 'perfect protein' containing all the essential amino acids in the proportions needed to build human tissues.

Regeneration — reheating chilled or frozen foods to 70°C as quickly as possible without affecting their quality.

Retrogradation — a change which occurs in starch gels on storage resulting in a deterioration of their texture.

Rigor mortis — stiffening of the muscles immediately after animals have been slaughtered.

Santos — an area in Brazil known for growing coffee.

Sanitizer — a substance which reduces the level of pathogens on a surface to an acceptable level.

Saprophytes — organisms which live on dead organic material e.g. dry rot fungus.

Sauerkraut — pickled cabbage.

Spores, fungal — reproductive bodies which spread the fungus from one food to another. **Endospores** — dormant bodies produced by some bacteria — very resistant to heat and chemicals.

St Vincent — an island in the West Indies known for producing arrowroot.

Smoke point — the temperature reached when a cooking oil or fat emits a blue smoke. Due to breakdown of the triglycerides.

Sterilant — a powerful disinfectant which will sterilise a surface if used correctly.

Sterilisation — the removal or destruction of all living organisms on a surface.

Stiff alive — a term used to indicate very fresh fish which is still stiff from rigor mortis.

Striped (striated) muscle — voluntary muscle tissue which has a striped appearance microscopically.

Surface tension — the force which gives liquid surfaces film-like properties.

Surfactants — surface active agents which lower the surface tension of water allowing it to wet surfaces more efficiently.

Thermic effect — (specific dynamic action) term applied to increase in energy output of the body following a meal.

Tissues — groups of cells of similar shape and function.

Trace elements — mineral elements required in the diet only in minute amounts e.g. copper, zinc, manganese.

Transamination — transfer of amino groups from one organic acid to another. Allows production of amino acids needed in the body from those in excess in the diet.

Trichinosis — disease due to consumption of meat infected with a nematode worm, *Trichinella spiralis.*

Trickling filter — method of making vinegar in which the liquid is trickled over wood shavings impregnated with acetic acid bacteria.

Toxin — a poison produced by a microorganism. **Exotoxin** a toxin which diffuses out of the cell into the surrounding food. **Enterotoxin** a poison which irritates the gut.

T.V.P. — textured vegetable protein — a product made from soya flour. Used as a meat extender and for vegetarian dishes.

U.H.T. — ultra high temperature method of sterilisation.

Urea — nitrogenous waste product formed by the liver and excreted by the kidneys.

V.C.M. — vertical cutter mincer. A machine which can purée soups, chop meat, make pastry dough, breadcrumbs and mayonnaise.

Vegans — vegetarians who eat only plant foods.

Velouté — a sauce or soup made from a blond roux and finished with liaison of egg yolk and cream.

Villi — the finger-like projections in the walls of the intestines which increase the surface area for absorption.

Volatile oils — oils which evaporate readily at room temperature.

Index

oily fish, 47, 52
osmophilic organisms, 90
osmosis, 70, 71
osteomalacia, 133, 135,
    156
osteoporosis, 157

pancreas, 145
parasites, 68, 219
pasteurisation, 187
pectin, 108, 160
pelagic fish, 47, 52, 54
Penicillium, 81, 195, 196
peptide bonds, 114
peptones, 143
pepsin, 143, 144
perimysium, 58
peristalsis, 141
pest control
    flies, 68, 241–242
    in food storage, 66–68
    rodents, 240–241
$_p$H, 91
    foods, 91, 92
    range of organisms,
        91, 92
phaeophytins, 123
photosynthesis, 24
phytic acid, 126
Pichia, 83
pickling, 192
pigments
    meat, 76–78
    effect of cooking, 120,
        123, 124
plant
    cells, 29–31
    storage organs, 23, 26
POEMS
        (polyoxyethylene
        monostearate), 36
polysaccharides, 162–163
poultry
    cooking, 120, 121
    types, 42–3
preservatives, 32–34
processed foods, 1,
    38–39
proteins, 113
    amino acids, 114, 131,
        177
    biological value, 178, 182
    complementation,
        179–180

cost, 183–184
sources, 177
protein values
    dishes and meals,
        181–183
    vegan meals, 180–181
    vegetarian meals,
        180–181
psyhrophiles, 87, 88
pyridoxine (vitamin B_6),
    136

QACs (quaternary
    ammonium
    compounds), 238
quantities (for portion
    control), 250, 251

rancidity, 71, 72
    hydrolytic, 75
    oxidative, 74
RDA (recommended
    daily allowances),
    150, 171
rechauffé dishes,
    207–208
reference protein, 178,
    180
refrigeration of
    chilled foods, 64
    fresh foods, 64
    frozen foods, 63
respiration
    aerobic, 90, 91
    anaerobic, 90, 91
retinol (vitamin A), 135
retrogradation, 112 ·
Rhizopus, 80
riboflavin (vitamin B_2),
    136
rice, 5
rigor mortis, 41, 75
rye, 5

saccharine, 35
saccharometer, 22
Saccharomyces, 83, 197
salad dressings, 117
Salmonellae, 214
salt
    content of foods, 155
    high blood pressure,
        154

preserving foods, 191
sanitisers, 236–238
sauerkraut, 197
saprophytes, 88
semolina, 4
shell fish, 48
slimming, 156, 173–176
smoke points, 121–122
smoking foods, 192
soaps, 233
spices, *see* flavourings
spores
    bacterial, 86
    fungal, 81, 82
Staphylococcus, 215
staple foods, 29
starch, 109
    factors affecting gels,
        111, 112
    gelatinisation, 110
sterilisation, 187
Streptococcus, 196
storeroom management,
    60, 61
sugar
    beet, 20
    cane, 20
    densities, 21, 22
    thermometer, 22
sugars
    culinary uses, 21,
        106–108
    food preservation, 191
    refining, 20
    relative sweetness, 109
    varieties of, 21
surface tension, 233–234
surfactants, 234
sweeteners, artificial, 35

table linen, 229
tapioca, 6
tapeworm, 219
tea, 16–17
teeth, 140–141
TVP (textured vegetable
    protein), 39,
    131–2
thermophiles, 87, 88
thiamin (vitamin B_1), 136
trace elements, 134
thermic effect of food,
    130

tissues
    animals, 56–57
    plants, 31
tocopherols (vitamin
    E_{12}), 135
toxins, 25
trichinosis, 219
triglycerides, 72, 73
trypsin, 143

urea, 147
UHT (ultra high
    temperature)
    treatment, 188

VCM (vertical cutting
    machine), 211
velouté, 117
vegetables, 6–8
vegetable oils, 14–16
    care of, 65, 122
    margarines, 15, 37
    refining, 14–15
    sources, 14
vegetarians, 155–156,
    180, 181
villi, 146
vinegars, 200–201
vitamins, *see* also under
    individual names,
    135, 138

water
    requirements of
        spoilage
        organisms, 89, 90
    activity, *see* A_w
washing up, 238, 239,
    225, 226
wine making, 198–199
weight watchers menu
    planner, 174, 175
    analysis, 174–176
wheat, 3
white fish, 47, 52
work flow in kitchens,
    222, 223
work surfaces, 209, 225

yoghurt, 196
yeasts, 82–84

zygospores, 82